Alpine Garden Society

Corydalis

a gardener's guide and

a monograph of the tuberous species

Magnus Lidén & Henrik Zetterlund

Christopher Grey-Wilson
Editor

A G S Publications Limited

First Published 1997

Published by AGS Publications Limited,
AGS Centre, Avon Bank, Pershore,
Worcestershire WR10 3JP

David Haselgrove
Managing Director,
Alpine Garden Society Publications Limited

Christopher Grey-Wilson
Editor, The Alpine Garden Society

ISBN 0-900048-66-2

Frontispiece
Colour variants in *Corydalis solida*,
from a painting by
Ingalill Axelsson

Printed by The Friary Press,
Bridport Road, Dorchester, Dorset DT1 1JL

Contents

Preface   5
Acknowledgements   5
Picture Credits   5
What is a *Corydalis*?   7
Corydalis in Medicine   9
Vernacular Names   10
Historical Résumé   10
Key to Genera of the Fumariaceae   11
Phylogeny and Subdivision   12
Pollination and Reproductive Systems   12
Seed and Dispersal   13
Cytology   14
Monsters   14
History of cultivation   14
Cultivation today   16
Pests in Nature   17
Pests and Diseases in Cultivation   17
The tuberous Species   18
    Seed Development and Germination   18
    Tuber Development   18
    Hybridisation   19
    Key to the Tuberous Sections   20
The Corydalis Flower   20
Section Corydalis   21
Section Radix-cava   76
Section Leonticoides   81
Section Dactylotuber   99
Section Duplotuber   112
Non-tuberous Species (a selection)   115
    Section Archaecapnos   115
    Other non-tuberous groups   120
Distribution Maps   134
References   139
Index   141

This book is dedicated to the late Professor Per Wendelbo (1927-1981)

PREFACE

We have chosen to dedicate this book to our friend, the late Professor Per Wendelbo. He was the major *Corydalis* authority of his time and he dealt with Fumariaceae for *Flora Iranica*, describing various new taxa in the genus. During his field trips in Turkey, Iran and Afghanistan he collected several tuberous species in the sections *Corydalis* and *Leonticoides*, most of which are still in cultivation today at the Gothenburg Botanic Garden. As director of the garden during the period 1965 to 1981, he managed to lay the foundation of its collection of tuberous plants and to initiate an interest in the alpine, Mediterranean, and Irano-Turanian floras amongst his staff, a tradition which has continued to the present day. Last, but not least, we owe to his curiosity, open mind and enthusiasm our own passion for *Corydalis*. Could he have offered a more precious gift to his disciples?

Our intention with this work was to make it relevant to the botanist as well as the gardener and indeed anyone who wishes to learn more about these noble plants. This means, however, that it will not be perfect for either the botanist who will have to put up with pots and poetry and the gardener who will, no doubt, be annoyed by the vast amount of petty scientific data in parts of the book.

ACKNOWLEDGEMENTS

Many people have supported this project in one way or another.

First of all we must thank our patient and tolerant families, our wives and children but then the following, in no particular order:

Tatsundo Fukuhara for sharing his knowledge of Japanese *Corydalis* species and seed anatomy, as well as for supplying live plants;

Janis Ruksans, Arnis Seisums and Mart Veerus for useful information and for enriching our gardens with some of the most exciting corydalis;

Tony Hall and Ron McBeath for inspiration and for access to two smashing gardens and their collections;

Brian Mathew for inspiration, information and for triggering the world-wide corydalis craze in 1981;

Kath Dryden, Roger Poulett, Norman Stevens and Erich Pasche, for plant material and cultural advice;

Antoine Hoog for *Corydalis solida* 'Zwanenburg' and access to the van Tubergen files;

Gale Masters of Mt Hood National Forest for help with *Corydalis caseana* subsp. *aquae-gelidae*;

The botanical departments of the Academia Sinica in Kunming and Chengdu for invaluable help in the field and in the herbarium.

Su Zhi-Yun, Marina Mikhailova, Irina Safonova and Byoung-Un Oh for hospitality, fruitful discussions, and access to type specimens and other herbarium material;

All herbarium curators who will now, at last, get their dried specimens returned;

Ingalill Axelsson for the watercolour drawings;

Robert Rolfe for histhoughtful reading of the proofs;

Friends of the Gothenburg Botanic Garden for financial support;

The country of Norway for Per Wendelbo.

PICTURE CREDITS

Unless otherwise stated the photographs are by Henrik Zetterlund
Mike Almond: plate 86; Niklas Ek: plates 55, 59, 60, 61;
Christopher Grey-Wilson: plates 49, 66, 83, 95, 98, 100, 103, 106, 107, 115, 117, 118;
Joseph Halda: plate 112; Magnus Lidén: plates 13, 14, 54, 68, 97, 102; B. Y. Oh: plates 38, 39.

WHAT IS A CORYDALIS?

*C*orydalis belongs in the family Papaveraceae in the broad sense, which altogether comprises about 750 species. Around 550 of these, including *Corydalis* species, are often separated out as a distinct family, the Fumariaceae, distinguished primarily by possessing a zygomorphic (unisymmetric) or bisymmetric corolla and by their lack of coloured sap. Among other genera in this group are *Fumaria* (the fumitories) and *Dicentra* (the bleeding hearts), the latter probably more welcome in your flower-beds than the former. However, if you study the *Fumaria*-flower in detail, you will be struck by its complicated structure, which differs little from that of *Corydalis* except for its smaller size. Those who have botanised in southern Spain may have come across the cushiony cliff-dwellers *Rupicapnos* and *Sarcocapnos* ('cliff-smoke' and 'flesh-smoke' if literally translated). A relative of the last genus grows as far north as Britain and Scandinavia, namely the scandent annual *Ceratocapnos* ('horn-smoke') *claviculata*, hitherto known as *Corydalis claviculata*.

What, is it no longer a *Corydalis*? It is often claimed that botanists change all familiar names just to see their own in print! Well, actually there are plenty of good reasons for this particular change. *Ceratocapnos claviculata* is much more closely related to *Fumaria* and so can not be retained in *Corydalis* if a meaningful system is attempted. Even more difficult to accept perhaps is that the frequently cultivated *Corydalis lutea* has been separated out as *Pseudofumaria lutea*, but a close study of the flowers reveals the same principal differences from *Corydalis* as are found in *Ceratocapnos*. A third taxon that had to be excluded from *Corydalis*, is the North American *C. sempervirens*, now assigned to the genus *Capnoides*. Basically, *Corydalis* embraces species with a zygomorphic (unisymmetric) corolla, a persistent style and a racemose inflorescence.

Classification of Fumariaceae
(number of species indicated)

subfamily Hypecoideae
        Hypecoum (18)
subfamily Fumarioideae
   tribe Corydaleae
        Dicentra sensu lato* (12)
        Adlumia (2)
        Capnoides (1)
        Dactylicapnos (10)
        Corydalis (c. 440)
   tribe Fumarieae
      (subtribe ined.)
        Cysticapnos (including *Phacocapnos*) (5)
      subtribe Sarcocapninae
        Platycapnos (3)
        Pseudofumaria (2)
        Sarcocapnos (4)
        Ceratocapnos (3)
      subtribe Fumariinae
        Fumariola (1)
        Fumaria (50)
        Cryptocapnos (1)
        Rupicapnos (7)
      subtribe Discocapninae
        Discocapnos (1)
        Trigonocapnos (1)

Dicentra as presently circumscribed is not a natural genus but should be split up into independent genera, corresponding to presently recognised subgenera

In spite of its larger size (as to the number of species), Fumariaceae is a much more uniform family than the Papaveraceae sensu stricto (in a narrow sense). Only the genus *Hypecoum* has at times been segregated as a separate family but shares a lot of characters with the Fumariaceae. *Hypecoum* consists of mostly yellow-flowered rosulate annual weeds that locally carpet the ground in olive groves in the Mediterranean area. A few species go as far east as China and Mongolia. Unlike the Fumarioideae they have petals that are free from each other. The inner ones are deeply three-cleft with a central fimbriate lobe clasping the stamens and style, while the outer ones are shallowly lobed and spreading. The corolla is disymmetric and there are no spurs.

The subfamily Fumarioideae is usually divided into two tribes: the chiefly Asiatic-American *Corydaleae*, recognised by a persistent style, and the mainly Mediterranean *Fumarieae*, characterised by a caducous (deciduous) style. Seed anatomy and DNA sequences (Fukuhara & Lidén 1995b; Lidén, Fukuhara & Axberg 1995) have revealed that *Corydaleae* in this sense is not a natural taxon, and should be broken up. This is not too surprising, considering that the only diagnostic character of *Corydaleae*, the persistent style, is found also in all related families (i.e. *Corydaleae* constitutes only what remains of the subfamily after the separation of the natural group *Fumarieae*). *Dicentra* in a broad sense is likewise defined only by its lack of characters and should be split into four more 'natural' genera.

Corydalis is distinguished by a zygomorphic (unisymmetric) corolla from *Adlumia, Dicentra* and *Dactylicapnos* which all have bisymmetric corollas. *Capnoides sempervirens* also has a zygomorphic corolla, but it looks rather like an oblique *Dicentra* flower. Furthermore, the inflorescence in *Capnoides* is terminated by a flower, whereas in *Corydalis* it is indeterminate. The stigmas also differ between all these genera, as between sections within *Corydalis*.

Corydalis DC., Flore de France ed. 3, 4: 601 (1805), *nomen conservandum* (Lidén 1981; Brummitt 1984), conserved against the homonyms *Corydalis* Medik. 1789 (=*Cysticapnos* Mill.), *Corydalis* Vent. 1803 (=*Capnoides* Mill.), and the synonym *Pistolochia* Bernh. (1800); later homotypic synonyms include: *Borckhausenia* Gaertn., Mey. & Scherb. (1803), *non* Roth, *Capnites* Dumort. (1827), *Bulbocapnos* Bernh. (1833). Type species: *C. solida* (L.) Clairv.
Calocapnos Spach (1839); *Capnogorium* Bernh. (1844). Type species: *Corydalis nobilis* (L.) Pers.
Sophorocapnos Turcz. (1848). Type species: *Corydalis pallida* (Thunb.) Pers.
Cryptoceras Schott & Kotschy (1854). Type species: *Corydalis rutifolia* (Sm.) DC.
Roborowskia Batalin (1893). Type species: *Corydalis mira* (Batalin) Z.Y. Su & X. Zhuang.
Cysticorydalis Fedde *nomen nudum*.

Annual to perennial soft and juicy herbs, usually glabrous, but sometimes papillose or papillose-hairy, very rarely (*C. chaerophylla* group) with septate hairs. *Cotyledons* flat, lanceolate, usually 2, but 1 in most of the tuberous species and in the sections Oocapnos and Fasciculatae. *Leaves* alternate (opposite in *C. enantiophylla* and sect. Leonticoides), pinnately or ternately divided (entire in *C. ludlowii*), green or often glaucous, especially below. *Stipules* usually absent but the petiole sometimes vaginate at base, or with stipule-like membranous appendages in some groups. *Inflorescence* racemose; each flower subtended by a bract; bracteoles absent. *Sepals* often small or minute, but sometimes prominent, dentate or entire, petaloid, sometimes falling early. *Corolla* zygomorphic (unisymmetric) with an upper petal equipped with a nectariferous spur, a spurless lower petal, and two apically fused inner petals that are jointed in the middle and provided with three parallel ridges or wings of which the central one is usually much wider (between the apex and the joint there is an upwardly directed tooth, important for the pollination mechanism). *Stamens* two, each with 4 thecae; filaments flat and translucent, each with three distinct veins, the central one supporting a dithecal anther, the lateral ones each a monothecal anther; anthers rounded to elliptic, opening by slits, closely adherent to the stigma. *Nectary* arising from the base of the upper stamen, usually prominent and protruding into the spur of the upper petal. *Stigma* very variable but often laterally flattened with few to several marginal papillae. *Fruit* usually a many-seeded bicarpellate septicidal capsule with a persistent style. *Seeds* black, carunculate (elaiosome or caruncle lacking in sect. Bipapillata), usually smooth but sometimes prominently ornamented (especially in the sections Sophorocapnos and Mucroniferae). Basic chromosome number 8: most species are diploid (2n=16) but tetraploids (2n=32) and, rarely, higher polyploids (2n=40, 48, c. 140) are also found.

The genus comprises a wide variety of forms from annual weedy species not unlike some of the European fumitories, to stout erect perennials reaching two metres or more. There are scandent species, climbing through the understory in humid Burmese forests, dwarf alpines only a couple of centimetres in height, as well as cushion-forming chasmophytes rooted in crevices of overhanging cliffs. They grow from sea-level up to the very limit of vascular plant vegetation in the Himalaya. Their latitudinal range spans from Thailand to the Siberian Arctic coast, with an odd outlier on the East African mountains (Lidén 1993b).

The stems are simple or branched, leafy or naked, stout and erect, or diffuse and decumbent; leaves can be alternate or opposite, entire or finely divided. The sepals are minute or absent to almost 10 mm in width, entire and shield-like to deeply fimbriate. The flowers vary from blue, purple, yellow, white, red, or orange, to various blends of these and they come in all forms and sizes, from 10 to almost 50 mm long.

It is a common misconception that most *Corydalis* are tuberous; from a European or Central Asiatic viewpoint, tuberous species certainly form the majority but if the whole distribution area is considered they comprise less than a quarter of the total number. This is due to the remarkable diversity of non-tuberous species in China and the Himalaya, reaching its peak (as in so many other genera) in the mountains of western China and south-eastern Tibet. China has some 300 species within its political boundaries and most of these are endemic (restricted to China). According to a recent estimate *Corydalis* is the sixth largest genus of flowering plants in China.

CORYDALIS IN MEDICINE

Like most papaveraceous plants and their allies, many species of *Corydalis* are, or have been, used pharmaceutically for a wide spectrum of conditions. *Corydalis cava* was commonly grown in monasteries in ancient times, and it still survives among the ruins in some places. One of its properties is said to have been its ability to ease menstruation. It was also used as a vermifuge (against intestinal worms). Dried and powdered it could be put on wounds to prevent bone-rot and (according to Hager 1883) it has also been used as false nict ('vegetable sulphur', the spores of club moss) by ruthless pharmacists.

A number of alkaloids (of which *protopin* and *bulbocapnin* are among the most important) are responsible for the medicinal powers of several of the tuberous species. In pure form they ease tension, are sedative, lower the blood pressure and prevent contractions of the muscles. *C. cava* is still used locally as a cure for Parkinson's disease, neurological aberrations, vertigo, and muscle tremor. It is also said to be a soothing medication before and after treatment with anaesthetics and it has hallucinogenic powers. A Danish authority states 'all the species [of *Corydalis*] I have tried are hallucinogenic if one smokes 1/2 a gramme of any part. The effect is pleasant, opium-like, but varies according to the present mood'. We would nevertheless strongly discourage anyone tempted to experiment. Bear in mind that several species are strongly poisonous and the concentration of alcaloids may vary a lot between species and between different parts of the same plant.

Which of the various reactions is responsible for the German epithet *Donnerwurzel* we do not know. Tubers of *C. cava* are included in the drug Phytonoxon for their sedative, antidepressive and hypnotic properties (Reimeier & al. 1995). *C. fumariifolia* is another species currently studied for its effects on the central nervous system (Zhu, 1991). It is also said to be 'a promising antithrombotic drug' (Xuan & al. 1994).

The Chinese *Yanhusuo* (*Yanfusuo*), the boiled and dried tubers of *C. yanhusuo* and several other tuberous species, 'one of the most famous chinese herbal drugs' (Fu & al. 1989), is an analgesic and antiarrythmic drug used for a variety of indications, including coronary heart disease. It is often given to women after childbirth. In Korea *C. ternata* is used and across the Pacific the Mexican Indians utilise the annual *C. aurea* subsp. *occidentalis* for the same purpose.

Corydalis crispa and *C. hamata* are used by the Tibetans as a remedy for hypertension. *CC. racemosa, incisa, decumbens, moupinensis, bungeana, edulis, balansae, linstowiana*, and many other species are also considered officinal. A Chinese expert has recorded no less than 60 species in the Tibetan pharmacopoeia. *C.*

govaniana, which has the power to cure syphilis, must be one of the more potent. It is also used to treat the eye disease Mamiran (Dymock 1890). *C. bulleyana* has been suggested as a good medication for paracetamol-induced liver injury.

Some species are strongly poisonous; *Corydalis caseana* has caused considerable losses among livestock in the western USA.

VERNACULAR NAMES

*K*orydallion was the name the ancient Greeks used for the crested or spurred lark and, due to the likeness of the flower to this bird (a great deal of imagination is needed) the names *Lerchensporn* and *Lerkespore* are indeed used for corydalis in Germany and Denmark respectively. In Britain, the epithet Larkspur has shifted to the genus *Consolida* in the Ranunculaceae, which has similarly spurred flowers.

In 'Flora von Mitteleuropa' (Hegi 1958) many names are mentioned, of which several relate to birds. The flower has been likened to a cock's comb (*Hähnchen; Hahner; Kikeriki; Crete de coq*), a goose beak (*bec d'oie*), a pigeon (*colombine*), a chicken (*poulette*), to a rocking horse (*Pferdchen*), or baby shoes. The names *Kuckuckblume* (German) and *gökstav* (Swedish) refer to early appearance of the flowers, at the time when the cuckoo starts singing. In Sweden *Corydalis* has been known as *nunneört* (nun's herb) since the 18th century, according to some authors because it has persisted by some old Swedish monasteries, but it is perhaps equally likely that the name is a translation of the German *Nunnenkraut*. *Hålört* (hollow herb) for *C. cava* alludes to the tuber.

HISTORICAL RÉSUMÉ

*C*arl Linnaeus included all Fumariaceous plants known to him in the genus *Fumaria*; thirteen species in all in his 'Species Plantarum' of 1753. Today they are dispersed in ten different genera. In *Corydalis* we find his *FF. capnoides, nobilis* and *'bulbosa'*. With the latter name Linnaeus covered the then known tuberous ones, recognising the three widespread Europeans *CC. cava, solida* and *intermedia* as varieties only (the number of tuberous species presently recognised is 95).

The first author to use the name *Corydalis* was Medikus (1789), though in relation to the south African genus now called *Cysticapnos*. Ventenat was next to go in 1803, referring to the species presently known as *Capnoides sempervirens* and *Adlumia fungosa*. According to the rules of priority laid down in the ICBN (International Code of Botanical Nomenclature) *Corydalis* should be used for *Cysticapnos* but the botanical scientific society has wisely construed an escape from such consequences; conservation of generic names enables us to adapt nomenclature to common usage. *Corydalis* in the modern conserved sense takes its starting point from de Candolle (in Lamarck & Candolle, 1805) and is typified by *C. solida*.

At this time, the name was used for almost all Fumariaceous taxa with many-seeded fruits but soon *Dicentra, Adlumia, Dactylicapnos,* and *Ceratocapnos* were segregated and *Corydalis* acquired more or less its present circumscription. *Capnoides* and *Pseudofumaria*, however, have only recently been reerected (Lidén 1986).

Since de Candolle (1821), who recognised 49 species, no comprehensive treatise of *Corydalis* has appeared, though regional accounts exist for many areas. A synopsis of the genus was presented by F. Fedde in 'Natürliche Pflanzenfamilien' (1936). He divided *Corydalis* into several sections, exemplifying each with a selection of the species known to him. An amended, but still very incomplete, sectional classification was given by Lidén (1986). A new subgeneric classification was suggested by Lidén *et al* (1997).

At present we estimate that the number of species in the whole genus will approach 440. A forthcoming volume of the flora of China, 'Flora Sinica' (Wu Zheng-Yih & al.) will cover the majority of the non-tuberous ones.

KEY TO THE GENERA OF THE FUMARIACEAE

1. Rosulate annuals with inner petals not apically united   *Hypecoum*
1. Inner petals coherent at the tip   **2**

2. Flowers bisymmetric   **3**
2. Flowers zygomorphic (unisymmetric)   **5**

3. Plants scandent   **4**
3. Plants not scandent   *Dicentra* **sensu lato**

4. Flowers yellow   *Dactylicapnos*
4. Flowers pink   *Adlumia*

5. Style persistent   **6**
5. Style early caducous   **9**

6. Plants not scandent   **7**
6. Plants scandent; leaves with tendrils   **8**

7. Inflorescence racemose; corolla not pink with a yellow tip   *Corydalis*
7. Inflorescence cymose; corolla pink or white with a yellow tip   *Capnoides*

8. Fruit one-seeded   *Discocapnos*
8. Fruit many-seeded   *Cysticapnos*

9. Fruit two to many-seeded   **10**
9. Fruit one-seeded   **12**

10. Leaves with tendrils   *Ceratocapnos*
10. Leaves without tendrils   **11**

11. Fruit many-seeded, dehiscent; seeds with elaiosomes   *Pseudofumaria*
11. Fruit two-seeded, semi-indehiscent; seeds lacking elaiosomes   *Sarcocapnos*

12. Leaves with tendrils   **13**
12. Leaves without tendrils   **14**

13. Fruit trigonous; pedicels long, capillary   *Trigonocapnos*
13. Fruit rectangular with ribbed or muricate walls; pedicels short, rather stout   *Ceratocapnos*

14. Racemes capitate   *Platycapnos*
14. Racemes not capitate   **15**

15. Fruit flat in cross-section, with a ribbed wall   *Sarcocapnos*
15. Fruit rounded in cross-section, without ribbed walls   **16**

16. Flowers yellow; fruit cylindrical   *Fumariola*
16. Flowers not yellow; fruit rounded   **17**

17. Racemes spike-like, with short equal pedicels   *Fumaria*
17. Racemes corymbose, with long geocarpic pedicels   **18**

18. Fruit with germination pores on a projecting beak   *Cryptocapnos*
18. Fruit beak without germination pores   *Rupicapnos*

PHYLOGENY AND SUBDIVISION

The genus can be divided into three subgenera according to seed-anatomy (Fukuhara & Lidén, 1995b) and DNA-sequences (Lidén *et al* 1995, 1997). The largest part, constituting the subgenus *Corydalis*, includes mainly mesophytic (i.e. plants adapted to a non-extreme water régime, like forest herbs) species with flattened stigmas with marginal papillae. Here belong for example all the tuberous species and nearly all forest, grassland, and scree species. The remaining two groups have flowers with blunt, short spurs, and small stigmas that are not laterally compressed. Furthermore, nearly all of them are yellow-flowered. The sections Strictae (exemplified by *C. rupestris*) and Bipapillata (*C. semenovii*) together constitute the subgenus *Chremnocapnos*, comprising more or less xerophytic (adapted to dry conditions) perennials. The subgenus *Sophorocapnos* is made up of four small sections where we find many annuals and biennials, but also some chasmophytic (growing on cliffs or rocks) perennials,

The large subgenus *Corydalis* comprises 28 sections. The largest of these is the mainly Chinese Fasciculatae (the famous *C. cashmeriana* is the type species of this section) with about 70 species, followed by the section Corydalis with 52 species, among them the common *C. solida*.

The tuberous species have frequently been segregated out as a separate subgenus or even genus but they do not form a coherent entity. It is obvious from morphology and DNA sequences that the section Duplotuber is not closely related to the other tuberous sections. The remaining ones (Radix-cava, Leonticoides, Dactylotuber, Corydalis) may perhaps constitute a natural group and are characterised, for example, by seed structure and the form of the single cotyledon, but the non-tuberous *C. nobilis* and its allies (sect. Capnogorium) have very similar seeds and fruits and are obviously closely related.

POLLINATION AND REPRODUCTIVE SYSTEMS

When the flowers are just about to open, the pollen is released from the anthers and deposited directly onto the stigmatic papillae but in most species the pollen is unable to germinate on its own stigma. This incompatibility can be partly broken in a few species by rupture of the stigmatic cells (a quite common phenomenon in flowering plants), which is of course one of the things that happens during insect-visits. Increased temperature has also been reported to enable selfing, though this is not in accordance with our experience. The pollen tubes of self pollen cannot compete with pollen from other individuals, however, and thus, under normal conditions, self-fertilisation is effectively prevented in the majority of species.

On the other hand, an evolutionary switch to self-fertilisation requires no morphological change, as the pollen is already in the right position. What is needed is a breakdown of the incompatibility system, which is relatively simple genetically, and obviously has happened repeatedly in the genus. The opposite change seems to be much less frequent, although the self-incompatibility of *C. longipes* is most easily explained as secondary, as the related species are all regular selfers.

There is a strong correlation between the breeding system and life-form. The annuals and biennials are self-fertile with very few exceptions, whereas most of the tuberous and rhizomatous ones are obligate out-crossers, though here the exceptions are more numerous.

Among the tuberous species, *C. cava* and its relatives all need pollen from another individual to set seed. In the section Leonticoides, *C. uniflora* is the sole self-compatible species. Not surprisingly, it is also the most insignificant in the section.

In sect. Corydalis, on the other hand, several species produce seeds by selfing; *CC. pumila, intermedia, gotlandica, caucasica, malkensis, angustifolia,* and *paczoskii*, are known to be self-fertile (and probably also *C. filistipes*), whereas the tiny (but pretty!) flowers of *C. orthoceras* require cross-pollination, as do the other species. In Duplotuber, *C. decumbens* is regularly selfing, whereas the other two are self-sterile. In the section Dactylotuber, *CC. benecincta* and *hemidicentra* are self-incompatible, whereas pods are spontaneously formed in cultivated plants of *CC. tianzhuensis, emanuelii, alpestris,* and *conorhiza*.

The self-compatible *C. pumila* has small flowers and a very faint smell, whereas the flowers of the related *C. solida* advertise their presence both olfactorily and visually. This correlation between breeding system and pollinator attractants is natural. Without insect-visits no fruits would be produced in *C. solida*. The cost of volatile compounds is on the other hand not negligible, and *C. pumila* prefers to invest its resources in a rich and secure seed set. A similar relation is seen between the self-sterile *C. longipes* and its self-fertile small-flowered relatives in the Himalaya (Lidén 1989). The prominent floral display in *C. caucasica* still suggests some caution before you jump to conclusions.

The high altitude perennials that have been checked so far, have proved self-sterile.

In natural habitats the early species are pollinated mainly by overwintering bumble bee queens (Ohara & Higashi 1994, Olesen & Knudsen 1994), or *Anthophora* bees (Hegi 1958), and in inhabited areas honey-bees are often important. The strongly scented *C. latiflora* is visited by bumble-bees, up to an altitude of at least 5000 m in the Himalaya. *C. hendersonii,* which can be found up to 6300 m above sea level, has quite large flowers and is probably insect-pollinated: to protect the sensitive parts, the flower is vertically held, with only the apices of the petals protruding above the densely packed leaves and bracts.

It is common to find the spur of almost all flowers pierced by nectar-thieves; bumble-bees are perhaps the most frequent sinners but the openings they make can later be utilised by other insects. An individual bee always uses the same strategy; some perform legitimate pollination during nectar search, while others regularly look for punctured spurs.

SEED AND DISPERSAL

The seeds of almost all species of *Corydalis* are equipped with fleshy appendages, known as elaiosomes. The sole exceptions are the two species of the section Bipapillata: *CC. semenovii* and *heracleifolia* from China. These appendages are rich in fat and are highly esteemed by ants. An investigation of the local distribution pattern of *C. aurea* in USA has shown that the plant sites are strongly correlated to ant nests (Beatty 1985). The distances covered by these small animals are not long, but still impressive considering their size; we have, for instance, noted an ant carrying a seed of *C. intermedia* about twenty metres.

In many species, especially the tuberous ones, the seeds are very sensitive to drought, and do not survive long periods of dry storage. The American and far East Asian annuals and biennials on the other hand (i. e. the subgenus *Sophorocapnos*), are quite resistant, and obviously have a different strategy. Their seeds are also different; they are usually flattened and strongly keeled and often have prominent ornamentation. The elaiosome is large, flat and membranous and is easily detached from the seed.

There are two different modes of primary seed-dispersal. Most non-tuberous species have explosively dehiscent capsules that scatter the seeds around to a distance of a couple of metres, and the same kind of dehiscence is found in most species of the section Dactylotuber. The other tuberous groups have capsules that gently open at the time of ripening. This includes *C. decumbens* and its allies, which are remotely related to the other tuberous sections, and also the non-tuberous section Capnogorium, i.e. *C. nobilis* and related species. The subgenera *Strictae* and *Sophorocapnos* also have non-explosive capsules. The mode of dehiscence is correlated with the presence or absence of papillae on the inner epidermis of the fruit (Brückner 1993).

There are two types of explosive dehiscence in the genus: in the sections Dactylotuber, Elatae, Archaecapnos, part of Fasciculatae (*curviflora*-group, *cashmeriana*-group), Hamatae, and in *C. incisa* and its allies, the fruiting pedicels are erect with pendent fruits, whereas in the sections Ramoso-sibiricae, Fumarioides, Chrysocapnos, Davidianae, and part of Fasciculatae (the *linarioides*-group and most scree-species) the pedicels are strongly recurved.

Vegetative dispersal is important in some groups. Old tubers of species in the sections Radix-cava and Leonticoides can attain a very large size and eventually disintegrate into independent parts. In the section Corydalis each full-grown tuber generally produces two flowering shoots. Each of the shoots will build up a fresh tuber for next season and thus the number of tubers will double each year. The Duplotuber species are very efficient in producing adventitious tubers, and also in some species of the section Corydalis, (*CC.*

gracilis, lineariloba, ohii, orthoceras, papilligera, repens, turtschaninovii, and *yanhusuo*) axillary tubers are formed from the scale-leaf. Several Chinese species (especially of the section Elatae), produce bulbils in the axils of cauline leaves (*CC. bulbilligera, dulongjianensis, esquirolii, flexuosa p.p., sheareri, schusteriana, schweriniana, vivipara*). The bulb-like hibernation buds in the section Fasciculatae (exemplified by *C. cashmeriana*) can, in some species, probably function as propagules. Last, stolons permit some species to exploit their immediate neighbourhoods, as with *C. scouleri,* the *C. polyphylla*-group, a few Fasciculatae species, and even in a few tuberous species like the above-mentioned *C. repens, lineariloba,* and *buschii.* It is notable (though hardly surprising) that vegetative multiplication is important mainly in self-incompatible perennials. In *C. pumila,* which is a regular selfer and produces abundant seeds, only one stem is usually produced from each tuber.

CYTOLOGY

The basic chromosome number in *Corydalis,* as in the rest of the family, is x=8 and the most common somatic number is 2n=16 (i. e. most species have the normal diploid condition). Especially in the tuberous sections there are also polyploid species, with twice or three times as many chromosomes or more. The highest chromosome number is found in the North American rhizomatous perennial *C. scouleri*; more than 140 chromosomes compete for space in its somatic cells (still, it is a long way to the 550 chromosomes of the palm *Voaniaola gerardii,* the angiosperm record holder, Johnson 1989).

The known tetraploids (2n=32) in sect. Leonticoides are *CC. afghanica, griffithii, popovii, ledebouriana,* and *maracandica.* The others are all diploid. In the section Corydalis, *CC. malkensis, ambigua, orthoceras* var. *orthoceras,* and *gotlandica* are tetraploid, while hexaploid (48), pentaploid (40), and tetraploid numbers have been found in the Japanese *C. lineariloba* complex and in *C. papilligera.* In the *C. cava* complex, diploids as well as tetraploids are found.

MONSTERS

Peloric flowers, where spurs are lacking or present on both of the outer petals (very rarely all four petals may be spurred) are not uncommon. On rare occasions wholly peloric plants are encountered. Sepals are sometimes transformed into malformed petals. In a *C. solida* from Macedonia (one of the clones of Strindberg & Zetterlund 88-17), the inflorescence is a much-branched pyramidal panicle, which is unique in the genus. One of our plants of *C. magadanica* produced several flowers with three or four carpels, instead of two.

HISTORY OF CULTIVATION

(Because of our limited acquaintance with the continental garden tradition, the following account is mainly based on British literature and may thus be rather insular in coverage)

The seeds' intolerance against dry storage has been a limiting factor to the introduction of new species into cultivation. For instance, we know that famous collectors like George Forrest, Frank Kingdon-Ward, Reginald Farrer, and others, sent home seeds of many of the Chinese species but still only the low altitude crevice species like *C. wilsonii* and *C. saxicola* became established in gardens. Today, collection is much easier and transport much faster; circumstances that have fostered the present plentitude of cultivated species.

The first cultivated *Corydalis* species were found at monasteries, where the Godly people used them for their pharmaceutic properties (see above). We believe, however, that some of the less pious monks and nuns appreciated them as much for their beauty as for their utility. *CC. cava, solida,* and a third species were grown in German gardens at least as early as 1561 and *C. cava* was cultivated in Britain by 1596.

The next species to make an impression in literature is *C. nobilis.* Seeds collected by Erik Laxmann in Siberia were sown in 1765 in Hammarby North of Stockholm, the garden of Carl von Linné (Linnaeus). The

Linnéan stock was probably the derivation of all other cultivated *nobilis* plants until very recently. In 1772 it was pictured in 'Hortus Vindobonensis', and introduced into Britain in 1783 by Mr. John Graefer. Linnaeus wrote that 'this plant that endures our winters, sets seed in abundance, and is so decorative, will without doubt be one of the most common plants in European gardens'. This has yet to happen.

In 1794 both *CC. cava* and *solida* are pictured in *Curtis's Botanical Magazine*. *C. angustifolia* was introduced in 1814, and *C. bracteata* appears nine years later (*Bot. Mag.* 1833).

During the period from 1830 to 1890, several species, like *CC. bracteata* (*Gartenflora* 1865), *schanginii* (*Bot. Mag.* 1833, *Gartenflora* 1865), *glaucescens* (Gartenflora 1878, Bot. Mag. 1887), *ledebouriana* (*Gartenflora* 1879, Bot. Mag. 1887), *sewerzowii* (*Gartenflora* 1882, *Bot. Mag.* 1886), *semenovii* (*The Garden* 1884, *Gartenflora* 1886), and *gortschakovii* (*Gartenflora* 1885) enters the horticultural stage. These introductions were mainly from Albert von Regel who travelled widely in Central Asia during this period and brought back plants that were distributed from St. Petersburg to prominent gardens and bulb-dealers in mainland Europe, as well as in the British Isles.

In 1880 *C. bracteata* was awarded an F.C.C. when 'exhibited by Mr. Elwes, a few weeks ago, at South Kensington, when it was considered by the Floral Committee to be worthy of a First Class Certificate. But....., we consider it by no means a fit subject for such distinction'. (*The Garden*, May 29, 1880).

The American species are first mentioned in 1886. The first record, to our surprise, is for *C. caseana* subsp. *caseana* (cultivated in Ipswich). *C. scouleri* was not mentioned in British journals until 1895, when it was imported from 'a continental nurseryman by the name of Meerbeck'.

From 1894 to 1904 the Chinese cliff species *CC. tomentella, saxicola* (as *thalictrifolia*; *Bot. Mag.* 1902), *tomentosa, wilsonii* (*Bot. Mag.* 1904) and the woodlander *C. cheilanthifolia* are frequently mentioned in horticultural literature. *C. saxicola* was awarded an F.C.C. in 1902 and *C. wilsonii* an A.M. in 1905. These species were mainly introduced by Ernest Henry Wilson in 1902 for Messrs. Veitch and Sons, though the presence of *C. tomentella* (A.M. 1937) is to be credited to M. de Vilmorin.

The sect. *Leonticoides* species *C. erdelii* (as *C. rutifolia*) and *C. popovii* make brief appearances during the same period and *C. angustifolia* was reintroduced by the Dutch firm of van Tubergen.

As Europe recovered from the First World War, *C. solida* 'Transsylvanica' appeared for the first time (1925). One year later *C. 'allenii'* appeared.

In the early 1930s the exquisite *C. verticillaris* (*Bot. Mag.* 1937) made a brief appearence on the scene, having been collected in Persia by E.K. Balls, and was awarded a P.C. in 1933 and an A.M. in 1934. The Cypriot *C. rutifolia* was also exhibited, whereas the Cretan *C. uniflora* was first collected in 1937 by Peter Davis who wrote that 'the tubers are hell to collect'.

The first of the blue-flowered species, *C. cashmeriana*, made its very first appearence at the Alpine Garden Society spring show in 1934 and was immediately rewarded with a Certificate of Merit, to be followed by an A.M. in 1938 and an F.C.C. in 1955. From then onwards it has proved to be the most frequently mentioned species.

The Second World War saw no further introductions and from 1949 the only species able to attract any attention were *C. cashmeriana* and *C. solida* 'transsylvanica'.

Little more happened before 1970. *C. solida* subsp. *incisa* was introduced and the A., C. & W. (Albury, Cheese and Watson) expedition collected plants of the *C. oppositifolia-erdelii* group in Turkey.

In 1969 *CC. ledebouriana, afghanica* and *griffithii* were introduced by Per Wendelbo and Ian Hedge and during the 1970s the Iranian *CC. chionophila* subsp. *chionophila* and subsp. *firouzii*, and the Central Asian *CC. aitchisonii* and *darwasica* were brought back by botanists of fame but they did not reach the gardening public until the 1980s.

The second of the blue species, *C. fumariifolia* (*Bot. Mag.* 1978, as *C. ambigua* var. *yezoensis*) received a P.C. when first staged in 1970 and yet another P.C. (as *C. ambigua v. yunnanensis*) in 1973. An A.M. was earned in 1979.

Corydalis caucasica and *C. malkensis* (as *C. caucasica* var. *alba*) are also mentioned for the first time in connection with P.C.s in 1973 (*C. malkensis* A.M. 1995).

In 1978 and 1979 the Royal Botanic Gardens, Kew, showed *CC. diphylla, C. oppositifolia* (as *C. rutifolia* subsp. *kurdica*) and *popovii* , all of which received P.C.s.

The introduction of the Himalayan *C. ecristata* marks the end of a century of slowly increasing corydalis interest. In 1981 Brian Mathew gave a lecture on the genus at the Fifth International Rock Garden Plant Conference held in Nottingham and so instigated the present craze for these charming little plants.

CULTIVATION TODAY

During the last fifteen years horticultural interest in the genus *Corydalis* has increased dramatically. During the late 1970s and the 1980s we were reaping the fruits of the botanical expeditions to Turkey, Iraq, Iran and Afghanistan that took place in the 1960s and the early 1970s. We owe much to people like Paul Furse and his followers.

The people that did most of the work, however, were plant-lovers trapped behind the iron-curtain. Gardeners from Czechoslovakia, Latvia, and Estonia travelled widely within the Soviet-empire, established contacts in the remotest areas and brought some fantastic plants into cultivation.

From the Caucasus came *CC. nariniana, seisumsiana, alexeenkoana, kuznetsovii,* and *vittae.* From C. Asia the following species were introduced: *CC. maracandica, macrocentra, nudicaulis, glaucescens, schanginii, schanginii* subsp. *ainae,* and *ruksansii.* From the easternmost part of Siberia they brought us *CC. turtschaninovii, ornata, buschii* and later (in the early 1990s) *CC. ussuriensis, gracilis, magadanica,* and *gorinensis.* We owe these 'botanical warriors' a great deal.

In the 1970s, tourism increased in Turkey and the Caucasus and many bulb-enthusiasts travelled there, revealing species like *CC. oppositifolia, erdelii, lydica, wendelboi, paschei, triternata, haussknechtii, henrikii, emanuelii, conorhiza* and *alpestris.*

New forms of common species have been selected in Europe and even a new species, *C. zetterlundii,* has been found.

From Japan better forms of *C. fumariifolia* have been introduced, as well as the tiny *CC. orthoceras, lineariloba, papilligera* and *fukuharae.*

The Himalaya has been exploited from 1970 onwards and perennial species like *CC. pakistanica, gortschakovii, ecristata, meifolia,* and *jigmei* have become established; others, for instance *C. latiflora* and *C. megacalyx,* smelled the low-land air and unfortunately soon succumbed.

From 1981 several (mostly British) expeditions have gone to China. The number one corydalis-country is gradually opening up and we face an exciting future. To date about 50 species have been introduced from there, most of them for the first time. The first to thrill us was the *C. cashmeriana*-like *C. pachycentra,* introduced from Cang Shan by the SBEC (Sino-British Expedition to Cangshan) expedition. Later expeditions have brought us *CC. flexuosa, elata, mucronata, adunca, atuntsuensis, balfouriana, benecincta, calcicola, densispica, eugeniae, hamata, hemidicentra, kokiana, lathyrophylla, melanochlora, pseudoadoxa, smithiana, taliensis, tenerrima, latiloba, yunnanensis* and others, but there are still many species awaiting introduction. Some are performing very well; *C. flexuosa* has made an unrivalled horticultural career; a few are sulking and seem bound to disappear.

The American subspecies of *C. caseana* have also been brought into cultivation and have become well established.

Todays corydalis-vogue is mirrored by the exhibitions and awards presented in recent times: 1986;—*C. nariniana* (as *C. persica*), P.C.; 1987;—*C. darwasica,* P.C.; 1988;—*C. solida* 'Beth Evans', P.C.; 1989;—*C. chionophila* subsp. *firouzii, C. aitchisonii* (as *nevskii*) & *C. maracandica,* P.C. 1990;—*C. flexuosa,* P.C. (A.M. 1991); 1992:—*C. solida* subsp. *incisa* & *C. integra* P.C.; 1994;—*C. solida* 'Nettleton Pink', *C. thyrsiflora,* P.C.; 1995;—*C. angustifolia, C. schanginii* subsp. *ainae, C. solida* 'Highland Mist', P.C.; *C. angustifolia, C. malkensis,* A.M.

Some horticultural hybridisation and selection has started, particularly with the red and pink forms of *C. solida* and there is a great scope for future cultivars. With more experience about natural growing conditions, we should be able to cultivate an increasing number of *Corydalis* in our gardens

At present perhaps 150 species are in cultivation in different gardens, a figure that will increase with new expeditions to Tibet (Xizang), China, and Korea........

Plate 1. *Corydalis alexeenkoana*
Plate 2. *Corydalis caucasica* subsp. *caucasica*
Plate 3. *Corydalis vittae*
Plate 4. *Corydalis vittae*
Plate 5. *Corydalis caucasica* subsp. *abantensis*

6

7

8

9

10

Plate 6. *Corydalis malkensis*
Plate 7. *Corydalis integra*
Plate 8. *Corydalis haussknechtii*
Plate 9. *Corydalis angustifolia*
Plate 10. *Corydalis zetterlundii*

PESTS IN NATURE

Corydalis are apparently not very palatable and have few enemies. One creature, the Clouded Apollo butterfly (*Parnassius mnemosyne*) is, however, wholly dependent on *Corydalis*. Its larvae feed on various species (in Europe mostly *CC. solida, intermedia* and *cava*). The sensory system of the female adult is indeed miraculous; Despite the fact that there is hardly any trace of the plant above ground by midsummer, she still manages to pick out the right spots, laying her eggs on withered leaves or grass, apparently guided by the smell of the dormant underground tubers. The Clouded Apollo is locally abundant in south and central Europe, and scattered northwards to central Norway. All above-ground parts of the plant are relished, and in some areas one frequently finds plants with the nutritious front part of the flowers consumed.

Wasps of the genus *Ailax* use corydalis-fruits as nurseries for their larvae. Infested fruits become swollen, spongy, and sterile. This has been recorded for corydalis species from many different sections but not on the spring ephemeral species. The rust *Cerotelium asari* switches between *Asarum* and *Corydalis lineariloba* (Ono 1995).

PESTS AND DISEASES IN CULTIVATION

The tuberous species are too ephemeral to host any serious diseases. In the early seedling-stage they are susceptible to fungal attacks but we have not identified either genus nor species. The typical propagation diseases are caused by a number of fungal genera like *Rhizoctonia, Phytium, Phytopthora, Fusarium, Alternaria* and *Botrytis*. Infections are triggered by the condition of the plant and the best way to prevent them is to use a sterilised growing-medium and to be cautious with water. If one is to use fungicides, one must remember that these various fungi are a heterogeneous group; a chemical that controls *Botrytis* has no effect on *Phytium* or *Phytophtora*. Since the chemicals vary from country to country and from time to time we are not giving any recommendations. *Botrytis* and other fungi can also attack the vegetative parts of adult plants under extreme conditions, such as during very mild winters, when plants come into growth far too early and become leggy and vulnerable.

Mice and voles can be serious pests, once they have acquired a taste for the tubers. Some seasons they neglect them entirely; other seasons they ruthlessly dig into every pot in their search for gourmet rodent-food (or, maybe, a hallucinatory trip). To be certain, take the greatest precaution to catch mice when they invade the alpine house in autumn, and do your very best to keep voles away from the open garden. An interesting observation on the field mouse by J. Wood of Kirkstall, was printed in *The Garden* 1889 (the first record we have seen of this pest, and it also gives us a clue to an unusual plant-dispersion) '... I have more than once heard surprise expressed as to how strong bulbs could have been carried some distance from the old clumps when no digging or hoeing had been done.... The field mouse is very fond of them, and what I saw was that when one tried to eat them, the marble-like tubers rolled away, followed by the little animal, until at last the partly-eaten tubers were carried several yards from their original place'.

Slugs can occasionally become a problem with the tuberous species and are a regular nuisance for the summer-growing ones.

Deer, roe deer, elk, hare and rabbit are all capable of ruining the spring display by browsing the flowering plants. The only remedies against these pests are better fences, a pet wolf or a shot-gun. In the Netherlands, bulbs are protected against browsing by spraying them with a very weak solution of tabasco (Pepper Sauce).

Red spider mite and powdery mildew are big problems when you grow summer-green species in the alpine house (but not in the open garden) and they have to be controlled. When you spot the damage it is generally too late, so keep a close eye on the plants. The mildew is probably *Erysyphe ranunculi*, since the attacks coincides with the same symptoms on various members of the *Ranunculaceae*. Downy mildew, caused by *Peronospora corydalis*, is a problem in the cultivation of *Yanhusuo* in China (Bao D. 1988). Its overwintering oospores on the plant remains are the main source of primary infection.

Greenfly can occasionally be a problem but they are easily controlled.

Be aware, however, the chemicals used to control red spider mite, greenfly and powdery mildew often tend to scorch the fragile foliage of *Corydalis*. The best thing is to find a better place to grow plants; spraying is a nasty and temporary action, not a solution.

THE TUBEROUS SPECIES

The tuberous *Corydalis* are most common in summer-dry areas, although several species of the sections *Duplotuber* and *Corydalis* can endure quite wet summers in Korea and Japan. The section *Dactylotuber* has some species at high altitudes in monsoon areas like Bhutan, SE Tibet and NW Yunnan.

The tuberous groups have at times been distinguished as a separate subgenus or even genus (*Pistolochia* Bernhardi). It is clear, however, that the tuberous sections do not form a natural entity. DNA-sequences suggest a rather distant relation between Duplotuber and the other tuberous sections. Dactylotuber stands out in the usually explosively dehiscent capsules, the usually crested petals and different stigma characteristics, and may possibly also constitute an independent tuberous lineage. Swollen underground structures are also present in other groups, take for example the radish-like or carrot-like tap-root of the biennials *CC. incisa* and *linstowiana* respectively, or the fasciculate fleshy storage roots of *C. cashmeriana* and its allies.

SEED DEVELOPMENT AND GERMINATION

At the time of dispersal the embryo of a tuberous species (*CC. solida* and *ledebouriana* have been investigated more closely) is still hardly discernible and growth is very slow during the summer. It is not until October that the embryo starts to enlarge, reaching its full size by the end of the year, then occupying more than half of the seed (Lidén & Staaf 1995). It is a combination of time and temperature that triggers the growth of the embryo. If the seeds are chilled too early, they cease to grow altogether. If kept at a constant temperature they will also not develop normally. They attain their full size in early winter and germinate in the following spring. This is in agreement with the behaviour of the American *C. flavula*, in which a hot summer period followed by a cold autumn is necessary for embryo growth (Baskin & Baskin 1994). That species, however, is a winter annual and the seeds germinate in the autumn.

The tuberous groups are remarkable in seedling structure; the seedling germinates with one cotyledon only and no other leaf appears in the first year (the section Duplotuber excepted). During the short growing season the cotyledon invests all of its assimilate into the formation of a tiny tuber which somehow manages to survive until the next spring. Single cotyledon seedlings are known from several other Fumariaceae, like *Corydalis* sect. Oocapnos and sect. Fasciculatae, *Dicentra peregrina* and *D. uniflora* and perhaps other species. Several other examples are known, mainly from geophytic representatives of the Umbelliferae and the Ranunculaceae.

In the section Corydalis, a single very small three-lobed leaf is formed next year, enough to secure a slightly bigger tuber for the third season. In the greenhouse a flowering stem is usually not produced until the fourth year, and under natural conditions it may take longer.

A second season seed-pan of a species of the section Leonticoides looks surprisingly similar to a first-year pan, except that the number of cotyledons has seemingly doubled, because each tuber has developed two small entire leaves. In the third season leaves more typical of the adult plant are produced. Plants will eventually flower at an age of four to six years.

TUBER DEVELOPMENT

The morphology and development of the tuber differ substantially between the sections. In Duplotuber it is a swollen stem-portion with several leaves from which flowering stems arise in axillary positions. In *C. decumbens* a few new tubers are formed each year in leaf-axils from the old tuber, as condensed leafy shoots producing numerous roots from their bases. The biggest of the new tubers is usually formed on top of the old tuber, and is, according to Ryberg (1960), formed by the surviving apical meristem and the tuber thus has a monopodial growth. *C. ternata* has a similar tuber development, but also produces axillary tubers from scale leaves in the lower part of the stems. In *C. buschii* the tubers are elongated structures, only swollen at the apex. In spite of superficial heterogeneity, however, the same basic pattern applies to all species of the section.

In the section Corydalis, on the other hand, the tuber is an annually regenerated rounded structure crowned at apex by a ring of scale-leaves. New buds are formed axillary to these scale leaves and radical leaves are wholly absent. At the base of the new shoot the incipient tuber penetrates the old tuber and a single fascicle of roots protrudes from its base. The new tuber(s) thus seems to consume the old tuber from the interior and the remnants of the latter will surround the fresh tuber as a thin papery skin (in *C. papilligera* this outer layer becomes rather tough and resistant). After flowering, new buds (usually one or two) are again initiated axillary to the lower scales. They will eventually give rise to next years flowering shoots and then die. The succession of shoot-generations is thus sympodial. Each flowering stem will build up one fresh tuber; if more than one, the daughter-tubers are usually free from each other, except in *CC. schanginii, nudicaulis,* and *ruksansii,* where they are often fused.

Corydalis cava has a perennial tuber, which enlarges outwards each year, becoming hollow with age. According to J. M. Olesen (1994) this is a necessary strategy for a forest plant with this kind of cambium, as otherwise the volume would become too large for the green parts to sustain. In the related species *C. blanda,* which grows in open alpine habitats, the tuber is more irregular and flattened.

In section Leonticoides the tuber can become very large and attain a more irregular form and will often divide into separate parts eventually. Roots are borne in fascicles whereas in section Radix-cava they are scattered singly over the surface, at least in young tubers. In these groups the apical meristem does not die away, but continues its growth in successive seasons (i.e. the growth point has a monopodial growth, and flowering stems arise from the axils of scale-leaves on a short indefinite axis). In contrast to the section Corydalis, mature specimens produce both flowering stems and radical leaves from the tuber.

The section Dactylotuber is, according to Ryberg (1955), sympodial, although very different in structure from section Corydalis.

HYBRIDISATION

Hybrids are easily produced in all the tuberous sections but crossings *between* the sections have not been successful. Natural hybrids between *CC. cava* and *solida* have repeatedly been reported but should be judged with some scepticism.

The primary hybrids have a reduced fertility but are usually not completely sterile, especially not in section Leonticoides. It seems as if the crossing barriers are generally higher between species of section Corydalis (*C. solida x bracteata* and *C. pumila x intermedia* for instance, both have 100% malformed and dwarf pollen), except when the parents are very closely related (as in *C. solida x pumila* and *C. wendelboi x tauricola*).

Even if the parental plants differ in ploidy-level (number of chromosome-sets) hybrids are easily formed, but they are then highly sterile. A cross between a diploid and a tetraploid (e.g. *C. chionophila* x *popovii, diphylla* x *afghanica, chionophila* x *ledebouriana*) will produce a triploid offspring which is often surprisingly similar to the tetraploid parent which contributes twice as much genetic material, so look twice before you conclude that the cross has failed.

The primary hybrid may sometimes show unexpected characteristics: for instance, a cross between a cream-flowered *C. alexeenkoana* and a pale red *C. solida* proved to be dark purple. The hybrid *C. afghanica* x *popovii* has normal green leaves but the racemes, including bracts, lack chlorophyll, while the fruits, on the other hand, are green! In this same hybrid another noteworthy effect occurs, namely loss of self-incompatibility.

The Baltic endemic *C. gotlandica* stems from a hybrid between *C. solida* and *intermedia,* a conclusion reached with the aid of DNA-analysis (RAPD). This species now grows in profusion in and around the village of Västergarn and is rapidly expanding, whereas the parental species are not found in the close vicinity. On the nearby little island of Stora Karlsö, however, all four Swedish species of the section *Corydalis* coexist, and the cradle of the new species might well have been sited there quite recently. This is a nice example of how a species of hybrid origin can exploit a niche not available to either of its parents, even if it is a poor competitor where it originated. Apparently, neither *C. intermedia* nor *C. solida* thrive well in the sandy soils at Västergarn.

KEY TO THE TUBEROUS SECTIONS

1. Stigma transversely oblong with 4 papillae; seeds keeled, papillose   **Section Duplotuber (p. 112)**
1. Stigma squarish, circular, or obtriangular; seeds neither keeled nor papillose   **2**

2. Leaves 2, opposite, usually sessile   **Section Leonticoides (p. 81)**
2. Leaves not opposite, usually clearly stalked   **3**

3. Stem with at least one conspicuous scale-leaf below the leaves   **4**
3. Stem without scale leaves   **Section Radix-cava (p. 76)**

4. Tuber rounded; stem usually with one scale-leaf and two leaves   **Section Corydalis (p. 21)**
4. Tuber often divided below; stem usually with 2-3 scale-leaves and 2-4 leaves

    Section Dactylotuber (p. 99)

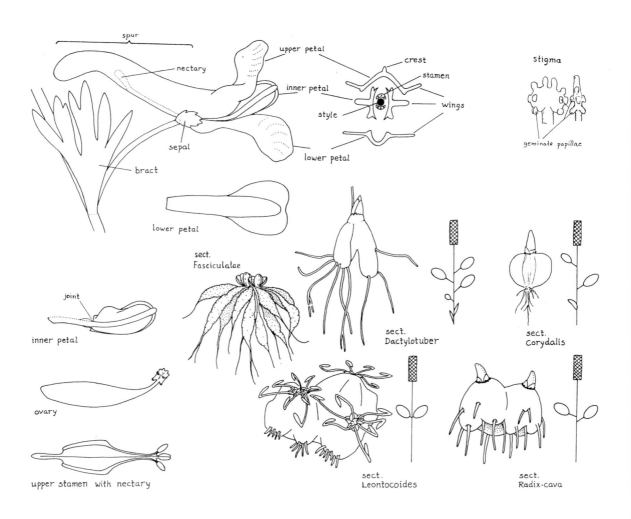

SECTION CORYDALIS

This is the largest of the tuberous sections and is second in size within the genus after section Fasciculatae. It has a wide distribution throughout temperate Eurasia, with an outlier in North Algeria (*C. densiflora*). Although including greater variability than the other tuberous sections, it is still easily recognised by its peculiar tuber structure, the single scale-leaf and the possession of usually two alternate stem-leaves. The stems range in length from about 5 cm in small individuals of *C. intermedia* and *C. pumila*, to about 40 cm in *C. schanginii*. They are (usually) glabrous but minute one-celled hairs are to be found now and then on petioles and peduncles in several species. However, this character is not even stable within individuals: one branch may be 'pubescent' while another is glabrous or, again, they may show pubescence one year and not the next. We have recorded such a phenomenon in *CC. fumariifolia, gorinensis , lineariloba, repens* and *solida*.

CULTIVATION. From the horticultural point of view this is the most important group within the entire genus. They are the easiest to grow, extremely hardy and accordingly long-lived. Striking variability has been revealed over the last decade; just consider *C. solida* with its red and pink forms from Romania, which have been a revelation, while only shallow investigations in the Balkans have presented us with numerous new forms in colours ranging from cherry-red to ice-blue and pure white. Yet there must be more to come and they will all make glorious garden-plants.

If given decent treatment all species will thrive in cultivation and some will produce fat tubers 3-4 cm in diameter. Bearing in mind that in nature the tubers are often minute (pea-size seems to be the optimum for many species) this development is astonishing. Plants in culture tend to become larger with more floriferous racemes and longer pedicels than plants in the wild. Flowers look especially good when a cold winter delays them until March; in a mild winter they start early and suffer from poor light and muggy weather and rarely produce their full potential under such conditions..

PROPAGATION. Seed is, of course, the best way to raise a good, numerous and healthy stock. Some of the species seed prolifically in the open garden while others need to be nursed under more controlled conditions. There are several obstacles which have to be overcome:

First, most species are self-sterile and have to be cross-pollinated with other individuals in order to yield seed. With the rarer species this is best done with a small paint-brush for, if you leave it to the insects, there is a chance that closely related species may hybridise.

The soft seed-pods tend to open up at the busiest time of the year, revealing the shiny black seeds with their white fatty appendages. They are easily forgotten though not by the ants who will carry them away out of reach. Inspect the capsules regularly, and give them friendly squeeze with your fingers along their sides: if ripe they will open readily.

If you have been devoted enough to secure a good crop of seeds, you should also take the time to sow them right away, when you can expect a 100% germination the following spring. If you delay, try not to wait any longer than August before sowing; seed that has been stored over the autumn may germinate but often does so very poorly and somewhat sporadically over several years.

Sow the seeds in pots or trays in a well-prepared, sterilised compost consisting of roughly equal parts loam, moss-peat, sand and coarse grit; the compost should be able to stay intact for three to four years. Sow thinly onto the surface and sieve on some clean fine sand so that it just covers the seeds and finally top with a grit-mulch that keeps the surface open and aerated. Water thoroughly and put the containers in a cool shady spot in the garden, preferably in a cold frame, and wait. It is important to ensure that the pots are never allowed to dry out. Frost is beneficial to good germination!

Germination takes place at the same time as the parent plants start to show, in February and March. Young seedlings are extremely thin-skinned and juicy and are prone to fungal attacks (damping off), particularly if the weather is rainy, foggy and cold. As soon as the cotyledons appear it is wise to take control: remove the grit-mulch, so that the moisture-level in the compost can be estimated and switch to a 'water when needed' regime. If you are an environmental-crook, then some fungicides can be used to control fungal attacks. Liquid fertilisers should be applied as a very weak solution.

When the seedlings have overcome the initial stress, continue a restrained approach by careful watering and routine checks. The seedlings will be in active growth for about as long as their parents. When dormancy sets in during May, watering should be decreased but not stopped: the compost should remain slightly moist during dormancy. The pea-sized corms could be left in their seed pots for at least another year, provided nutrients are applied. We sprinkle each pot with a teaspoon of bonemeal each September and, sometimes, apply liquid (standard) feeds once or twice during the spring. After a second growing season the tubers will have become crowded and they may need to be divided up when the planting season starts in August. Pay attention to the depth that the tubers have placed themselves and use this measurement for all future planting. Seedlings will flower after two to four years from sowing.

In Section *Corydalis* the tubers renew themselves annually and divide regularly at the same time. Examination of the tubers in the autumn will reveal the number of divisions each will separate into the following year, for each bud will develop into a new tuber. Normally one good-sized tuber will double or triple in one season and this means that in order to produce commercial quantities it is necessary to have a large motherstock. Some species produce axillary tubers in the scale-leaves: these tubers are not like the others in that they are more irregular (amorphic) but they will look normal after another growing season.

HORTICULTURAL DIVISIONS. The Section can be divided into three groups horticulturally; the Western Woodlanders, the Bulb-belt Species and the Eastern Woodlanders.

The Western Woodlanders

This group consists of *CC. angustifolia, caucasica, gotlandica, intermedia, malkensis, paczoskii, pumila, solida* and the *alexeenkoana* group. Some of these may grow in meadows at higher altitudes but their requirements in cultivation are the same.

They are the easiest to please: all can be grown out-doors under normal garden-conditions, in the rock-garden, the flower border, in woodland and, under favourable conditions, they may even become naturalised in grass.

In nature their tubers are found at a shallow depth and this is the way they should be planted in cultivation. Plant them approximately 10 cm deep in a fertile, neutral to slightly acid, well-drained loam

and they will thrive. A thin mulch of leaves, coarse peat, or bark may also prove beneficial and this will give the buds some protection from intermittent frosts. It will also prevent the soil from dirtying the plant in rainy spring weather.

Planting may be carried out during the dormant period (June to September), from the point when the leaves are yellow until the developing roots make the tuber difficult to handle. The most important thing is to keep the tubers juicy and plump; they do not like drying, though they will stand some desiccation.

In pots. Pot-grown specimens will flourish in any decent growing medium. The best compost is a good bulb-compost (i.e. a free-draining mixture with a rather high nutrient level). John Innes No. 2 mixed with 1/3 chippings + sand will work fine. In this they should be planted with the bud at least 5 cm below the surface. They look best if three adult tubers are planted together in a 12 cm pot. For a single tuber, an 8 cm pot is sufficient. A large pan packed with tubers may be impressive but can become a bit too crowded to be really beautiful.

Potting is normally done in August or September. If they have been rested correctly there will be no roots to be seen; if they have been too moist through the last period of the dormancy the roots may well have started to grow; if so they must be handled with care. Clean them from remnants of dead tissues but take care, for it is easy to damage the thin skin. Plant them, cover them, finish with a layer of grit and plunge the pots into a suitable medium.

By the end of September it is time to start watering. The roots will emerge directly if the nights are cool and the compost is moist (if, for some reason, you want to delay action, then store the tubers at an even temperature of around 18°C). After the first watering the pots must be kept moist thereafter.

From September onwards the plants are going through intense activity; cells are dividing and stem, leaves and flowers are formed and they will start to grow slowly upwards. By December or January they are just below the surface, the shoot lying developed and ready, folded within its scale-leaf. In this position it will remain until temperature and (to a minor extent) daylength, are favourable. Then they rapidly emerge, mainly as a result of a potent cell-elongation.

Drying out during this final phase can be fatal. We do not even keep them 'just moist' as is often recommended, but keep them moist from planting time until the leaves are about to wither. In the winter-months the pots are often frozen solid but this does not harm the plants. However, late frosts, after a mild winter, can be disastrous and sometimes kill off a year's growth. The plants will usually survive but they will be severely weakened.

In spring they require plenty of water: dry them out and you will understand why. A corydalis is primarily water temporarily contained within a thin skin. Supporting tissue is almost absent and lack of water causes immediate wilting. They demand a lot of water during the first period and not until the flowers are wholly expanded will they show some moderation.

Since we use a compost which is rather rich in nutrients we do not feed our pot-grown corydalis but if a leaner compost is used, feeding is essential. Use a weak liquid fertiliser (0.1-0.2 per cent) from the point when the flowers are wholly developed until the leaves start to fade.

When flowering is over and seed, it is hoped, set, the leaves will quickly turn yellow and, within a week, start to shrivel. Give them water to this point, and they will get the opportunity to withdraw as much nutrient as possible into the tuber which will become plump, pregnant-looking, and shiny.

Over the summer it is wise to keep the pots shaded and plunged in sand. This keeps the compost a little cooler and, with clay-pots, enables plants to be supplied with a small amount of moisture through the plunge. With this group we prefer to water the plunge every week or every second week (depending on the weather) through the summer. As the cool autumn approaches, one has to show some restraint with watering in order to delay rooting.

The 'Bulb-Belt' Species

This is a large group of species rather vaguely defined from the group above; *CC. glaucescens, haussknechtii, henrikii, integra, nudicaulis, paschei, ruksansii, schanginii, tauricola, triternata, wendelboi* and *zetterlundii* are probably best placed here. They come from woods, oak-scrub, meadows and screes at Mediterranean latitudes, as does an overwhelming majority of the Eurasian geophytes (summer-dormant bulbous, tuberous and rhizomatous plants) and are accustomed to a drier summer than the species already dealt with. All of them have been tried in the open garden and have done quite well. However, they do not show such sparkling enthusiasm as the members of the previous group. The best position is in the sunnier parts of the rock-garden but better still is a

bulb frame which can be covered in summer to control moisture level. The ambitious gardener can ensure their survival by lifting the tubers when the foliage is about to wither (see section Leonticoides) and storing them in a cool shady position. Since they want a dry but not desiccating rest it is wise to pack them in dry peat or sand in a plastic bag. Otherwise the horticultural requirements are more or less the same as for the Western Woodlanders except that the pH can vary from neutral to slightly basic.

They are all marvellous pot-subjects in a well-lit alpine house and can be grown as the former group, except that the dormant period should be drier. This does not mean dust-dry and if the plunge is watered every second week this will be sufficient, even in a sunnier spot in the alpine house or the bulb frame. Under such treatment they are not prone to early rooting and they can be the last 'solidas' to be repotted in the autumn. Otherwise, the watering regime is the same as for the Western Woodlanders.

The Eastern Woodlanders

In this group we include the species from eastern Siberia, Manchuria, Korea and Japan; *CC. ambigua, fumariifolia, gorinensis, lineariloba, magadanica, ornata, orthoceras, papilligera, turtschaninovii* and *ussuriensis* are included here.

Since they come from a region where the summers are cool and humid these plants will not tolerate a dry and hot summer. They want a peaty compost and love leaf-mould, so providing peat-wall conditions and light shade is the key to success. One disadvantage with these plants is that they emerge too early in a mild winter. It is wise to check them regularly and give them a protective mulch of peat, conifer-needles or leaves if the shoots are showing in January-February.

So far we have tried *CC. fumariifolia, gorinensis lineariloba, magadanica, ornata, papilligera* and *turtschaninovii* in the open and they seem quite happy.

They do not mind pot-culture; plant them in a rich peaty compost of the kind that the hungrier Asiatic primulas like. Since they demand a moist rest, they are early rooters and should be the first to be repotted; the safest time is the first half of August. After planting, plunge them in a cool, shaded corner in the alpine-house and water, because from now on they are active and roots will have started to grow before the end of the month. They need to be kept continuously moist but not wet, from potting until the top growth withers. Before they emerge it is often enough to moisten the plunge, with occasional watering from above. In spring, as growth commences, watering should increase. Feeding is as for the Western Woodlanders but plenty of leaf-mould and well-rotted manure in the compost will make supplementary feeding superfluous.

The dormant period is important; these species hate being dried. In Gothenburg we keep them plunged in a shady corner and water the sand once or twice a week, depending on the weather.

Corydalis Section Corydalis

Pes-gallinaceus, T. Irmisch, Abh. Naturf. Ges. Halle 6: 273 (1867); *Pes-gallinaceus* subsect. *Globosae*, von Poellnitz, Repert. Spec. nov. Regni veg. 42: 101 (1937).

Seedlings with one cotyledon. *Tuber* solid, rounded, 1-2.5(-4) cm in diameter, with an apical crown of small scales and a single tuft of roots at the base. *Stem* tapering towards the base with 2 (rarely 1 or 3) stalked alternate leaves, which are 1-4 times ternately divided. *Scale-leaf* present, located a few centimetres above the base of the stem, ovate, membranous, enclosing the developing stem, and from the axil of which one or a few branches usually grow out at a later stage. *Racemes* simple. *Bracts* large, green, entire to deeply divided. *Sepals* small or absent, rarely prominent. *Outer petals* not cristate, obtuse to emarginate at apex. *Nectary* variable; most species have a short nectary tapering to a slender apex but there are several exceptions.

Five well circumscribed subsections of Section Corydalis can be distinguished:

Subsection 1 Corydalis
    <u>Series 1 Helicosyne</u> (*CC. alexeenkoana, angustifolia, caucasica, gotlandica, haussknechtii, integra, intermedia, kusnetzovii, malkensis, paschei, paczoskii, tarkiensis, tauricola, vittae, wendelboi, zetterlundii*)
    <u>Series 2 Corydalis</u> (*CC. bracteata, densiflora, gracilis, pumila, solida*)
    <u>Series 3 Repentes</u> (*CC. ambigua, fukuharae, fumariifolia, grandicalyx, hallaisanensis, humilis, kiaotschouensis, lineariloba, linjiangensis, maculata, ohii, orthoceras, papilligera, repens, ussuriensis*)
    <u>Series 4 Raphanituber</u> (*CC. gorinensis, gorodkovii, magadanica*)
    <u>Series 6 Adianta</u> (*CC. henrikii, triternata*)
Subsection 2 Brevinectaria (*CC. glaucescens, nudicaulis, ruksansii, schanginii*)
Subsection 3 Officinales (*gamosepala, ornata, turtschaninovii, yanhusuo*)
Subsection 4 Numullaria (*caudata, humosa*)
Subsection 5 Monstruosa (*filistipes*)

KEY TO SUBSECTIONS

1. Nectary acute, often tapering to a slender tail	**Subsection 1 Corydalis**
1. Nectary obtuse	**2**
2. Flowers yellowish white, 10 mm long	**Subsection 5 Monstruosa**
2. Flowers not yellow, or more than 10 mm long	**3**
3. Nectary very short; inner petals with dark brownish purple apex; daughter-tubers frequently coherent (C. Asia)	**Subsection 2 Brevinectaria**
3. Nectary usually long; inner petals not tipped with dark brownish purple; daughter-tubers not coherent (E Asia)	**4**
4. Fruit broadly ovate; leaflets rounded on long petiolules; pedicels 15-40 mm	**Subsection 3 Numullaria**
4. Fruit linear; leaves different; pedicels 5-15 mm	**Subsection 4 Officinales**

Plate 11. *Corydalis wendelboi* subsp. *congesta*
Plate 12. *Corydalis paschei*
Plate 13. *Corydalis densiflora*
Plate 14. *Corydalis gotlandica*
Plate 15. *Corydalis tauricola*

16

17

18

19

20

Plate 16. *Corydalis solida* subsp. *solida* 'Ice Nine'
Plate 17. *Corydalis solida* subsp. *incisa*
Plate 18. *Corydalis solida* subsp. *solida*, a pink form
Plate 19. *Corydalis solida* subsp. *solida*, pure white form from Macedonia
Plate 20. *Corydalis orthoceras*

KEY TO SPECIES OF SECTION CORYDALIS

SOUTH-WEST ASIA AND CAUCASUS

1. Nectary one fifth to one third as long as spur   **2**
1. Nectary about half as long as spur   **3**

2. Flowers horizontal; limb of lower petal 4-6 mm broad; seed with a short beak   **41. *C. henrikii***
2. Flowers nodding; limb of lower petal 6-8 mm broad; seed without a beak   **40. *C. triternata***

3. Bracts much shorter than pedicels, rounded; racemes very lax; fruit lanceolate   **13. *C. paschei***
3. Bracts almost equalling to longer than pedicels   **4**

4. Bracts entire, or rarely the lowermost slightly divided   **5**
4. Bracts divided, or the uppermost entire   **10**

5. Inner petals externally tipped with dark purple   **6**
5. Inner petals only internally tipped with purple   **7**

6. Lateral stigma-papillae simple; seeds with a thick border around the hilum (Kurdistan)   **8. *C. haussknechtii***
6. Lateral stigma papillae geminate; seeds without a thick collar surrounding the hilum (NW Anatolia)   **6. *C. integra***

7. Stigma broader than long; fruit rounded in cross-section; inner epidermis of fruit wrinkled   **8**
7. Stigma about as broad as long; fruit dorsiventrally flattened; inner epidermis of fruit not wrinkled   **9**

8. Limb of lower petal undulate; spur straight, somewhat upwardly directed   **3. *C. vittae***
8. Margin of lower petal not undulate, usually incurved; spur often recurved at apex, especially in bud   **2. *C. kusnetzovii***

9. Raceme distinctly stalked, rather dense; flowers white with spur strongly curved upwards   **5. *C. malkensis***
9. Raceme indistinctly stalked, very lax; flowers usually lilac with straight spur   **4. *C. caucasica***

10. Stigma broader than long; flowers robust, creamy white; inner epidermis of fruit wrinkled   **1. *C. alexeenkoana***

10. Stigma about as broad as long; flowers slender   **11**

11. Self-compatible; bracts 3-fid, or the upper entire; fruit linear   **12**
11. Self-incompatible; all bracts divided, usually with more than 3 divisions; fruit ovate-lanceolate or linear   **13**

12. Spur shorter than limb; flowers cream, rarely pale purple   **9. *C. angustifolia***
12. Spur equalling limb; flowers purple   **11. *C. tarkiensis***

13. Pedicels 7-15 mm, equalling bracts; lower petal emarginate at apex; fruit linear or linear-lanceolate   **14. *C. tauricola***
13. Pedicels 2-7 mm, shorter than bracts; lower petal not or only slightly emarginate; fruit lanceolate   **12. *C. wendelboi***

EUROPE, CENTRAL ASIA AND SIBERIA, WEST OF BAIKAL

1. Bracts entire, or rarely the lowermost slightly divided   **2**
1. Bracts divided, except sometimes the uppermost   **9**

2. Bracts ovate-lanceolate; nectary very short, obtuse   **3**
2. Bracts broadly ovate to obovate; nectary long-tapering   **6**

3. Inner petals only internally tipped with purple; flowers broadly winged, emarginate at apex   **45. *C. glaucescens***
Inner petals externally tipped with dark purple; flowers narrowly winged, acute to obtuse at apex   **4**

4. Spur 21-27 mm long   **44. *C. schanginii***
4. Spur shorter than 15 mm   **5**

5. Outer petals suffused with brown; seeds 1-1.5 mm, about 20   **42. *C. nudicaulis***
5. Outer petals not suffused with brown, seeds 2.5 mm, 2-5   **43. *C. ruksansii***

6. Corolla yellow, scale-leaf with adventitious tuber **21. *C. gracilis***
6. Corolla pink, purple or white; adventitious tuber absent **7**

7. Racemes long and lax; pedicels 5-14 mm; fruit linear **6. *C. integra***
7. Racemes very dense; pedicels 2-4 mm; fruit ovate **8**

8. Lower petal 4 mm broad at apex; capsule ovate-lanceolate **15. *C. intermedia***
8. Lower petal 8 mm broad at apex; capsule broadly ovate, long-acuminate **16. *C. gotlandica***

9. Flowers yellow (rarely white); lower petal 10-15 mm broad **10**
9. Flowers pink, purple or white; lower petal up to 10 mm broad **11**

10. With adventitious tuber in scale-leaf; fruit oblong; racemes 2-4-flowered, elaiosome broad **21. *C. gracilis***
10. Without adventitious tuber; fruit ovate; racemes 5-15-flowered; elaiosome small, globular **20. *C. bracteata***

11. Fruit linear; elaiosome spirally twisted; bracts with 1-4 deep divisions, central lobe largest **12**
11. Fruit ovate to elliptic; elaiosome not twisted ; bracts apically incised to digitately divided into 4-8 lobes **14**

12. Regular selfer; racemes 3-10-flowered; inner petals tipped with dark purple (Crimea) **10. *C. paczoskii***
12. Self-incompatible; racemes 10-20-flowered; inner petals not tipped with dark purple **13**

13. Outer petals with dentate obtuse apices (Macedonia) **7. *C. zetterlundii***
13. Outer petals with broad emarginate apices, not dentate **6. *C. integra***

14. Racemes loose; bracts usually longer than broad; pedicels 5-15 mm **19. *C. solida***
14. Racemes compact; bracts at least as broad as long; pedicels 3-8 mm **15**

15. Bracts simply divided; lower petal 7-10 mm **17. *C. pumila***
15. Bract lobes dentate or divided; lower petal 10-12 mm **18. *C. densiflora***

ASIA EAST OF BAIKAL

1. Nectary acute to acuminate **2**
1. Nectary obtuse **19**

2. Stems branched from cauline leaves (E Siberia: Magadan) **38. *C. magadanica***
2. Stems branched from scale leaf only **3**

3. Flowers yellow to yellowish white (E Siberia) **4**
3. Flowers blue, purple or pure white **5**

4. Leaves small, rounded with crowded segments; racemes very dense **37. *C. gorodkovii***
4. Leaves triangular with narrow discrete lobes **39. *C. gorinensis***

5. Lower petal with very broad strongly auriculate claw (S. Korea) **36. *C. maculata***
5. Claw of lower petal not auriculate **6**

6. Sepals 5 x 8 mm, deeply fimbriate; bracts divided into several acute narrow lobes (S. Korea) **31. *C. grandicalyx***
6. Sepals much smaller; bracts usually less divided **7**

7. Tuber with a firm outer layer; capsule very broadly ovate, flat with thick valves; seeds spinulose **35. *C. papilligera***
7. Tuber with thin papery outer layer; capsule different; seeds smooth **8**

8. Spur of upper petal 2-6 mm; inner petals 5-6 mm long (Honshu) **34. *C. orthoceras***
8. Spur and inner petals longer **9**

9. Inner petals 5-8 mm long **33. *C. repens***
9. Inner petals 9-12 mm long **10**

10. Stems straight and erect **11**
10. Stems geniculate at nodes (lineariloba group) **15**

11. Capsule ovate-lanceolate; flowers 'bladdery' **25. *C. ussuriensis***
11. Capsule linear to narrowly lanceolate; flowers not bladdery **12**

12. Nectary about half as long as spur; spur cylindrical, 12-16 mm long **13**
12. Nectary about one third as long as spur; spur broad-based, 8-11 mm long (see also *C. ornata*, lead 23) **14**

13. Bracts ovate, divided (S Manchuria)
26. *C. linjiangensis*
13. Bracts linear to lanceolate, entire (Honshu)
24. *C. fukuarae*

14. Lower petal conspicuously saccate; leaves glaucous (Kamtchatka) **22. *C. ambigua***
14. Lower petal straight or shallowly saccate; leaves green (Hokkaido; Sakhalin; SE Siberia)
23. *C. fumariifolia*

15. Stem with axillary tuber in the scale-leaf **16**
15. Stem without axillary tuber **17**

16. Inner petals 12-13 mm; fruit narrowly oblong; crests of inner petals not overtopping the apex
30. *C. ohii*
16. Inner petals 9-10 mm; fruit ovate-lanceolate; crests of inner petals clearly overtopping the apex **29. *C. lineariloba***

17. Crests of inner petals acute, much overtopping the apex (Shandong) **28. *C. kiaotschouensis***
17. Crests of inner petals not or only slightly overtopping the apex (Korea; NE China) **18**

18. Spur triangular, tapering towards the apex (Chejudo; SE South Korea) **32. *C. hallaisanensis***
18. Spur oblong, obtuse (N South Korea; North Korea; NE China) **27. *C. humilis***

19. Flowers yellowish white, 10-13 mm long with very short saccate spur **52. *C. filistipes***
19. Flowers larger, blue, purple or white **20**

20. Fruit broadly ovate; petiolules long; racemes 3-8 flowered; pedicels 15-40 mm **21**
20. Fruit linear; petiolules indistinct; racemes 8-20-flowered; pedicels 5-15 mm **22**

21. Spur 5-7 mm; inner petals 4 mm long
47. *C. humosa*
21. Spur 12-14 mm; inner petals 7-8 mm long
46. *C. caudata*

22. Leaflets entire, lanceolate; most bracts entire; axillary tuber present; corolla strongly curved
51. *C. yanhusuo*
22. Leaflets divided; most bracts divided; axillary tuber present or absent; corolla straight or curved **23**

23. Stems often branched from cauline leaves; petiole bases vaginate; axillary tuber absent
50. *C. gamosepala*
23. Stems usually branched from the scale-leaf only; petioles not or very slightly vaginate at base, axillary tuber sometimes present; corolla usually straight **24**

24. Nectary less than one fourth as long as spur
49. *C. ornata*
24. Nectary at least one third as long as spur
48. *C. turtschaninovii*

SUBSECTION CORYDALIS
Nectary acute, often tapering to a slender tail. 41 species distributed throughout most of the area of the section but only in Manchuria and Shandong/Jiangsu in China.

Series Helicosyne Lidén
Willdenowia 26:23 (1996). Type species: *C. caucasica* DC.

Nectary long-tapering, slender. *Elaiosome* spirally twisted. *Fruit* lanceolate to narrowly elliptic. 16 species; Europe, Caucasus, W Asia.

1-3 *C. alexeenkoana* Group
Stigma broader than long. *Fruit* with inner epidermis wrinkled.

1. *C. alexeenkoana* N. Busch in Acta Horti Tiflis 9, suppl. (Fl. Cauc. crit. 3): 56 (1905). Type: Armenia, Imeretia,1800 m, 26.4.1899, *Radde* (LE, lecto, selected by Prokhanov 1961, see *C. tarkiensis* for reference). Note: Two specimens were cited in the original description: *Alexeenko* 5304 from Tarki, and *Radde* s.n. Prokhanov (1961) claimed that, as the plant from Tarki is purple and not white, it does not fit the protologue. His lectotypification is in accordance with current usage, e.g. Grossheim (1950). Alexeenko's plant serves as the type of *C. tarkiensis* Prokh. (species no. 11).

DESCRIPTION. *Plant* robust, erect, 10-20 cm (or more in etiolated plants). *Leaves* twice to three times ternately divided with leaflets more or less deeply divided into 2-3 narrowly obovate to linear lobes. *Racemes* dense, 3-10-flowered (up to 15-flowered in cultivated plants), usually with a distinct stalk. *Bracts* usually divided into 3 to 5(-8) lobes, rarely the

Fig. 1. a, *Corydalis alexeenkoana* (cult. from H. Andersson, *sine coll.*, S Georgia); **b**, *C. vittae* (cult., Seisums, *locus classicus*); **c**, *C. kusnetsovii* (cult. from E. Pasche, *sine coll.*, W Caucasus, Teberda 1990).

uppermost entire. *Pedicels* 5-20 mm. *Sepals* minute or absent. *Corolla* straight, creamy white to pale yellow, of a very robust construction; inner petals 11-12 mm; lower petal with a straight or slightly saccate claw and a rounded shallowly emarginate blade, often with incurved margins, not undulate. *Spur* 11-14 mm long with nectary a third to almost half as long, shortly tapering. *Stigma* much broader than long with several papillae, of which the basal ones are geminate, but the lateral ones only indistinctly so. *Fruit* fusiform, rounded in cross-section, 15-20 x 4-5 mm, with a very short and narrow style, clearly set off from the capsule ; inner epidermis of fruit conspicuously wrinkled. *Seeds* 5-9, 2-2.3 mm with broad, spirally twisted elaiosome. 2n=16. Self-incompatible. Fig. 1a; Pl. 1.

DISTRIBUTION. Transcaucasus. Amongst shrubs. Map 2.

A stout species with large pale yellow to creamy white flowers in a densely packed raceme. It varies considerably in leaf: in some specimens they can be as deeply incised

as in *C. angustifolia,* whereas other individuals approach *C. solida.* Though not as elegant or broad-lipped as *C. malkensis,* its vigour and size make it a perfect garden plant. We have grown it for years in a peaty soil in light shade and each season it becomes stronger.

2. C. kusnetzovii Khokhr. in Bull. Princ. Bot. Gard. Acad. Sci. URSS 56: 42 (1964). Type: NW Caucasus, Russia, prov. Krasnodarsk, distr. Adler: Krasnaja poljana, Mt Aczischo, 21.5.1959, *A. P. Khokhrjakov* (MHA, holo).
C. teberdensis Khokhr., Tr. sev.-vost. kompl. inst. (Magadan) 42: 175 (1971). Type: NW Caucasus, prov. Stauropolitana, pagus Verchnjaja Teberda, sloping *Quercus* woods by the river Teberda, 1300 m, 6.4.1970, *A. P. Khokhrjakov* (MHA).
C. alboviana nomen nudum.

DESCRIPTION. *Plant* stout and erect, 10-15(-20) cm. *Leaves* twice to almost three times ternately divided with leaflets deeply divided into obovate obtuse lobes. *Racemes* 3-10-flowered. *Bracts* all entire. *Pedicels*

5-15 (-20) mm long, suberect to patent in fruit. *Corolla* white, creamy white or pale yellow, often slightly suffused with a dirty purple, rather robust, often nodding; inner petals 9-11 mm long; limb of lower petal with incurved margins as in *C. alexeenkoana*, the claw often broadly saccate. *Spur* 10-15 mm long, sometimes curved down at the very apex, with a nectary about half as long. *Fruit* and seed as in *C. alexeenkoana*. 2n=16. Self-incompatible. Fig. 1c.

DISTRIBUTION. W part of the main Caucasus. Woods, 1000-2000 m. Map 2.

Closely related to *C. alexeenkoana* but with entire bracts. It is very variable in leaf division, flower size and colour, from one population to another or within a single population. The type of *C. kusnetzovii* has flowers which are quite reddish.

Some clones have been in cultivation masquerading as *C. vittae*. They vary considerably in flower size and the larger types challenge *C. malkensis* in beauty. They are all easy to grow.

3. *C. vittae* Kolak. in Dokl. Akad. Nauk Armyanskoi SSR 5: 87 (1946). Type: W Caucasus, Georgia, distr. Gagra, Mt Gagry near Mt Ach-Ag, subalpine meadows on limestone, 2200 m, 9.7.1940, *Kolakovsky & Vitta Jabrova* (LE, holo).

DESCRIPTION. Similar to the previous species but: *Plant* less robust and with more ascending stems, 10-15 cm high. *Leaves* three times ternately divided with small stalked leaflets deeply divided into 3-5 obovate lobes. *Racemes* rather dense, distinctly stalked, 6-15-flowered. *Bracts* entire or the lowermost slightly divided. *Corolla* white or with a slight purplish tinge; inner petals 11 mm long; lower petal straight or slightly saccate with an ovate truncate blade with undulate margins. *Spur* 13-15 mm long with nectary about half as long. *Fruit* 20-23 mm long, often strongly suffused with purple. 2n=16. Self-incompatible. Fig. 1b; Pl. 3, 4.

DISTRIBUTION. W Caucasus. Map 2.

Differs from the very closely related *C. kusnetzovii* in the more delicate corolla with its long straight, slightly upwardly directed spur, undulate outer petals and longer and narrower nectary.

It has the same demands in cultivation as *C. alexeenkoana* but does not become as large.

4. *C. caucasica* DC., Syst. 2: 119 (1821). Type: 'Kaukasus, in montibus sylvaticis', *M. von Bieberstein* (LE?, not found; 'type' in P (DC.) is *C. angustifolia*).

4a. subsp. *caucasica*
C. tenella Ledeb. in Bull. Acad. Imp. Sci. Saint-Petersbourg 2: 313 (1837). Type: SW Georgia, Source of Kura, Mt Adshara, 2300 m (LE).

DESCRIPTION. *Stems* sub-erect, 10-20 cm high. *Leaves* usually situated towards the base, bi-ternate or almost so with rather long petioles; leaflets clearly stalked, entire or cleft into 2-3 oblong to obovate, usually mucronate lobes. *Racemes* lax, subsecund, usually with rather short peduncle, 2-6-flowered (rarely up to 15-flowered in cultivation). *Bracts* ovate, entire, or the lowermost slightly divided, usually slightly pointed. *Pedicels* equalling bracts, 4-10 mm and erecto-patent in flower, 9-13 mm and patent to slightly recurved in fruit. *Sepals* 1.5-2 mm long, deeply divided into a few narrow laciniae. *Corolla* lilac, very rarely white; outer petals with broad emarginate somewhat undulate limbs; inner petals white (often becoming yellow in the press), 9-10 mm. *Spur* rather straight, 12-16 mm long, with a very slender nectary at least half as long. *Fruit* pendulous, oblong, somewhat flattened, 20-25 x 3-4 mm, with a short beak and a 3 mm long style. *Seeds* 8-13(-16), smooth, 2-2.5 mm with spirally twisted elaiosome. 2n=16. Self-compatible. Fig. 2a.

DISTRIBUTION. Caucasus Mountains. 'Forests and shrubs', 1000-2000 m. Map 3.

One of the most garden-worthy species with broad-faced purplish-pink to lilac flowers and thin, subordinate leaves. Only a few years ago it was a rarity in gardens but it is now in general cultivation and offered by many nurseries. It is equally easy in a pot as as it is in the open garden where it seeds profusely in the right spot.

4b. subsp. *abantensis* Lidén & Zetterlund in Lidén Willdenowia 26:26 (1996). Type: NW Turkey, Vil. Bolu, Bolu to Gerede, beech scrub facing N, 1050 m, 31.3.1957, *Davis & hedge 26286* (E, holo; K, iso).

We have recently received in cultivation a single plant from Lake Abant, far to the west of the other known localities, which deviates from typical *C. caucasica* in its dense-flowered, not one-sided racemes, less

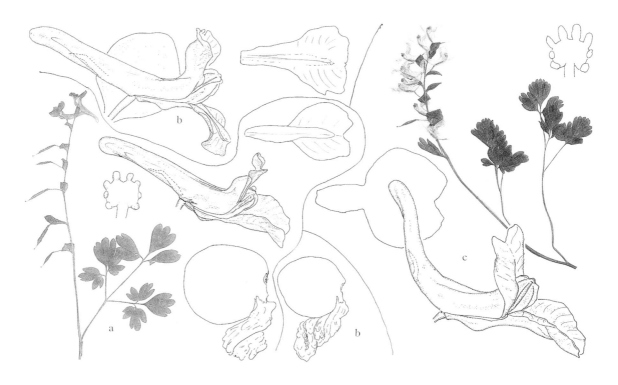

Fig. 2. a, *Corydalis caucasica* subsp. *caucasica* (cult. from E. Pasche 87, *sine coll.*, Caucasus, Saguramo, 1000 m); **b**, *C. caucasica* subsp. *abantensis* (cult. Hanslik, NW Turkey, Vil. Bolu, N of Abant); **c**, *C. malkensis* (cult. hort.)

flattened fruit, a different shape of the lower petal, and smaller seeds. It is self-incompatible but produces a full seed-set when crossed with *C. caucasica*. Herbarium specimens of this form are previously known from NW Anatolia and have been confused with *C. integra*, from which they differ in the differently shaped fruit, the absence of a dark apex to the inner petals and the form of the lower petal.). Fig. 2b; Pl. 5; Map 5.

5. *C. malkensis* Galushko in Novosti Sist. Vyssh. Rast. 13: 251 (1975). Type: N Caucasus, river Malka, Khabas, April 1960, *Galushko & Romanenko* ('LE', not found). Note: The identity is not quite certain, as the type has not been traced. *C. kusnetzovii* and *C. caucasica* are also known from the same area.

DESCRIPTION. *Stems* 7-20 cm, erect, with one or two branches from the scale-leaf. *Leaves* once to twice ternately divided with leaflets deeply cleft into obovate lobes, that may again be shallowly lobed at apex. *Racemes* 5-10 flowered (to 15-flowered in cultivation), rather dense, with a distinct peduncle.

Bracts entire, ovate to obovate, obtuse or acute. *Pedicels* slender, 6-10 mm, equalling the bracts, elongating to 17 mm in fruit. *Sepals* minute. *Corolla* with very broad outer petals, with a yellowish green tint in bud but becoming pure white; lower petal saccate at base, with a very broad spreading limb; inner petals 11-12 mm. *Spur* strongly upward-curved, 14-17 mm long. *Stigma* about as long as broad, sometimes with the lateral papillae simple. *Fruit* broadly lanceolate, somewhat flattened dorsiventrally, 18-20 x 4-5 mm. *Seeds* 5-9, 2.5 mm, with a spirally twisted elaiosome. 2n=32. Somewhat self-compatible but probably mainly cross-pollinated. Fig. 2c; Pl. 6.

DISTRIBUTION. C and NW Caucasus, at least in the upper valleys of the Kuban and Malka rivers. Woods. Due to confusion with *C. kusnetzovii* and white forms of *C. caucasica*, the distribution cannot be given with certainty. Map 3.

A most delightful plant, distributed among gardeners as *C. caucasica* 'Alba' but clearly distinguished from *C. caucasica* by the often more divided leaves, dense stalked racemes, minute sepals, very broad-lipped showy white flowers with long upwardly curved spurs and broader and shorter fruits. In addition, the chromosome number and breeding system are different. It has been in cultivation for a long time (at least since the 1960s), cherished by growers and is one of the true aristocrats in this section. It received a P.C. in 1973 and an A.M. in 1995.

It is superb as a pot-subject and seductive in the rock-garden if grown in a raised position, where it may be admired with the kneeling adoration deserved. It often seeds itself freely in gardens. The occasional seedling may attain a pink, brownish or lilac flush on the limbs and this is probably due to hybridisation. Being a tetraploid, it will contribute two thirds of the genetic material in hybrids with diploid species and hybrids will be very similar to the tetraploid parent. Accordingly, it is a good parent for hybrids since the lip-size is dominant.

6. C. integra Barbey & Fors.-Major in Stefani, C. I. Forsyth-Major & W. Barbey, Samos 30 (1892); *C. majori* Poelln., Repert. Spec. nov. Regni veg. 45: 104 (1938). Type: Greece, Samos, Mont Kerki, *Major* 625 (K; LE).
C. wettsteinii Adamovic in Österr. Bot. Z. 56: 174 (1906); *C. solida* subsp. *wettsteinii* (Adamovic) Hayek, Prodr. Fl. Penins. Balcan. 1: 364 (1925). Type: Greece, Mt Athos, Hagion Oros, Adamovic 1906 (not seen).

DESCRIPTION. *Stem* suberect, rather robust, 10-20(-35 in cult.) cm with 1-3 branches. *Leaves* very glaucous, mostly biternate with more or less divided leaflets with obovate to oblong segments. *Racemes* 5-20-flowered, long and lax. *Bracts* entire, broadly elliptic, or (in European plants) often divided into 2 to 5 segments, about equalling the straight 5-10(-14) mm long pedicels. *Corolla* pale pink to almost white, with inner petals tipped blackish purple; lower petal with a narrow claw gradually dilated into a broad, usually emarginate limb; inner petals 9-11(-12) mm. *Spur* 12-13 mm long. *Fruit* 15-20(-27) x 2-3 mm, linear to narrowly lanceolate with prominent midveins. *Seeds* 5-8(-14), smooth, 2-2.3 mm, with spirally twisted elaiosome. 2n=16. Self-incompatible. Fig. 3b; Pl. 7.

DISTRIBUTION. Mountain slopes, N-facing cliffs. March-April. E Balkans, Aegean region, NW Anatolia (Turkey). Map 4.

A rather variable species which is perhaps divisible into subspecies. The Greek plants differ from the east Aegean and Anatolian ones in their more robust habit, the frequently divided bracts, narrower lower petal and shorter fruits. Plants from Naxos occupy an intermediate position. A form from Chios is notable for its very long fruits and large, slightly divided bracts.

The form that we grow hails from Mt Cholomon in Greece and is very robust with white to pale pinkish flowers and dark-tipped inner petals. In the rock-garden the basic colour attains a more bluish tinge. The foliage is distinctly glaucous and a prominent and attractive feature.

This is a splendid garden-plant and has proved wholly hardy in the open. It received a P.C. in 1992 and an A.M. in 1995.

7. C. zetterlundii Lidén in Willdenowia 21: 178 (1991). Type: Skopje-Macedonia, WSW of Titov Veles, a few km NW Bogomila by the railway between Titov Veles and Prilep, deciduous woodland, 580 m., 21.4.1988, *Zetterlund & Strindberg* 8864 (GB, holo; LE, iso).

DESCRIPTION. *Stems* ascending, 8-15 cm high (-25 in cult.). *Leaves* slightly glaucous, closely set towards the base of the stem, small, 3-5 cm long (to 8 cm in cult.) including a short petiole 1-2 cm, two (to almost three) times ternate with long petiolules; leaflets deeply divided, the ultimate lobes narrowly obovate, acute. *Racemes* long and shortly stalked, much overtopping the leaves, 10-12-flowered (-25 in cult.). *Bracts* with an oblanceolate to obovate central portion with one to three long teeth or narrow laciniae on each side. *Pedicels* slightly shorter than the bracts, 3-5 mm long (-11 mm in cult.) in flower, elongating to 5-6 mm, basally reflexed in fruit. *Sepals* minute. *Corolla* white or usually variegated with purple, the wings and inner petals paler; outer petals narrowly winged, obtuse, with eroded-dentate apices; lower petal subspathulate, obtuse; inner petals 10-11 mm long, pale with rather broad angular crest, only internally blotched with dark purple at apex. *Spur* not or slightly tapering towards a blunt apex, 11-14 mm long, the nectary tapering to a long slender apex, reaching more than halfway along the spur. *Fruit* narrowly lanceolate, flattened and angular in cross-section, uni- to sub-bi-seriate, 20-25 x 3 mm, including a seed-less portion ca 4 mm long, and a style 1.5 mm long. *Seeds* 6-10, 2.4 x 1.8 mm, with a

Fig. 3. a, *Corydalis zetterlundii*, (cult. type); **b**, *C. integra* (cult. Papanicolau, Greece, Khalkidhiki, Mt Cholomon 750 m, 1982)

spirally twisted usually long elaiosome. 2n=16. Self-incompatible. Fig. 3a; Pl. 10.

DISTRIBUTION. Only known from the type locality in Skopje-Macedonia. Map 4.

An isolated species, perhaps closest to *C. integra* but readily distinguished by its different growth habit, the division of bracts and the narrow, obtuse, dentate outer petals.

This new European species was dicovered in the wooded foothills of the Jakupica range in Macedonia as late as 1988. Its small dissected leaves are produced at ground-level and the long dense racemes are boldly presented well above the ground. The flower-colour may be a reddish-lilac or white, the latter is definitely to be preferred horticulturally. It is an early starter but the flowers take a long time to unfold. At dusk they produce a bewildering spicy scent. It has taken well to cultivation and stock is now being built up. In 1992 it was collected in its *locus classicus* by a commercial 'gold-digger' and directly offered in the trade.

8-14 *C. wendelboi* Group

This group is recognised by its straight lower petal, a long caudate nectary and a peculiar stigma which lacks geminate (double) lateral papillae. The elaiosome is spirally twisted, although only indistinctly so in *C. haussknechtii*. Two or three axillary branches usually grow out from the scale-leaf. The inner petals may or may not be tipped externally with dark purple.

There are 4 self-incompatible species in Anatolia and Iraqi Kurdistan, and two self-compatible ones, *C. angustifolia*, *C. paczoskii* (and perhaps *C. tarkiensis*), found outside of this area, in the Caucasus/Elburz and Crimea regions. The closely related species *CC. tauricola* and *wendelboi* form a series of vicariant races throughout western Anatolia, whereas *C. paschei* is found in a small area within the distribution area of *C. wendelboi* subsp. *wendelboi*. Map 5.

8. *C. haussknechtii* **Lidén** in Notes Roy. Bot. Gard. Edinb. 45: 358 (1989[1988]). Type: SE Turkey, Vil. Mardin, Derik, April 1867, *Haussknecht* 28 (BM, holo; G (BOISS.), iso).

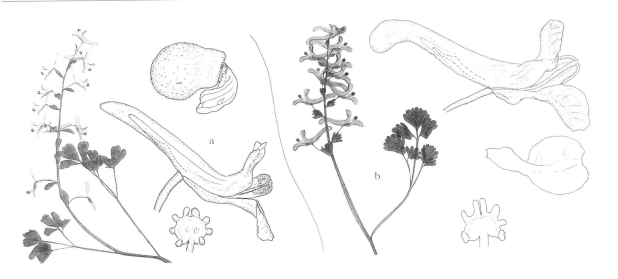

Fig. 4. a, *Corydalis haussknechtii* (cult. KPPZ 168, Turkey, Vil. Mardin, Hop Geçedi); **b**, *C. paschei*, (cult. type)

DESCRIPTION. *Stems* sub-erect, 10-22 cm. *Leaves* rather dark green, thickish, biternate with shallowly to deeply divided leaflets; segments broadly obovate to lanceolate, obtuse or acute, often greatly differing in size. *Racemes* long and lax, 6-22-flowered without a distinct peduncle. *Bracts* obovate-lanceolate, entire, 6-15 mm in flower, often lengthening considerably in fruit up to 30 mm. *Pedicels* 8-15(-23)mm, reflexed in fruit. *Corolla* white, creamy white, or pale lilac, always with the inner petals tipped with a contrasting blackish purple; outer petals broadly emarginate; lower petal 12-15 mm long, without a basal pouch; inner petals (10-)11 mm. *Spur* (10-)13-17 mm long. *Fruit* lanceolate, 17-21 x 4 mm, including a 4 mm style. *Seeds* 4-10, 2 x 1.7 mm with a thick protruding collar surrounding the hilum area and a prominent, slightly twisted elaiosome. 2n=16. Self-sterile. Fig. 4a; Pl. 8.

DISTRIBUTION. Turkish and Iraqi Kurdistan. 1000-2800 m. 'Rich soil between rocks'. Map 5.

We were lucky enough to come across a few specimens of this Kurdish endemic whilst searching for *Iris bakeriana* at Hop Geçidi near Mardin in SE Turkey in 1990 (KPPZ 90-168). Here it was seeking protection in the crannies at the base of limestone outcrops in dense oak scrub at an altitude of 1200 m.

It is very variable in flower-size, as we have been able to judge both from herbarium specimens and from our cultivated plants.

In cultivation it is an early starter, quite pretty though not exciting, but the largest-flowered forms are definitely worthy of a place in a collection.

9. C. angustifolia (M.Bieb.) DC., Syst. 2: 120 (1821); *Fumaria angustifolia* M.Bieb., Fl. Taur.-Cauc. 2: 146 (1808). Type: 'Habitat in Iberia' (LE).

DESCRIPTION. *Stem* slender, 8-16 cm. *Leaves* green, bi- to tri-ternate with leaflets deeply divided into linear-lanceolate to narrowly oblong or narrowly obovate segments. *Racemes* short, 2-10-flowered (longer and 10-23-flowered in cult.), secund. *Bracts* cuneate, shallowly to deeply 3-5-cleft with linear lobes, or the uppermost entire, lanceolate 6-10 mm. *Pedicels* 5-10 mm in flower, somewhat lengthening in fruit. *Corolla* usually white, or with a lilac suffusion (especially in plants from N Iran), rarely cream, the inner petals internally tipped with dark purple, sometimes also partly externally; lower petal straight, 12-16(-18) mm long, with a narrow obtuse limb; inner petals 12-14(-16) mm. *Spur* upward-directed, 9-13 mm long, distinctly shorter than the lower petal. *Fruit* 23-33 mm long, linear, nodding on slender pedicels. *Seeds* 10-20, almost 2 mm. 2n=16. Self-compatible and regularly selfing. Almost cleistogamous strains occur (Nakhichevan, Zangezur Mt). Pl. 9.

DISTRIBUTION. N Iran (Elburz Mountains), Caucasus, Turkey (NE Anatolia). Forests and scrub. Map 5.

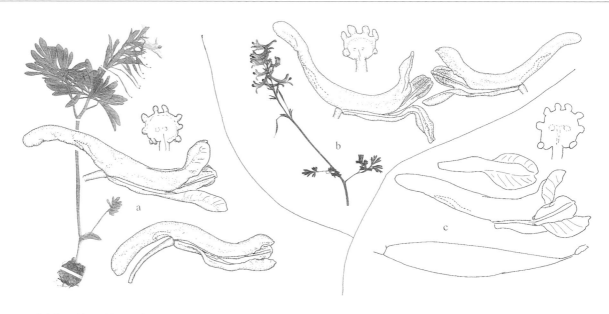

no data); **c**, *C. tarkiensis* (type)

An elegant forest species with much-dissected leaves and long-petalled, short-spurred flowers. The flower colour is sometimes described as yellow in floras but living plants are normally ivory-white. Iranian specimens tend to be larger-flowered, with broader leaf segments. They often favour more open situations at higher altitudes (c. 2000 m).

Although it has been grown since the early 1800s, and has been firmly in cultivation since about 1900, it has never been common; it is a plant for enthusiasts. In the 1930s a pink form (= *C. tarkiensis*?) was grown as well as the ivory-white but only the latter prevailed. With us it is first in bloom each spring and is invariably subjected to harsh weather; despite this it has survived since 1955. Most of the material in cultivation seems to have its origin from near Tbilisi in Georgia.

Due to its habit of being self-fertilised at an early stage, the flowers soon fade away. Seed is produced in profusion and it is advisable to remove the racemes before seed-fall if it is grown under glass, otherwise seedlings will pop up everywhere. In contrast, in the open ground it will never become a nuisance.

It received a P.C. from the Royal Horticultural Society in 1995.

Three cultivars have recently been released by Janis Ruksans:
'Georgian White'. Flowers cold white.
'Thalysh Dawn'
'Touch of Gold'. A 'yellow-flowered' form.

10. *C. paczoskii* N. Busch in Acta Horti Tiflis 9, suppl. (Fl. Cauc. crit. 3): 55 (1905); *C. solida* var. *ramosa* Pacz.in Zap. Novorossiisk. Obshch. Estestvoisp. 15: 68 (1890); *C. ramosa* B.Fedtsch. in Bull. Herb. Boissier 7: 806 (1899), non Wall.; *C. solida* var. *pauciflora* Pacz. in Zap. Kievsk. Obshch. Estestvoisp. 10: 421 (1899). Type: Ukraine, Crimea 16.4.1889, *Paczosk* (LE)

DESCRIPTION. *Stem* slender, 8-15 cm, with 1-3 ascending branches from the scale-leaf. *Leaves* dark green, biternate with leaflets deeply divided into lanceolate to narrowly oblong segments, rarely entire. *Racemes* 3-10-flowered. *Bracts* cuneate, shallowly to deeply divided into 3-5 linear acute lobes, or the uppermost entire, lanceolate, 6-10 mm long. *Pedicels* 4-8 mm, slightly elongating in fruit up to 14 mm. *Corolla* purple with the apices of the inner petals blotched with blackish purple; lower petal 11-13 mm long, without a basal pouch, with a narrow obtuse limb; inner petals 10-11 mm long. *Spur* straight or slightly sigmoidally curved, 10-13 mm long. *Fruit* sub-pendent, 18-23 x 3 mm, narrowly lanceolate. *Seeds* 7-14, 1.9-2.4 mm. 2n=16. Self-compatible and regularly selfing. Fig. 5b.

DISTRIBUTION. Ukraine; Crimea. Map 5.

Corydalis paczoskii is related to *C. angustifolia*, but readily distinguished by its purple corolla with a

Fig. 6. a, *Corydalis tauricola* (cult. KPPZ96, Turkey, Vil. Kahramanmaras, Kurt Kalesi); **b**, *C. wendelboi* subsp. *wendelboi* (cult. type); **c**, *C. wendelboi* subsp. *congesta* (cult. type)

comparatively longer spur and shorter fruits. It is hardy and permanent in the open with a quiet charm that appeals to the enthusiast. A regular selfer that may seed around under favourable conditions in the garden.

11. *C. tarkiensis* Prokh. in Bot. Mater. Gerb. Bot. Inst. Komarova Akad. Nauk SSSR. 21: 423 (1961); *C. alexeenkoana* N.Busch *pro parte* excl. type. Type: S Russia, N Dagestan, near Petrowsk (Makhatchkala), Mt Tarki, 90 m, 28. 3. 1902, *Th. Alexeenko* 5304 (LE, holo).

DESCRIPTION. *Stems* 7-15 cm, with one or rarely two branches. *Leaves* bi- to tri-ternate with entire to deeply divided leaflets, the ultimate segments lanceolate to oblanceolate, acute to obtuse. *Racemes* 4-10(-15)-flowered. *Bracts* equalling the pedicels, cuneate, more or less deeply divided into three lanceolate lobes; upper bracts sometimes entire. *Pedicels* 5-10 mm long, slightly elongating in fruit. *Sepals* 1-2 mm. *Corolla* purple with the tips of the

inner petals dark; outer petals more broadly winged than in *CC. paczoskii* and *angustifolia* and slightly emarginate at apex; inner petals 10-11 mm long. *Spur* straight, 12-13 mm long, with a slender nectary reaching at least half-way. *Capsule* lanceolate, 16-23 x 3-4 mm (8-13 x 2 mm according to the type description). *Seeds* c. 12, 2 mm with a spirally twisted elaiosome. Fig. 5c.

DISTRIBUTION. E Caucasus; Makhatchkala area. Map 5.

Evidently close to *C. paczoskii* but apparently a more robust and less-branched plant with more floriferous racemes, the lower petal being more broadly winged and emarginate at apex. Not in cultivation.

12. *C. wendelboi* Lidén in Notes Roy. Bot. Gard. Edinb. 45: 355 (1989[1988]). Type: SW Turkey, Yesil Göl Dagh, between the peaks, limestone, 1500-1800 m., 23. 4. 1972, *Runemark & Wendelbo* 219 (GB, holo).

DESCRIPTION. *Stem* suberect, (5-)10-15(-20) cm. *Leaves* two to four times ternate; leaflets deeply divided into narrowly obovate to linear obtuse segments. *Racemes* shortly stalked, (5-)10-25(-40!)-flowered, nodding at apex in bud, becoming straight. *Bracts* c. 10 mm long, broadly flabellate, usually divided into several lobes which are often again divided or dentate. *Pedicels* short, (2-)3-5(-7) mm long (or longer in cultivated plants, even up to 12 mm), patent or recurved in fruit. *Corolla* very variable in colour from white to pink, maroon, red and purple, sometimes bicoloured; outer petals obtuse to truncate. *Lower petal* 10-12 mm long; inner petals 9-10 mm long. *Spur* cylindrical to narrowly conical, 9-12 mm long, straight or usually slightly recurved, with a slender nectary at least half as long. *Fruit* lanceolate, 10-24 x 3-5 mm. *Seeds* 4-11, 1.5-1.8 mm.

12a. subsp. *wendelboi*

C. solida var. *tenuisecta* Boiss., Fl. Or. 1: 129 (1867); *C. solida* var. *densiflora* subvar. *tenuisecta* (Boiss.) Poelln. in Repert Sp. nov. Regni veg. 45: 111 (1938). Type: SW Turkey, 'in montibus Cariae', *Pinard* s.n. (G (BOISS.)).
C. solida subsp. *solida* sensu Cullen & Davis in Davis, P. H., Fl. Turkey vol. 1 (1965).
C. brevipedicellata Lidén in Notes Roy. Bot. Gard. Edinb. 45: 360 (1989). Type: W Turkey, Mahmud Dagh above Armutli, 21.4.1933, *O. Schwarz* 485 (B, holo).

DESCRIPTION. *Racemes* not very dense. *Lower petal* oblong, or slightly widened towards the apex, 2-4 mm broad. *Capsule* narrowly lanceolate, 15-24 mm long. 2n=16. Self-incompatible. Fig. 6b.

DISTRIBUTION. Turkey, SW Anatolia eastwards to the W Taurus Mountains (Ermenek). Map 5.

This subspecies has been in cultivation for a long time, masquerading until 1989 as *C. solida* var. *densiflora* or just *C. solida*. It is very common in SW Turkey between 700 and 2000 m altitude and grows in all sorts of environs.

It varies in form, number of flowers, division of bracts, size of capsule, etc. The flower colour varies from white to purple or a smoky lilac, bicolored. Large-flowered, long-fruited, fragrant, usually white-flowered plants are found in the west of its range. In the easternmost localities, near Ermenek, introgression with *C. tauricola* is apparent.

For ornamental purposes the best forms will have to be searched out. Most introductions have not proved particularly exciting, although it does well in the open garden.

12b. subsp. *congesta* Lidén & Zetterlund in M. Lidén in Willdenowia 26:26 (1996). Type: NW Turkey, Anatolia, Ulu Dag˘, *Brian Mathew* s. n. (GB, holo). *C. solida* var. *densiflora* sensu Rix & Phillips, The Bulb Book (1981).

DESCRIPTION. Distinguished from subsp. *wendelboi* by: *Racemes* dense, with much broader flowers; lower petal 4-6 mm broad. *Capsule* 10-16 mm long. 2n=16. Self-incompatible. Fig. 6c; Pl. 11.

DISTRIBUTION. Turkey, NW Anatolia from Ulu Dağ eastwards to 36°E. Map 5.

A homogeneous taxon throughout most of the distribution area but in Ankara Vilayet very narrow-lobed forms are found.

The dense racemes of broad flowers makes this a much prettier plant than its southern counterpart. It is a good rock-garden plant but is also suitable for the alpine house. The colour is normally a greyish blue or different shades of purple, but red forms are also known. Two fine cultivars have been named:

'Abant Wine'. For long this was distributed as *Corydalis* sp. Kartal Tepe. It was originally collected above Lake Abant (prov. Bolu) by Eugen Schleipfer who picked out some cherry-red forms amongst the ordinary purples. The plants in circulation are the deep wine-purple seed offspring from these noble ancestors. It is a nice plant but where is the cherry-red one hiding out?

'Hotlips'. A sterile hybrid-offspring from the above, most probably with a red *C. solida* as pollen-parent. Very beautiful! An intense red on the cold side, slightly speckled.

13. *C. paschei* Lidén in Notes Roy. Bot. Gard. Edinb. 45: 357 (1989[1988]). Type: SW Turkey, Vil. Antalya, Kas to Elmali, south side of Sinekçibeli pass, 1400 m, eroded ditch, 2. 4. 1985, *E. Pasche & M. Koenen* 8505, cultivated Gothenburg Botanic Garden (GB, holo; E, iso; LE, iso).

DESCRIPTION. *Stems* 10-15 cm (-20 in cult.), decumbent at first, later suberect. *Leaves* (and leaflets) long-stalked, bi- to sub-triternate with ultimate lobes rounded, ± imbricate, rarely obovate and free. *Racemes* very lax, 4-12(-19)-flowered. *Bracts* small, rounded, entire or usually shallowly incised. *Pedicels* much longer than the bracts, 10-20mm, becoming arcuate in fruit. *Corolla* pink with the outer petals broadly winged and emarginate at apex; lower petal with a slight subbasal pouch or almost straight, 11-12 mm, abruptly dilated into a rounded, slightly emarginate limb 5-7 mm broad; inner petals 10-11 mm. *Spur* somewhat inflated at apex, sub-sigmoidally curved, 14-15 mm long. *Fruit* lanceolate, 12-15 x 3-4 mm long. *Seeds* 4-6, 2.5 mm, smooth. 2n=16. Self-incompatible. Fig. 4b; Pl. 12.

DISTRIBUTION. Turkey, SW Anatolia, just W of Antalya. 900-1400 m. March-April. Map 5.

A most distinctive species known from two localities within the distribution of *C. wendelboi*. It was first collected by Erich Pasche and Manfred Koenen on the Sinekçibeli pass W of Antalya in SW Turkey. Here it grows on west-exposed moist rocky slopes in pine and cedar woodland. It has since been found at Termessos where it grows along with masses of *Colchicum baytopiorum* and the giant celandine, *Ranunculus ficaria* subsp. *ficariiformis*. Its sporadic distribution remains a mystery. In 1988 we had expected to find it at the Avlanbeli Pass in the vicinity of Sinekçibeli but to our surprise *C. paschei* was absent while *C. wendelboi* was present.

It is a vigorous and handsome species. The lax raceme with long pedicels, small rounded bracts, comparatively broad flowers and distinctive foliage makes it easily distinguishable. It has been successfully grown outdoors at Gothenburg.

14. *C. tauricola* (Cullen & P.H.Davis) Lidén in Notes Roy. Bot. Gard. Edinb. 45: 357 (1989[1988]); *C. solida* subsp. *tauricola* Cullen & P.H.Davis in Notes Roy. Bot. Gard. Edinb. 25: 45 (1963). Type: S Turkey, Vil. Içel, Namrun, 1000-1800 m, rocky limestone, 15.4.1933, *Balls* 176 (E, holo; K, iso).

DESCRIPTION. *Stems* horizontal at first, becoming suberect, 10-25 cm. *Leaves* bi- to tri-ternate, with obovate to oblanceolate segments. *Racemes* long and lax, 5-15 (-20)-flowered. *Pedicels* 7-15 mm (-20 in cult.), straight to arcuate in fruit. *Bracts* equalling pedicels or often shorter, 3-6-fid, often with a large central lobe and smaller lateral lobes. *Corolla* white

to pale purple; outer petals rather broadly winged, obtuse or emarginate at apex; inner petals 10-13(-14) mm long, darker at the apex, but often with the dorsal crest pale. *Spur* 12-15 mm long, nectary from half to two thirds as long. *Fruit* linear or (in the east) narrowly lanceolate, 18-28 x 2(-4) mm. *Seeds* 3-8, 1.7-2.2 mm. 2n=16. Self-incompatible. Fig. 6a; Pl. 15.

DISTRIBUTION. Turkey, S Anatolia; E Taurus and Amanus Mts. Map 5.

Closely related to *C. wendelboi*, with which it is nearly perfectly vicariant. In the narrow zone of overlap signs of introgression have been noted. Forms from the Amanus range are notable for their large flowers and broader fruits.

It is a delightful plant, suitable for pot-cultivation, and much prettier than *C. wendelboi*. We have seen it in the foothills of the N Amanus mountains where it frequents the hornbeam woods together with *Cyclamen pseudibericum* and *Crocus adanensis*. Here it was the frailest, most pathetic plant to be seen and the tubers hardly reached the size of a pea. In cultivation it remains low but with a stouter constitution and surprisingly large, broad-lipped flowers from white to pale pinkish purple.

For horticultural purposes the easternmost forms are the most valuable. It has proved amenable in the open garden.

C. intermedia Group
Bracts entire or almost so. *Inner petals* with wings reaching beyond the apex, not tipped externally with dark purple. 2 species; Europe.

15. *C. intermedia* (L.) Mérat, Nouv. fl. env. Paris: 272 (1812); *Fumaria bulbosa β intermedia* L., Sp. Pl.: 699 (1753); *F. fabacea* Retz., Fl. scand. prodr. ed. 2: 167 (1795) *nomen illegit*; *C. fabacea* (Retz.) Pers. Syn. 2: 269 (1806). Type: Burser Hortus Siccus VII(1)102 (UPS, lecto).
C. alpina J.Gay in Ann. Sci. Nat. (Paris) 26: 252 (1832). Type: numerous syntypes.

DESCRIPTION. *Tuber* 1-2.5 cm, usually with one stem only but large tubers may have two. *Stem* 4-10(-20) cm with two (rarely one or three) leaves. *Leaves* once or usually twice ternate with entire to deeply divided leaflets; ultimate lobes obovate to narrowly obovate. *Racemes* 1-5-flowered (rarely to 10-), nodding, not becoming erect in fruit. *Bracts*

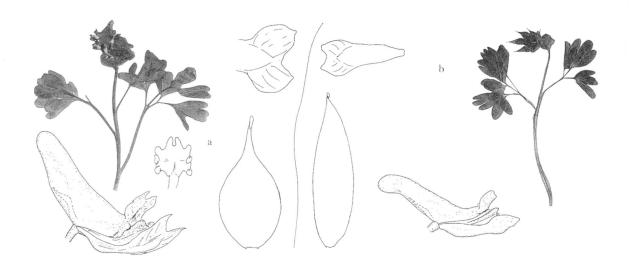

Fig. 7. a, *Corydalis gotlandica* (cult. Lidén s.n., *locus classicus*); **b**, *C. intermedia* (cult. Lidén s.n., Sweden, Gotland, Stora Karlsö)

entire, broadly obovate; on extremely rare occasions the lowermost bract can be divided. *Pedicels* very short, erect and stout, 2-4 mm. *Sepals* minute or absent. *Corolla* pale to dark reddish purple; outer petals each with a broad apical notch creating two acute lobes.; inner petals with broad triangular-acute crests, overtopping the apex; lower petal straight, 4 mm broad at apex. *Spur* 5-10 mm long. *Capsule* ovate-lanceolate, (10-)15-20 x 4-5 mm. *Seeds* 4-9, 2.2 mm, with a long spirally twisted elaiosome. 2n=16 (several from Sweden and central Europe); 2n=40 and 42 have been reported but we have been unable to confirm this. Self-compatible and predominantly autogamous; the flowers have no discernible scent. Fig. 7b.

DISTRIBUTION. Europe from Scandinavia (70°N) southwards to central Spain. March-early May. Map 6.

In the wild *C. intermedia* prefers well-drained soil in shady situations in deciduous woods, especially by the base of trees where the soil dries out in summer; sometimes in more open situations in park environments. It is the most common corydalis in large areas of Europe, but due to its small size and early appearance it is often overlooked.

In one of its two known localities in Spain it has, in addition to its normal appearance in spring, been found flowering in the late autumn.

It is easy in gardens but will only appeal to the enthusiast. Due to the fact that self-pollination

happens at an early stage, fruits are formed very early and the flowers quickly vanish. Hybrids are known with *CC. pumila* and *solida*.

16. C. gotlandica Lidén in Nord. J. Bot. 11: 132 (1991). Type: Sweden, Gotland, Västergarn, N of the church, among *Prunus spinosa*, 6.5.1947, *E. Th. Fries* 6. 5. 1947 (GB, holo; S, iso).

DESCRIPTION. *Plant* rather glaucous. *Tuber* 1.5-4 cm, usually rounded but sometimes elongated or lobed in large individuals. *Stems* 10-20 cm, rather robust, with 2 or often 3 leaves on the flowering stems. *Leaves* biternate with deeply divided leaflets; ultimate lobes acute to subobtuse. *Racemes* very dense and (compared to those of *C. intermedia*) showy, 2-3 cm long, (3-) 5-15-flowered, slightly nodding, becoming erect in fruit. *Bracts* broadly obovate to rounded, entire, or usually the lowermost bract with a few divisions. *Pedicels* very short and stout, 2-3 (-4) mm, erect in fruit. *Corolla* reddish purple to red, strongly curved; upper petal apically emarginate; lower petal 11-12 mm long, not reflexed, slightly saccate at the middle but without a basal pouch, with an emarginate limb 7-9 mm broad, with acute divisions; crests of inner petals triangular, barely overtopping apex. *Spur* upward-directed, 10-13 mm long. *Capsule* 13-17 x 7-8 mm, broad and flattened, ovate, long-acuminate. *Seeds* 3-6, 2-2.2 mm, with a straight or slightly twisted elaiosome. 2n=32. Self-compatible. Fig. 7a; Pl. 14.

Fig. 8. a, *Corydalis pumila* (cult. Strindberg & Zetterlund 40, Skopje-Macedonia, near Kicevo, *Fagus* woodland, 900 m); **b, c**, *C. densiflora* (b, cult. A. Edwards, Sicily, Mt Madonie, Piano Zucchi; c, Huter, Porta & Rigo 324, Italy,

DISTRIBUTION. Sweden: Gotland, 1-10 m. April-early May. Map 6.

This recently described species is known only from Västergarn, Gotland, and from the nearby island of Stora Karlsö. In the sandy area of Västergarn it is very numerous and mostly confined to man-made habitats: fertile grassland, margins of fields and shrubberies (both planted and natural). It was first discovered in the ruin of an old 'kastal', part of a fortification from the 12th century.

The chromosome number immediately sets *C. gotlandica* apart from the other European species of section Corydalis. Although most similar to *C. intermedia*, it has a few characters in common with *C. solida* (lowermost bract usually divided, racemes erect in fruit) and was recently shown to be a chromosome-doubled hybrid between these two. The 'DNA fingerprint' of *C. gotlandica* corresponds to the sum of that of the other two species. As both parental candidates are found in close proximity to *C. gotlandica* on the island of Stora Karlsö, whereas they are lacking in Västergarn, it is tempting to suggest that Stora Karlsö was the cradle of this species. It is also possible that it occurred quite recently, as it is currently expanding in distribution and benefits from human disturbance.

In early bud stage it may be confused with *C. intermedia*. However, in *C. gotlandica* the lowermost bract is usually divided and as soon as the much larger densely packed flowers develop, mistaken identity is out of the question. It is an early species, flowering only slightly later than *C. intermedia* and *C. pumila*.

In the wild it usually has its peak flowering in late April.

It can be quite eye-catching in open places, when lots of reddish purple flower-heads dot the ground.

Series Corydalis

Bracts usually divided. *Inner petals* not tipped externally with dark purple. *Nectary* tapering to a slender tail. *Elaiosome* flat or globular, not spirally twisted. 5 species.

17. *C. pumila* (Host) Rchb., Fl. Germ. excurs.: 698 (1832); *Fumaria pumila* Host, Fl. Austriaca 2: 304 (1832); *Corydalis lobelii* Tausch, Flora 22: 379 (1839), *nomen illegit.* Type: From Austria, near Vienna (not seen).

C. depauperata Schur, Verh. Mitth. Siebenbürg. Vereins Naturwiss. Hermannstadt: 51 (1853). Type: 'reg. subarctica in locis humidis lapidosis calcareis. Am Bulafall in den Kerzeschoarer Gebirgen, 6000'. *Schur*, Sertum Florae Transs. nr. 159 (ex descr., not seen).

DESCRIPTION. *Tuber* 1-3 cm. *Stem* usually single from each tuber, 5-16(-20) cm. *Leaves* twice or rarely once ternate with entire or deeply divided leaflets; leaf-lobes broadly or rarely narrowly obovate, obtuse. *Racemes* dense, 4-10 (-14)-flowered; flowers usually horizontal, partly concealed by the bracts. *Bracts* broadly obovate to almost orbicular, with 4-6 spreading obovate obtuse lobes, very rarely almost entire. *Pedicels* short and rather stout, 3-5(-8) mm, erectopatent in flower. *Corolla* white to pale reddish purple except for the wings of the outer petals which are a contrasting dark purple (forms that are reddish purple all over are occasionally encountered); upper petal obtuse to slightly emarginate; lower petal 7-10(-11) mm long, with a straight claw and a rounded to slightly emarginate 4-6 mm broad shallowly dentate limb; inner petals with crests low and rounded, not overtopping the apex. Spur straight, 6-10 mm long. *Ovary* gradually attenuate into a short style. *Capsule* elliptic-acuminate, dorsiventrally flattened, suberect, 14-20 x 5-6 mm. *Seeds* 5-10, 2.2 mm, with an obovate flat elaiosome. 2n=16. Self-compatible, probably often autogamous. Fig. 8a.

DISTRIBUTION. Confined to a belt across Europe from central Scandinavia southwards to northern Greece and central Italy; it has become rarer in recent years in parts of central Europe. March-April. 0-1000 m. Map 7.

Corydalis pumila prefers neutral and alkaline soils and tolerates drier and more open situations better than either *CC. solida* or *intermedia*. In the Scandinavian countries it has a pronounced coastal distribution and sometimes grows even in the upper littoral belt, but it also inhabits lawns and yards. In southern Europe we have encountered it in forests and in subalpine meadows.

Hybrids with *C. solida* are occasionally produced. The hybrids are partially fertile and may, through back-crossing and introgression, form extensive and highly variable hybrid-swarms, especially in parks, gardens, and other disturbed habitats.

Vegetatively, it is similar to *C. intermedia*, and scarcely more attractive. A collectors item, its small flowers are hidden behind the incised bracts and the dense little raceme is hardly raised from the ground on a short stem.

17b. C. laxa auct. In the Mälaren area in east-central Sweden morphological intermediates between *C. pumila* and *C. solida* are found. Their flowering period coincides with that of *C solida*, while being considerably later than *C. pumila*. In natural habitats the populations are rather uniform but differ greatly from place to place, sometimes approaching *C. pumila*, sometimes *C. solida*. These forms are probably a result of ancient introgression between *C. solida* and *C. pumila* at their westernmost and northernmost limits respectively. DNA studies support this conclusion.

18. C. densiflora C. & J.Presl, Del. Prag. 1:10 (1882). *C. solida* var. *densiflora* (C. & J.Presl) Boiss., Fl. Or. 1: 129 (1867); *C. solida* subsp. *densiflora* (C. & J.Presl) Hayek, Prodr. Fl. Penins. Balcan. 1: 364 (1925) (*nomen, non planta*). Type: Sicily, 'In nemorosis Nebrodum' (not seen).
C. solida var. *bracteosa* Batt. & Trab. in Bull. Soc. Bot. France 52: 498 (1905); *C. solida* subsp. *bracteosa* (Batt. & Trab.) Greuter & Burdet, Willdenowia 10:231 (1980). Type: Algeria, L'Haizer, Tizi-n-Teselent, 2100 m, 25.5.1905, *Battandier* (L).

DESCRIPTION. Similar to *C. pumila* but: *Plant* much more robust. *Stems* 10-15(-20) cm. *Leaves* usually biternate. *Leaves* usually with very broad leaflets, shallowly cut apically, or rarely deeply cut into narrowly obovate segments. *Raceme* usually dense, 5-15 (-20)-flowered. *Bracts* short and broad, apically divided into short segments that are usually again dentate or shallowly cut at apex. *Pedicels* 3-8 mm, erect and stout, straight or very slightly recurved in fruit. *Corolla* whitish to pale pink with red margins, or sometimes wholly reddish purple or with purple streaks, obtuse at apex, slightly sinuose-dentate; inner petals 9-10 mm long; lower petal without a basal pouch. *Spur* 8-12 mm long. *Capsule* dorsiventrally flattened, rather firm with thick marginal veins, broadly elliptic, acuminate at apex, 10-18 x 5-7 mm including a short straight style. *Seeds* 3-8, 2-2.5 mm. 2n=16. Self-incompatible. Fig. 8a,b; Pl. 13.

DISTRIBUTION. S Italy, N Sicily and one locality in Algeria. 700-2100 m. May-June. Map 7.

This species was previously considered to be the same as the Balkan *C. solida* subsp. *incisa* but the morphological differences are substantial. It is very similar to *C. pumila* in the broad bracts, the suberect thick pedicels, the short straight style and in the form and coloration of the corolla. However, the longer erect racemes and the larger flowers are distinctive. Furthermore, it is not a regular selfer and produces very few seeds when self-pollinated.

So far we only grow a single plant from Sicily (Mt Madonie); a pretty thing with flowers dramatically striped with pinkish veins and purplish lipstick.

19. C. solida (L.) Clairv., Man. herbor. Suisse: 371 (1811); *Fumaria bulbosa* γ. *solida* L., Sp. pl. 699 (1753); *F. bulbosa* L. emend. Mill., Gard. dict. ed. 8

Plate 21. *Corydalis solida* subsp. *solida* Penza group
Plate 22. *Corydalis solida* subsp. *solida*, white form from Macedonia
Plate 23. *Corydalis solida* subsp. *solida*, form from Austrian
Plate 24. *Corydalis solida* subsp. *solida* 'George Baker'
Plate 25. *Corydalis solida* subsp. *solida*, 'Prasil Strain'

26

27

28

29

30

Plate 26. *Corydalis solida* subsp. *solida* 'Blushing Girl'
Plate 27. *Corydalis solida* subsp. *incisa* 'Cirrus'
Plate 28. *Corydalis bracteata*
Plate 29. *Corydalis bracteata*, close up of flowers
Plate 30. *Corydalis* x *allenii*

Fig. 9. a-d, *Corydalis solida* subsp. *solida* (a, cult. Vitek s.n., Austria; b, cult. Lidén s.n., Sweden, Gotland, Stora Karlsö; c, cult. from KP 27/72, Romania, Paringului Mts); **e**, *C. solida* subsp. *subremota* (cult. Seisums & Veerus 147, Siberia, Krasnojarsk, Stolbi, GB)

(1768); *F. solida* (L.) Mill., Gard. abr. dict., ed. 6: 110 (1771); *F. halleri* Willd., Fl. Berol.: 229 (1787); *F. minor* Roth, Tent. fl. Ger., 1: 300 (1788); *F. digitata* Schrank, Baier. fl. 2: 242 (1789); *Corydalis bulbosa* (L.) DC., in Lamarck & de Candolle, Fl. Fr. ed. 3, 4: 637 (1805) *nomen rejic.*; *C. digitata* (Schrank) Pers., Syn. 2: 269 (1806); *C. halleri* (Willd.) Willd., Enum. hort. Berol. 740 (1809). Type: Burser Hortus Siccus VII (UPS, lecto).

DESCRIPTION. *Stems* erect, usually with a late branch from the scale leaf axil. *Leaves* (once) two to four times ternate with entire or deeply cleft leaflets; ultimate lobes variable, usually rather narrow, but sometimes very broad, glaucous below. *Racemes* rather dense, somewhat elongating in fruit; flowers usually nodding. *Bracts* usually longer than broad, apically more or less deeply divided into usually acute lobes, rarely entire. *Pedicels* slender, 5-15(-20) mm, more or less recurved in fruit. *Corolla* variable in colour; outer petals broadly winged and usually

emarginate at apex, often with a shallowly dentate margin; lower petal with or without a basal pouch; inner petals pale, only internally blotched with dark reddish purple at apex, and with rather narrow dorsal crests that do not overtop the apex. *Spur* straight or apically recurved, the n*ectary* tapering to a long slender tail, reaching halfway through the spur or more. *Style* usually long, often geniculate at base. *Capsule* broadly lanceolate to elliptic, dorsiventrally flattened, pendent. *Seeds* 2-12, with a flat obovoid elaiosome.

Although easily circumscribed, *C. solida* has a large amplitude of variation and even when four subspecies are distinguished, some remain extremely variable. The subspecies are mostly vicariant and generally distinct, but intermediate forms are found in areas of overlap between subsp. *incisa* and subsp. *solida*. Due partly to its great variability and partly to its horticultural significance, *C. solida* will be given a more exhaustive treatment than the other species.

KEY TO THE SUBSPECIES

1. Capsule 20-27 mm long, 5 times as long as broad, 2-7-seeded (Aegean: Andros; Yenisey area) **4**
1. Capsule 12-20 mm, 3-4 times as long as broad, 3-12-seeded **2**

2. Bracts with divisions again divided or dentate **19d. subsp. *incisa***
2. Bracts entire or simply lobed **3**

3. Lower petal often saccate; flowers usually purple; spur 10-14 mm long (Europe) **19b. subsp. *solida***
3. Lower petal not saccate; flowers blue; spur 7-10 mm long (Yenisey area) **19a. subsp. *subremota***

4. Flowers reddish purple; lower petal 12-14 mm long; fruit 2-7-seeded with a seedless distal third (Aegean: Andros) **19c. subsp. *longicarpa***
4. Flowers blue to bluish purple; lower petal 10-11 mm long; fruit 3-12-seeded without a seedless portion (Yenisey area) **19a. subsp. *subremota***

19a. subsp. *subremota* Popov ex Lidén & Zetterlund in Willdenowia 26:26 (1996). Type: Siberia: Yenisey, Krasnojarsk, 56°N, high grass, shady place by a brook, 13. 6. 1876, *H. W. Arnell* (S, holo). *C. halleri* var. *subremota* Popov in Flora USSR 7: 672 (1937) *nomen nudum*.

DESCRIPTION. *Stem* very slender, 10-25 cm, with rather small, twice to three times ternate leaves; ultimate leaf-lobes narrowly obovate to oblanceolate or linear. *Racemes* 4-12-flowered, very dense at first, elongating in fruit; flowers narrow and small. *Pedicels* short and slender, 5-8 mm long, patent to slightly arcuate-recurved in fruit. *Bracts* equalling the pedicels, narrowly obtriangular, digitately divided into narrow acute lobes. *Corolla* blue to purplish blue; inner petals 9-10 mm; lower petal with claw narrow and straight without any trace of gibbosity, the limb broad and emarginate (or sometimes rather narrow and obtuse), often with a short mucro in the notch. *Spur* straight and slender, 7-10(-13) mm long. *Capsule* 13-27 x 4-5 mm, 3-12 seeded, gradually narrowed into a short style. *Seeds* 1.5-2 mm long. Fig. 9e.

DISTRIBUTION. Russia: Middle and Upper Yenisey: Krasnojarski kray; Tuva. May to June. Map 8.

The bluest *C. solida* subspecies which is immediately distinguished from the other subspecies by its very slender habit and small bluish flowers. The capsules vary considerably in length but are always narrower, paler and more delicate in texture than those of subsp. *solida*. Only after considerable hesitation did we decide to keep it in *C. solida* rather than treat it as a separate species.

In the wild it grows with *C. gracilis* in deciduous humid forests at low altitudes. This subspecies has been recently introduced to cultivation but it is scarcely a traffic-stopper, although it has a delicate charm all of its own.

19b. subsp. *solida*
C. solida var. *speciosa transsilvanica* Schur, Enum. pl. Trans.:52 (1853), *nomen illegit.*
C. solida var. *australis* Hausm., Fl. Tirol. 42 (1854); *C. australis* (Hausm.) Host in J. Hort. Pract. Gard. ser 3, 45: 205 (1902). Note: from the southern slopes of the Alps; intermediate between subsp. *solida* and subsp. *incisa,* for example in the division of bracts. Not studied in cultivation.
C. slivenensis Velen., Fl. Bulg. 20 (1881). *C. solida* subsp. *slivenensis* (Velen.) Hayek, Prodr. Fl. Penins. Balcan. 1: 364 (1925). Type: Bulgaria, Sliven, *Skorpil* 1884 (PRC, not seen).
C. bicalcarata Velen. Fl. Bulg. 20 (1881). Type: Bulgaria, Mt Vitosa, *Skorpil* (PRC, not seen); see also subsp. *incisa*.
C. pirotensis Adamowiç in Allg. Bot. Z. Syst.: 79 (1896); *C. solida* var. *densiflora* subvar. *balcanica* f. *pirotensis* (Adamovic) Poelln. in Repert. Spec. nov. Regni veg. 45: 111 (1938). Type: Serbia, Sabanov Trap and Mt Belava near Pirot, calcareous soil, 400-500 m, April, *Adamovic* (L).
C. feddeana Poelln., Repert. Spec. nov. Regni veg. 14: 101 (1938), non H.Lév. (1913). Type: Odessa, 20. 4. 1883, *Schumann* (B, holo).

DESCRIPTION. *Stems* 10-25 cm (-35 in cult.). *Leaves* twice or usually three times ternate, with oblanceolate to obovate obtuse segments, usually less than three times as long as broad. *Racemes* with a distinct stalk, rather dense at first, elongating in fruit, 5-20(-25)-flowered. *Bracts* nearly always longer than broad, obovate to oblong, shallowly or deeply divided into four to eight more or less parallel to slightly diverging acute lobes, or rarely entire. *Pedicels* roughly equalling the bracts, 7-15(-20) mm long and somewhat recurved in fruit. *Corolla* with outer petals broadly emarginate, rarely obtuse; lower petal usually with a prominent pouch at base; *inner petals* 10-12 mm long. *Spur* (6-) 10-14 (-16) mm long. *Ovary* usually distinctly geniculate at base of long style. *Capsule* sub-pendent, 15-20 x 5 mm. *Seeds* 5-11, c. 2 mm. 2n=16 (24, 32). Self-incompatible. Fig. 9a-d; Pl. 18, 19, 22, 23.

DISTRIBUTION. From east-central Sweden and Gotland through south Finland, eastwards to the Urals and slightly beyond; central Europe southwards to N Greece, N Italy and N Spain. It is only known as a garden escape or semi-naturalised plant in most of north-western Europe. There are occasional finds from the N Caucasus and Tashkent (?). 0-1000 m. Flowering late April-May. Map 8.

The flower colour is very variable; reddish purple to dull greyish purple (or to quote a distinguished grower 'a murky pale puce') is the norm in most parts of the distribution area. White flowered forms are common in E Macedonia, Bulgaria and parts of Russia. In east Finland and the Baltic states the flowers tend to be rather bluish and in the Ukraine they attain an attractive deep purple. Some sources claim the presence of individuals with yellowish flowers in Bulgaria, an idea that stems from Velenovsky (1881). As white flowers frequently turn yellowish in the press a mistake cannot be excluded.

Contrary to 'Flora Bulgarica' (Stojanov *et al*, 1966) and Lidén (1988) we have not recognised *C. slivenensis* as a separate taxon. Even if the supposedly distinguishing characters (broad entire leaflets and white flowers) are found primarily in Bulgaria and E Yugoslavia, they are not correlated and are found with 'normal' *C. solida* characters. In natural populations individuals with all possible combinations of characters co-occur.

Corydalis solida subsp. *solida* is known to hybridise with *C. pumila* and may in these instances give rise to hybrid swarms, especially in parks, gardens and similar environments. This is especially pronounced in east-central Sweden (cf. 17b, *C. laxa*), and a successful clone from such a hybrid-swarm growing in Linnaeus' own garden (Hammarby) was in fact once described as a distinct species, *C. rutacea* (Th. Fries 1854). Hybrids with *C. intermedia* are known from Sweden and Austria.

According to Henry and Margaret Taylor, forms of *C. solida* from the Pyrenees do not cross easily with the central European ones but we have not had the opportunity to investigate this.

Sterile hybrids with *C. wendelboi* and *bracteata* are also known (see under those species).

CULTIVATION. The most common form in cultivation is the 'weedy' *puce malade*-coloured one which spreads rapidly and can be found in park environments all over Europe. Used as a landscape plant it is quite charming if associated with other spring-flowers. When plain *C. solida* is offered by European nurseries this is the plant you will undoubtedly receive.

Two quotations may serve to illustrate the different opinions concerning the horticultural merits of this form: 'As a spring plant, it deserves a place in the garden; in point of ornament, it is applicable to the same purposes as the Primrose, will grow in almost every soil or situation....' (*Curtis's Botanical Magazine*, 1794). The famous Sam Arnott (*The Garden*, 1898) speaks for its slanderers: 'I do not think, however, that many would resent being advised not to add Haller's Fumitory to their gardens....'.

If one wants plants of clearer colours, named cultivars should be chosen. These have been multiplied by division or as controlled seed-strains and are often horribly expensive when first marketed.

In the past there were few cultivars around. The plant known as *C. solida* 'George Baker' was the first of any note. A number of new cultivars and strains have now appeared on the scene and our guess is that this development will continue. To date the selection has concentrated on the white, pink and red forms but some gorgeous deep violet and plum-purple plants, that well deserve attention, are found in certain populations and we hope that they will find their way into general cultivation before long.

The Transsylvanians. This group has been subject to much interest and some confusion. Originating in present day Romania, it was first introduced by the famous firm van Tubergen in 1925 under the names *Corydalis solida transsylvanica* 'rubra', 'salmonea' and 'alba'. This stock was sent by Dr. A. Amlacher from Orastie-Broos, Romania, who wrote: *'Corydalis 'cava' speciosa transsilvanica*, a magnificent *Lerchensporn* in mixed colours, white, white-red-spotted, red-purple, pink etc in all shades of colour, 100 tubers, 10 Mark'.

The second introduction was collected in 1972 by Josef Kupeç and Milan Prasil (KP 27/72) in the Transsylvanian Alps, at 1500 m (which is exceptionally high for subsp. *solida*!) in the Paringului Mountains, 2 km from the Chalet Cabana Rusu (9 km from Petroseni). In one mountain meadow a small patch of red and salmon-red plants was found amongst the ordinary purples, as well as some intermediates. There have been other introductions as well but these have not been as widely distributed.

For a group of such recent introduction one is surprised to find so many question marks and contradictions in the commentaries dealing with these popular plants. Therefore it is necessary to make a more extensive summary of their history in cultivation:

1925. Introduced by the van Tubergen nurseries. Th. Hoog writes in the *Gardeners Chronicle*, 1960, 'In about 1930 [turned out to be 1925] we were in touch with a collector in Transsylvania and in that year I offered in my catalogue *C. solida transsylvanica alba* with white flowers, and *C. s. t. rubra* with claret-red flowers. We also had a limited stock of *C. s. t. salmonea* with salmon-pink flowers'.

1931. Mentioned by Karl Foerster in an article.

1935. *C. s. t. salmonea*, exhibited by Lady Iris Lawrence, Dorking.

1936. Written up by Karl Foerster and beautifully illustrated in his book 'Der Steingarten'. His plants were of different shades and the very best forms had orange-red flowers.

1940s. Munich Botanic Garden (Wilhelm Schacht) received plants from Karl Foerster.

1959. *C. s. t.* exhibited by Messrs. W. E. Th. Ingwersen Ltd. at the Royal Horticultural Society when it received an Award of Merit (A.M.).

1966. Written up in the *Gardeners Chronicle* by Will Ingwersen, whom we quote: '... It extends over the past 30 years from one small tuber which was given to my father by the late Sir William Lawrence... after all these years I now possess four tubers.... these few treasured tubers are the only plants of *C. transylvanica* now in cultivation..'.

1968. Written up in the *Gardeners Chronicle* by W. Ingwersen 'Nearly 40 years ago, the late Sir William Lawrence, a great gardener and plant collector, gave my father one tuber of *C. transylvanica*, this being one of the only two in cultivation as far as was known. The one he retained eventually perished but our plant survived and flowered each year'.

1977. *C. solida* 'George Baker', first time mentioned!: *Bulletin Alpine Garden Society* vol. 45. Editor's note: 'Since the name *'transsylvanica'*, however

admirable, is not in accordance with the International Rules of Nomenclature, this plant has now been given the cultivar name *Corydalis solida* 'George Baker', in commemoration of the fine plantsman G.P. Baker, who first introduced it to cultivation in the early 1930s'.

1980. *C. solida* 'transsylvanica' written up in *The Plantsman* by Will Ingwersen: '.. originated from one tuber given by the late G.P. Baker of Sevenoaks many years ago (sic!)...... flowers of a rich terra-cotta pink....'.

1984. The following statement appears in the *Bulletin Alpine Garden Society*: '.... 'George Baker' (once *transsilvanica*) refers only to the rich red form'.

1988. *C. solida* 'George Baker'. According to Alan Leslie (*The Garden*, July 1992) awarded a First Class Certificate (F.C.C.).

From the above it seems probable that the plant that bears George Baker's name never passed through his hands. Two great plantsmen became mixed up in the 1970s. It is likely that *C. transylvanica salmonea* was imported by Sir William Lawrence when listed by van Tubergen, that it was exhibited by his wife in 1935 and that the Ingwersen statements from 1966 and 1968 are more reliable than that of 1980. Furthermore, it is a fair assumption that the Karl Foerster plant and also the Munich strain hail from van Tubergen in Holland.

A fog still surrounds the origin of *C. solida* 'George Baker'. The colour of the original Ingwersen plant is described as 'RHS colour-chart; spur 51C, lip 56A', 'good large flowers of a beautiful rosy-pink', 'a rich terra-cotta pink', 'salmon-pink blossoms of considerable beauty', 'bright coral pink overlaid by lavender blue' and 'terra-cotta red'. As the cultivar-name 'George Baker' only refers to the rich red form the obvious conclusion is that it is not the same plant as that staged by the Ingwersen Nursery in 1959. This is supported by Jim Jermyn, proprietor of Edrom Nurseries, who trained at Birch Farm Nursery in the 1970s and says that 'there was no such plant ('G.B.') grown there but a paler form of a weaker stature. The glorious red one suddenly appeared on the scene in the late seventies'.

In fact, the name 'George Baker' may have been applied to an individual of the 1972 introduction since in the 1977 note in the *Bulletin Alpine Garden Society* the collective name 'transsylvanica' is transferred to 'George Baker' without pointing out any particular clone: indeed for a while many pink- and red-flowered

C. solida were called 'George Baker'. Another introduction might well have been distributed by the Ingwersens as they would probably be the first to receive an improved 'transsylvanica'.

Dr. Alan Leslie (*The Garden*, July 1992) justly expresses a fear concering 'an undesirable proliferation of cultivar names'. He suggests Sunrise Group as a collective name for the pink forms and Sunset Group for the redder forms and so adds to the 'proliferation'. In fact, the intensity of the red pigmentation depends to a large extent on the climate and is particularly prominent when plants have been grown in the open garden, especially when cold weather has delayed them. This would make it possible for a plant in the mid-shades of red-pink to fit into both groups depending on how, where and when it had been grown.

Recognised cultivars:

'Beth Evans'. Soft pink with a white flash on the spur. Edinburgh Botanic Garden raised this from seed, probably received from Munich Botanic Garden. It was named to commemorate Alf Evans' late wife, and received an A.M. in 1988.

'Dieter Schacht'. A selected clone from Munich Botanic Garden. Similar to 'Beth Evans' but a better increaser.

'George Baker'. The red corydalis of great fame; really a superb plant. Pl. 24.

'Highland Mist'. A cross between a Pyrenean *C. solida* and 'Prasil Strain' produced by Henry and Margaret Taylor with a 'smoky bluish-pink'colour. A good increaser but expensive. P.C. in 1995.

'Kissproof'. A Dutch selection by W. van Eeden from a naturalised colony. White flowers with rosy-violet lips.

'Lahovice'. (KP 27/72). A refined, more uniform selection of the 'Prasil Strain'. A number of tubers were sent by M. Prasil to Paul Christian who selected the best and deepest red forms. From these the 'Lahovice' stock has been worked up.

'Munich Form'. A temporary British name applied to the striking coral red (on the Continent) form from Munich Botanic Garden. It has been distributed in Britain from the vegetative increase of an initial introduction of four tubers in 1981.

'Nettleton Pink'. P.C. in 1994, exhibited by Potterton & Martin. A vigorous clone with attractive rich pink flowers.

'Nymphenburg'. Same as 'Munich form'.

'Prasil Strain'. (KP 27/72). A seed-strain in which the flowers vary from scarlet-red to salmon-orange and pink. Pl. 25.

'Sixtus'. A recent pink-flowered introduction from Romania named after its collector.

'Zwanenburg'. (KP 27/72). A selected clone from the 'Prasil Strain' that appeared in Michael Hoog's catalogue in 1990 as 'J. 10'. It was described as 'the sensation of the genus *Corydalis*; a true break, a mutation with bright luminous scarlet flowers'. From what we have seen this really is the reddest but, unfortunately, it is still very rare.

The Latvians. Even if these are not yet readily available we expect them to be future favourites. Much selection has been made by Janis Ruksans, a distinguished Latvian horticulturist. Some of his plants have just appeared in the trade:

'Blushing Girl'. A pink form, a sport found by Janis Ruksans in a Latvian garden. It has entire obovate bracts and pale warm-pink (a touch of cream) flowers in a compact raceme. Pl. 26.

'Snowstorm'. A stout and vigorous milky-white cultivar from the banks of River Ogre in Latvia selected by J. Ruksans.

The Penza solidas. A remarkable group collected in one locality near Penza in European Russia. Here the colour-variability within *C. solida* is developed to the extreme. Apart from ordinary 'pale puce', white, pale to darker blue, pink, wine-red (Pl. 21) and brownish purple plants are to be found:

'Blue Dream'. A compact violet-blue form.

'Blue Giant'. Strong-growing, lilac-blue Penza.

'Blue Pearl'. A Ruksans selection with pale blue flowers, the colour like *Crocus chrysanthus* 'Blue Pearl'.

'Evening Shade'. Faintly light blue Penza.

'Jaroslavna'. A nice brownish red clone.

'White Knight'. Robust, pure white.

The Macedonian solidas. Another area where subsp. *solida* shows an exceptional variation is southern Bulgaria, southern Serbia and Skopje-Macedonia. Here pure white ones are common as well as bright lilac-purple and pale blue shades. In this area, individuals with less-divided or even entire primary leaflets are frequently found intermingled with the more normal ones. The most intriguing forms in cultivation are **'Ice Nine'** (Pl. 16), a delicious white form with an ice-blue face, and another white one, flushed red with the mouth touched with cherry-red lipstick.

19c. subsp. *longicarpa* Lidén in Willdenowia 26:27 (1996). Type: Greece, Andros: N slope of Mt Kouvara (Petalon Oros), 2 km SW Arnas, 500-600 m, 2. 4. 1971, *Snogerup & Gustafsson* 41876 (L, holo).

DESCRIPTION. *Stem* slender, 15-25 cm. *Leaves* thin, biternate with discrete broadly obovate leaflets deeply divided into oblong to obovate obtuse lobes. *Racemes* 3-10-flowered, becoming very lax, and further elongating in fruit. *Pedicels* patent to recurved, 5-10 mm in flower, up to 15 mm in fruit. *Bracts* deeply divided with acute lobes, sometimes with the primary lobes dentate. *Corolla* pale purple, darker at apex; lower petal 12-15 mm long, straight, without any trace of gibbosity. *Spur* 12-16 mm long. *Capsule* 20-25 x 3 mm, incl. a straight beak 4-8 mm, 2-7-seeded. *Mature* seeds unknown. Fig. 10b.

DISTRIBUTION. Greece, Andros, 500-900 m. March. Map 8.

This subspecies, which occupies the south-east extreme of the distribution area of the species, is similar to subsp. *solida* in general habit but is readily distinguished by its long pale flowers with a straight lower petal, as well as the long and narrow capsules.

19d. subsp. *incisa* Lidén in Notes Roy. Bot. Gard. Edinb. 45: 349-363 (1989[1988]). Type: Greece, Peloponnese, Chelmos, 1800 m, 7. 6. 1933, *O. Cyrén* s. n. (GB, holo; S, iso).
C. decipiens Nyman, Schott & Kotschy, Anal. Bot. 42 (1854). Type: Montenegro (?), above Krajuluj, amongst *Pinus pumila*, near melting snow, 1770 m, 24.8.(!) 1850, *Kotschy* 401, (BM, K; L).
C. tenuis Schott, Nyman, & Kotschy in Anal. Bot. 42 (1854). Type: Dalmatia, *Fr. Maly* s.n. (L).
C. balcanica Velen., Fl. Bulg. 21 (1881); *C. solida* var. *densiflora* subvar. *balcanica* (Velen.) Poelln., Repert. Spec. nov. Regni veg. 45: 111 (1938). Type: Bulgaria, summit of Mt Vitosa, *Skorpil* (PRC, not seen; description and other material from the type locality indicate this species).
C. densiflora sensu Haláczy, Consp. Fl. Graec. 1:44 (1901) and Papanicolau in A. Strid (ed.), Mountain Flora of Greece 1 (1985), non C. & J.Presl.

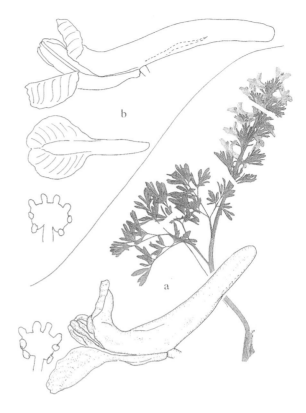

Fig. 10. a, *Corydalis solida* subsp. *incisa* (cult. Ek21, Greece, Mt Parnassus); b, *C. solida* subsp. *longicarpa* (type)

C. solida var. *densiflora* subvar. *taygetana* Fedde, Repert. Spec. nov. Regni veg. 16: 190 (1919). Type: Greece, Taygetos, 11.4.1849, *Heldreich* 239 (B; GB).
C. solida subsp. *densiflora* (C. & J.Presl) Hayek, Prodr. Fl. Penins. Balc. 1:364 (1925), *sensu* Hayek, excl. type.
C. solida var. *densiflora* subvar. *tenuisecta* (Boiss.) Poelln., Repert. Spec. nov. Regni. veg. 45: 111 (1938) *sensu* von Poellnitz, excl. type.
?*C. thasia* (Stoj. & Kitan.) Stoj. & Kitan. Fl. ins. Thasos. Ann. Univ. Sofia, Fac. Phys. Mat. xli, livr. 3, Sci. Nat.: 304 (1945); *C. solida* var. *thasia* Stoj. & Kitan. Type: NE Greece, Thasos (not seen, but the description and photos of wild plants indicate that it could possibly belong here).

DESCRIPTION. *Plant* robust and erect, 6-15 (-25) cm. *Leaves* three to four times ternate with lanceolate to linear leaf-lobes. *Raceme* showy, (3-)8-22-flowered, more short-stalked than in subsp. *solida*. *Bracts* large, deeply divided with the primary divisions again divided or dentate, usually enlarging in fruit. *Pedicels* shorter than the bracts, 5-10 mm in flower, somewhat longer and strongly reflexed in fruit. *Corolla* large, white to pale purple; lower petal 13-14 mm long. *Spur* 11-15 mm long. *Ovary* usually with a long basally geniculate style. *Capsule* 15-18 x 5 mm. *Seeds* 5-10, 2 mm with large obovate straight elaiosome. 2n=16. Self-incompatible. Fig. 10a; Pl. 17.

DISTRIBUTION. Albania, Skopje-Macedonia, Montenegro, Greece, Bulgaria (Mt Vitosa). Very common in alpine meadows and pastures over a large part of the Balkan peninsula, usually on limestone. 1000-2300 m. March-June. Map 8.

Subsp. *incisa* is usually a more robust and firm plant than subsp. *solida* and its leaves and bracts are thicker. The longer, denser and shorter-stalked racemes are also distinctive. As subsp. *solida* and subsp. *incisa* occupy different habitats and altitudes, they rarely get a chance to meet in nature but intermediate forms are found in areas of overlap at intermediate altitudes, especially in north-east Greece and Bulgaria. Plants from the north-western part of the distribution area are generally smaller, with smaller and darker flowers.

Horticulturally, we find it the most elegant member within *C. solida*. Its finely dissected leaves and deeply divided bracts bring out the bright flowers in a most attractive way. It shimmers in the sun and on a warm day it produces a heavenly scent.

The colour is mostly pale: white to pink or lilac. The best forms are to be found in Greece. Although sometimes pitiable dwarfs in nature they become large and handsome in cultivation. The north-western forms keep their compact habit in cultivation.

This subspecies has been in cultivation since the late 1800s, being regularly found in literature as *C. densiflora*. In 1992 it was awarded a Preliminary Commendation (P.C.) by the Royal Horticultural Society in London in one of its fine white forms.

P. Christian & A. Hoog 821 from the Vermion mountain in N Greece has been in circulation for a few years. A most delightful plant with olive-green foliage and red pedicels, contrasting perfectly with the pure white flowers. Highly recommended!

'Vermion Snow'. A white selection from B. Mathew 6999 B, collected on Mt Vermion in N Greece.

'Cirrus'. A dove-grey large-flowered form from Mt Taygetos, collected by Bengt Oxelman. Pl. 27.

'Altostratus'. A pure pink equivalent of the above.

C. solida incisa forma PA 600. This is a rogue, apparently collected in Greece but the collection-data has been lost. The largest *solida* seen so far and distributed by the Copenhagen Botanic Garden. The colour is a deep lilac and it is a good garden-plant.

***C. decipiens* Hort.** A semi-sterile clone of obscure origin, possibly a hybrid of subsp. *incisa* ancestry. It has been in the trade for a long time; an early-flowering large plant with reddish purple flowers, 'an improved *solida*' (Dutch grower).

Uncertain Taxa:

C. solida subsp. *oligantha* (Trinajstic) Greuter & Burdet, Willdenowia 19:38 (1989); *Bulbocapnos solidus* subsp. *oliganthus* Trinajstic, Suppl. Fl. Anal. Jugosl. 1: 19. Type: Croatia, Brač, *Trinajstic* 11557 (Herb. Trinajstic, not seen).

20. *C. bracteata* (Willd.) Pers., Syn. 2: 269 (1806); *Fumaria bracteata* Stephan ex. Willd., Spec. pl. 3: 858 (1800). Type: Siberia, Altai, *Stephan* (B (WILLD.) 12914; LE).

C. hybrida Michajlova, Novosti Sist. Vyssh. Rast. 25: 88 (1988). Type: W Russia, St Petersburg, Komarov Institute, *Michajlova* (LE): see below.

DESCRIPTION. *Stems* erect, 15-30 cm (up to 40 cm in cultivation), unbranched or usually with a single late branch from the scale-leaf. *Leaves* long-petioled, thin, once to three times ternate, often more than two; leaflets more or less deeply divided into narrowly obovate lobes. *Racemes* 5-13-flowered (-20 in cult.). *Bracts* ovate-flabellate, apically cleft into 4-7 narrow lobes. *Pedicels* slender, 10-15 mm long, patent to slightly arcuate in fruit. *Corolla* large, broadly winged, cream to yellow, rarely white; lower petal with a broad saccate claw abruptly dilated into an emarginate limb 9-15 mm broad; inner petals 11-14 mm long. *Spur* 12-15 mm long, with nectary one third to half as long. *Stigma* broader than long. *Capsule* elliptic, 15-18 x 5 mm, with very short style. *Seeds* 5-10, about 2 mm, with a minute globular elaiosome on a distinct dark stalk. 2n=16. Self-incompatible. Fig. 11b; Pl. 28, 29.

DISTRIBUTION. Russia: Novosibirsk, Altai, Tomsk, Kuznetsky Alatau. Map 9.

Fig. 11. a, *Corydalis gracilis* (cult. S. & V. 145, Siberia, Krasnojarsk, Stolbi, GB); **b**, *C. bracteata* (cult. from J. Ruksans, *sine coll.*, Siberia, Kemorova distr., Leninsk Kuznetski).

Similar to *C. solida* subsp. *solida* in vegetative characters but more robust and with much broader yellow or yellowish, lemon-scented, flowers. The peculiar elaiosome is worth noting.

This lovely species has been in cultivation since the 1820s but has never secured a stronghold in British gardens. It is the only yellow representative of the section in general cultivation and for that reason it is always in great demand. There are records that it has been successfully grown previously: in 1920 H. J. Elwes refers to it as a 'beautiful weed which comes up everywhere but [is] not very easy to pull up'. It was also well established in different collections, notably at the Royal Botanic Gardens Kew, in the 1880s. In *The Garden*, 1880, May 29, there is a reference to it obtaining a First Class Certificate (F.C.C.) from the Royal Horticultural Society when exhibited by Mr. Elwes!

Recent literature tells us more about the despair it has caused in Britain. It is a continental species and it is likely that the series of unreliable mild and muggy British winters broken by cold spells has eliminated established colonies. It needs cold in order to remain safely underground in winter, then warmth in April to get it into growth. If the climate is slightly more continental it will prove quite vigorous. It has managed to naturalise in both Moscow and St. Petersburg.

In Gothenburg it was planted in the north face of a peat-wall, where it thrives and seeds around into mats. When the herbage is about to become too dense we are saved by the voles that have a feast every fourth or fifth year, after which the remaining plants have to build up once again.

Corydalis bracteata is not always happy in the alpine-house; the extra few degrees afforded by the house confuses the plant: by growing it under glass we create a mild Atlantic climate and in some seasons it will work, while in others it will not. If one is determined to grow it in a pot the compost should be a peaty, slightly acid one that is rather rich. The shoots will normally emerge late in the corydalis-season; in too mild a winter it will come up in February and will then not develop satisfactorily.

Plate 31. *Corydalis fumariifolia* subsp. *fumariifolia*
Plate 32. *Corydalis fumariifolia* subsp. *azurea,* from Japan
Plate 33. *Corydalis fumariifolia* subsp. *azurea,* from Sakhalin
Plate 34. *Corydalis ussuriensis*
Plate 35. *Corydalis papilligera,* hexaploid form

36

37

38

39

40

41

Plate 36. *Corydalis lineariloba*
Plate 37. *Corydalis papilligera*, hexaploid form
Plate 38. *Corydalis grandicalyx*
Plate 39. *Corydalis hallaisanensis*
Plate 40. *Corydalis triternata*
Plate 41. *Corydalis magadanica*

'**Marina**'. A pale sulphur form from the Kemerovsk district that becomes almost white with age. Distributed by J. Ruksans.

C. (x) hybrida appeared spontaneously in the lawn at the Komarov Institute, St Petersburg. The supposed parentage is the same as for *C. allenii* auct. (see below) but it is rather like *C. bracteata*, except for the purple flowers. The pollen is of normal appearance and stainability, which does not suggest hybridity.

20b. C. x allenii Irwing, invalid name (non Fedde). A completely sterile diploid hybrid of garden-origin, widely distributed as *C. allenii* Irwing, with *C. bracteata* and *C. solida* as its parents. It is intermediate between the parents but with creamy pink-veined flowers in a shade that appeals to some but repels others. A vigorous grower that has to be frequently divided. Pl. 30.

21. C. gracilis Ledeb., Fl. Ross. 1: 101 (1842); *C. bracteata* var. *gracilis* (Ledeb.) N.Busch in Acta Horti Tiflis 9, suppl. (Fl. Cauc. crit. 3): 66 (1905). Type: Siberia, Yenisey, *Fischer* (LE).

DESCRIPTION. Like *C. bracteata* but: *Plant* with an accessory tuber in the scale-leaf, unbranched, or with a single leaf in connection with the axillary tuber. *Stem* slender. *Leaves* once to twice ternately divided; leaflets usually divided into oblong or narrowly obovate lobes. *Racemes* 2-4-flowered, rarely with up to 7 flowers. *Bracts* ovate, shallowly cut into acute lobes, rarely entire. *Corolla* with outer petals lemon yellow and with broad emarginate limbs; lower petal abruptly dilated into an emarginate limb 12-17 mm broad; inner petals 12-14 mm long. *Spur* 12-20 mm long, with a very slender nectary 9-13 mm long. *Stigma* larger and more squarish in outline than that of *C. bracteata*. *Fruit* linear, 20-25 x 2-3 mm. *Seeds* 4-7(-10), the elaiosomes much larger, not globular. Self-incompatible. Fig. 11a.

DISTRIBUTION. E Russia: Irkutsk, Krasnojarsk district, Mt Sajan. Map 9.

Very similar to the vicariant *C. bracteata* but a smaller plant with an accessory tuber in the scale-leaf, more ovate bracts with more acute lobules, fewer and usually broader flowers, linear fruits and a very distinctive elaiosome.

It has only recently been introduced in cultivation but shows great promise. To the gardener this is like a miniature *C. bracteata*: the flowers are about the same size and colour as *C. bracteata* but the tubers are much smaller and the height only around 15 cm. Its ability to multiply is due to the additional tuber that is formed in the scale leaf.

So far it has grown well in the alpine house as well as in the open garden, given the same treatment as the above.

Series Repentes Aparina

Novosti Sist. Vyssh. Rast. 7: 166 [1970] (1971). Type species: *C. repens* Mandl & Mühld.

This series is distinguishable with difficulty from the series Corydalis and Raphanituber, but the nectary is often shortly acute and the flowers usually blue. The outer petals are broadly winged, with a characteristic lower petal-limb which is broadest at the base, and usually with a smooth apical emargination (but see *C. fukuharae*). The inner petals are not tipped with dark purple externally.

Some species have stems more or less geniculate at the nodes and often form pale subterranean 'stolons', frequently with axillary tubers in the scale-leaves. These tubers are usually small, irregular and compact, (similar to chick-peas); they do not develop the internal structure of normal tubers until their second season. In these same species, the inner petals have rather broad dorsal wings which often protrude beyond the apex, sometimes conspicuously so. 15 species from eastern Asia.

Only a few of the species in the series *Repentes* are in cultivation and this treatment is tentative.

22. C. ambigua Cham. & Schltdl. in Linnaea 1:558 (1826). Type: E Siberia, Kamtchatka, near Petropavlosk, *von Chamisso* (B; LE; UPS)

DESCRIPTION. *Plant* glaucous, 9-18 cm. *Leaves* biternate, rather small; leaflets obovate, entire or shallowly divided into a few large teeth, rarely deeply divided into lanceolate lobes. *Racemes* much overtopping the leaves, 4-12-flowered, rather lax. *Bracts* ovate-lanceolate, acute, entire. *Pedicels* slender, 6-12 mm long, or up to 16 mm long in fruit. *Sepals* minute, or sometimes up to 1.5 mm, filiform. *Corolla* blue to purple; outer petals with rounded emarginate limbs; inner petals 8-9(-10) mm; lower petal broadly saccate at base, with a rounded emarginate limb. *Spur* 7-11 mm long, with the

Fig. 12. **a**, *Corydalis fumariifolia* subsp. *azurea* (cult. type); **b**, *C. fumariifolia* subsp. *fumariifolia* (cult. S. & V. 58, *pro parte*, SE Siberia, Chasan distr., Kedrovaja Padj, ussuriensis-locus); **c**, *C. ambigua* (isotype UPS)

nectary reaching to about one third. 2n=28 (Sokolovskaya, 1960). Fig. 12c.

DISTRIBUTION. Russia: Kamtchatka, perhaps also on the Siberian east coast. The distribution is imperfectly known due to confusion with the next species. 'Shrubs, forests, sandy or stony soil, in the north along shores of seas and rivers'. Map 9.

Closely related to *C. fumariifolia* but differing in several minor details: leaves rather small, glaucous above (large and green above in *C. fumariifolia*); the dorsal wings of the inner petals are more angular and usually broader in *C. fumariifolia*; in *C. ambigua* the lower petal has a broad saccate claw, whereas in *C. fumariifolia* the lower petal is usually straight or shallowly saccate but often angular at the very point of insertion. The fruit of *C. fumariifolia* is linear and uniseriate, dorsiventrally flattened with a distinct margin, while in *C. ambigua* the fruit is shorter and broader, uniseriate to biseriate. The chromosome

numbers are also said to differ, *C. ambigua* being tetraploid (Sokolovskaya 1960).

Plants under the name *C. ambigua* have been in circulation for at least 25 years but most, if not all, of this material belongs to *C. fumariifolia*.

23. *C. fumariifolia* Maxim., Prim. fl. Amur.: 37 (1859); *C. ambigua* f. *fumariifolia* (Maxim.) Kitag. in Rep. Inst. Sci. Res. Manchoukuo 3: 232 (1939); *C. remota* var. *fumariifolia* (Maxim.) Kom. in Acta Horti Petrop. 22: 351 (1903); *C. lineariloba* var. *fumariifolia* (Maxim.) Kitag., Neolineam. fl. Mansh.: 321 (1979); *C. turtschaninovii* f. *fumariifolia* (Maxim.) Y.H.Chou, Fl. pl. herb. Chin. bor.-or. 4: 229 (1980). Type: E Siberia, Lower Amur, Köurmi (Kkhurti), 10.5.1855, *Maxim.* (LE, holo).

DESCRIPTION. Similar to the preceding species but: *Leaves* thin green, usually larger, glabrous or sometimes papillose-hairy on the stem, or papillose-scabrid along veins and margins of leaves. *Stems* simple or usually with one branch 8-20(-28) cm. *Racemes* 5-12(-25!)-flowered. *Bracts* broadly lanceolate to ovate or obovate, entire to pectinately dentate or flabellately divided. *Pedicels* slender, erectopatent, 5-14 mm long (up to 25 mm in cultivation), not or only slightly arcuate in fruit. *Corolla* pale to bright blue or bluish purple, rarely purple or white, usually with the broad wings of the outer petals darker, and the inner petals contrastingly white; lower petal with the claw straight or saccate, but often with a distinct angular base, the limb broad at base, narrowed towards the apex, and with a broad emargination; margin entire, rarely slightly dentate. *Spur* straight, sometimes slightly recurved at apex, 8-11 mm long, often triangular in form with broad base; nectary very shortly acuminate, up to one third as long as the spur. *Fruit* linear, dorsiventrally flattened with thin valves and a more or less undulate marginal rim, often streaked with reddish brown when mature, (15-)20-25(-30) x 2.5-3 mm, uniseriate. *Seeds* 5-15, 2 mm, smooth, with obovate elaiosome.

23a. subsp. *fumariifolia*

C. ambigua var. *amurensis* Maxim., Prim. fl. Amur.: 37 (1859). Type: Lower Amur, Köurmi (Kkhurti), 10.5.1855, *Maxim.* (LE, holo).

C. ambigua var. *amurensis* lusus *rotundiloba* Maxim., Prim. fl. Amur.: 37 (1859; *C. ambigua* f. *rotundiloba* (Maxim.) Kitag., Rep. Inst. Sci. Res. Manchoukuo 3: 233 (1939). Type: none designated.

C. ambigua var. *amurensis* lusus *lineariloba* Maxim., Prim. fl. Amur.: 37 (1859); *C. ambigua* f. *lineariloba* (Maxim.) C.Y.Wu & Z.Y.Su *illegit.* in Acta Bot. Yunnanica 7: 266 (1985), non (Siebold & Zucc.) Kitag. (1939). Type: none designated.

C. remota var. *pectinata* Kom. in Acta Horti Petrop. 22: 351 (1903); *C. ambigua* f. *pectinata* (Kom..) Kitag. in Rep. Inst. Sci. Res. Manchoukuo 3: 233 (1939); *C. lineariloba* f. *pectinata* (Kom.) Kitag., Neolineam. fl. Mansh.: 321 (1979). Type: not seen.

C. ambigua f. *dentata* Y.H.Chou, Fl. herb. Chin. bor.-or. 4: 229 (1980). Type: not seen.

C. ambigua f. *multifida* Y.H.Chou, Fl. herb. Chin. bor.-or. 4: 229 (1980). Type: not seen.

DESCRIPTION. *Tuber* pale grey. *Leaves* twice to three times ternate with entire to deeply divided leaflets; ultimate lobes narrowly linear to lanceolate, elliptic or ovate, entire to deeply divided, sometimes serrate or crenate-dentate. *Bracts* lanceolate and entire (especially in the north of its range) or deeply dissected or pectinate-dentate. *Corolla* with inner petals 8-11(-13) mm long; limb of lower petal 6-10 mm broad. 2n=16. Self-incompatible. Fig. 12b; Pl. 31.

DISTRIBUTION. Russia from the lower Amur southwards to Vladivostok, NE Korea and E Manchuria. 'Forests and shrubs'. April-May. Map 9.

A very variable species, especially in the degree of division of leaves and bracts, width of leaflets, hairiness and size of the flowers. Several forms and varieties have been described. This variability is developed to the extreme in the south of the area, where formas *dentata*, *lineariloba*, *multifida*, *pectinata*, etc., are all found growing intermingled. It is interesting to note that the same variability in leaf form is found in *C. turtschaninovii*, which often grows together with *C. fumariifolia* in this area.

Recently introduced in cultivation by Janis Ruksans. Easy to grow in the woodland and the peatgarden as well as in the alpine house. The *lineariloba* forms are particularly graceful and will probably, in due time, become popular garden-plants.

23b. subsp. *azurea* Lidén & Zetterlund in M. Lidén, Willdenowia 26:27 (1996). Type: Japan, Hokkaido: Abashiri, *Rokujo, s.n., s.d.,* cultivated in Gothenburg Botanic Garden (GB, holo).

?*C. jezoensis* Miq. in Ann. Mus. Bot. Lugduno-Batavum 3: 205 (1867). Type: Japan, Hokkaido (= Jezo), *Siebold* (not seen).

C. ambigua var. *glabra* Takeda in Bot. Mag. (Tokyo) 24: 7 (1910). Type: (K).

C. ambigua var. *papillosa* Takeda in Bot. Mag. (Tokyo) 24:9 (1910). Type: (K).

?*C. ambigua* var. *angustifolia* Yatabe apud Matsum., Enum. pl. Japon. 2: 142 (1912). Type: not seen.

DESCRIPTION. *Leaves* once to twice ternate, usually with broadly ovate leaflets, although forms with linear or crenate-dentate leaflets are also found. *Bracts* ovate to narrowly ovate-lanceolate, usually entire. *Corolla* with inner petals 10-12(-13) mm long; limb of lower petal 7-11 mm broad. *Spur* usually distinctly triangular and somewhat laterally compressed. 2n=16. Self-incompatible. Fig. 12a; Pl. 32, 33.

DISTRIBUTION. Hokkaido; Sakhalin. Map 9.

'Woods and meadows from lowlands to mountains'. April-May. Map 9.

This beautiful plant is a surprisingly recent introduction to European gardens. It is distinguished from the previous subspecies mainly by the usually broader leaflets and by its more triangular spur. It first started to appear in garden literature as *C. ambigua* in 1970. It received a P.C. that year under the name *C. ambigua* var. *jezoensis* and in 1973 as *C. a.* var. *'yunnanensis'*. In 1981, Jack Crosland kindly presented us with some tubers of a plant that was awarded an A.M. in 1979. This form has extraordinarily nice, clean sky-blue flowers and frail, light-green foliage which is very sensitive to dry, hot weather.

Fig. 13. *Corydalis ussuriensis* (cult. S. & V. 59, *locus classicus*)

The colour varies from clear-blue to shades of bluish-purple and many growers have expressed disappointment over their expensively acquired plants. In literature, it has been claimed to be a worthy substitute for *C. cashmeriana* in the south of Britain. In mild winters, however, it may appear too early and suffer badly from hard frosts. Still, it is probably better delayed outside in a cool peat-bed than grown in the alpine-house where its early appearance may cause its flowerbuds to abort.

24. *C. fukuharae* Lidén in Willdenowia 26:27 (1996). Type: Japan, Honshu, Tohoku distr., Akita pref., Yamauchi-mura, Kurosawa (39° 16'N; 140°

43'E), 4.5.1995, 250 m, *T. Fukuhara* (GB, holo; KYO, iso).

DESCRIPTION. *Stems* slender, 9-20 cm, suberect, branched from the scale-leaf (and very rarely from the lower cauline leaf). *Leaves* thin, green above, slightly glaucous beneath, twice to almost three times ternate with entire to dentate or deeply divided leaflets; ultimate lobes obovate, obtuse to acute. *Racemes* rather dense at first, soon elongating, 3-13 flowered. *Bracts* oblong to lanceolate, entire, or rarely the lowermost slightly divided, acute to obtuse. *Pedicels* slender, 5-12 (-18) mm long, equalling the bracts, arcuate-recurved in fruit. *Sepals* (0.3-)1-1.5 mm long, ovate to linear, entire to coarsely dentate. *Corolla* blue to purplish blue; inner petals 10-12 mm long; lower petal with a long, sometimes saccate claw, abruptly dilated into an emarginate limb with entire to usually somewhat crenulate margins, with a small spur at the base of the petal. *Spur* (of upper petal) oblong, straight, rather narrow at base and not, or only slightly tapering towards the obtuse apex, (9-)12-16 mm long, with a slender caudate nectary about half as long. *Fruit* linear (but ovary lanceolate), 20-25 x 2 mm, similar to that of *C. fumariifolia*. *Seeds* about 10. Apparently self-fertile. Fig. 14d.

DISTRIBUTION. Japan: central and northern Honshu southwards at least to distr. Nagano (Shinano), Niigata and Gumma prefectures, growing in forests from 150 up to at least 900 m. Flowering in May. Map 10.

A rather variable species related to *C. fumariifolia* but easily distinguished by the longer and much narrower spur, a distinct spur on the lower petal, a more slender nectary, as well as by its green stigma.

A welcome addition to our collection with its green dissected foliage. The large flowers resemble those of *C. fumariifolia* with an open clear pale blue face but with a long narrow spur of a more slaty blue.

25. *C. ussuriensis* Aparina in Novosti Sist. Vyssh. Rast. 3: 168 (1966). Type: SE Siberia, near Vladivostok, distr. Chasan, park 'Kedrovaja padj' upper Garajskij river, 7.5.1964, *T. Aparina* (BM; C; E; K; LE).
C. vorobievii Nedulushko & Urussov ined.9.5.1977, *Nedulushko & Urussov* (MHA).

DESCRIPTION. *Stems* suberect to erect, 15-25 cm high. *Leaves* biternate, thin and delicate, with stalked

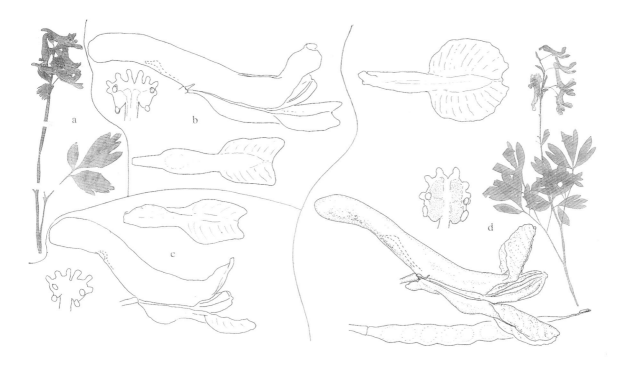

Fig. 14. a-c, *Corydalis linjiangensis* (a, Webster 299, NE China, Liaoning, Mukden to Yaloo river, K; b, type; c, *sine coll.*, NE China, Liaoning, Dadong, Daliang, PE), **d**, *C. fukuharae* (cult. type)

entire or sparingly crenate-dentate rounded to obovate leaflets, sometimes coarsely dentate or deeply divided into broadly lanceolate, acute to obtuse lobes. *Racemes* 3-10(-15)-flowered, rather dense at anthesis, elongating greatly in fruit. *Bracts* broadly lanceolate to obovate, entire or divided to about half into narrow acute lobes. *Pedicels* slender, 10-18 mm long, up to 25(-40) and more or less erect (rarely spreading) in fruit. *Corolla* blue (?to purple) with white centre, very broad, appearing somewhat inflated, especially by the insertion of the pedicel, strongly fragrant.; inner petals 10-13 mm long; dorsal crests not overtopping the apex; lower petal with a broadly saccate claw and very broad shallowly emarginate limb up to 14 mm broad. *Spur* thick, 10-12 mm long, with an acute nectary less than one third as long as the spur. *Fruit* broadly lanceolate to elliptic, 10-15 x 5-6 mm. *Seeds* 4-9, 1.8 mm with a botryoid elaiosome rather like that of *C. lineariloba*. Self-incompatible. Fig. 13; Pl. 34.

DISTRIBUTION. E Russia: Ussuri. May. Map 10.

Habitually similar to *C. fumariifolia*, from which it differs in the short broad fruit and its bladdery flower. It has been likened to *C. repens* but is readily distinguished from that species by the taller erect stem, large strongly fragrant flowers with short nectaries and by the crests of the inner petals which do not protrude beyond the apex.

In the type locality it grows together with extremely variable populations of *C. fumariifolia* subsp. *fumariifolia* and *C. turtschaninovii*.

This is one of the most beautiful and eye-catching species in the genus. The flowers are among the largest of this group, rather tubby and they emit a delightful scent. The blue is, in our plants, a little clouded in a tasteful way. It will, hopefully, be an easy plant but few plants are in cultivation.

26. C. linjiangensis Z.Y.Su in Willdenowia 26:28 (1996). Type: NE China; Jilin, Linjiang, Manjiang, Nanshan, 990 m, 13.5.1959, *Biol. Res. Exp.* 18466 (NENU).

Fig. 15. a, b, *Corydalis kiaotschouensis* (a, Hancock 16, E China, Shandong, Chefoo (= Yantai), Pecheli, K; b, *sine coll.*, 'Heilongjiang', PE?); **c-e**, *C. humilis* (c, type; d, e, Oh s.n., S Korea, Kyonggi-do, Chonmasan, GB)

DESCRIPTION. *Stems* suberect, 10 to 20 cm. *Leaves* ternate to biternate with rhombic, obovate or linear, crenate-dentate to pectinate dentate or entire leaflets, hairy below in the vein-furcations. *Racemes* 7-15-flowered. *Bracts* usually ovate, pectinate-dentate. *Corolla* blue; lower petal with long claw, usually more or less saccate, but sometimes straight and with a rather small sharply set off, slightly emarginate blade; inner petals 13-14 mm long. *Spur* straight, cylindrical, 12-13 mm long, the nectary at least half as long as the spur. *Stigma* broad with six apical papillae and pronounced geminate papillae. *Fruit* (immature) linear. *Seeds* up to 10. Fig. 14a-c.

DISTRIBUTION. China; mountains of W Liaoning and S Jilin provinces, 800-1200 m. Map 10.

Somewhat similar to *C. humilis* but easily distinguished by the more erect habit, the narrower and less sharply emarginate petal-limbs and the linear fruit. It is also similar to *C. fumariifolia* but has longer flowers and a much longer nectary.

Not known to be in cultivation.

27. *C. humilis* B.U.Oh & Y.S.Kim in Korean J. Pl. Taxon. 17: 24 (1987). Type: S Korea, Kyonggi-do, Kap'yong-gun, Hyondungsan, 22.4.1986, *B.-U. Oh* (KU, holo; GB, iso)

C. remota sensu B.U.Oh (1986).

DESCRIPTION. *Stems* weak, suberect to ascending, 4-15 cm. *Leaves* somewhat glaucous, sometimes with white spots, once to twice ternate; leaflets entire to divided with obovate obtuse ultimate segments, entire or sometimes crenulate-dentate, rarely divided into long narrow lobes. *Racemes* (1-)4-10-flowered, dense. *Bracts* flabellately or sub-pectinately dentate or lobed, rarely entire. *Pedicels* longer than the bracts, 6-14 mm; 10-15 in fruit, straight. *Corolla* blue, with or without a purplish hue, with whitish inner petals; outer petals rather broadly winged; inner petals 8-11 mm long, with rounded dorsal wings that do not protrude beyond the apex, or very slightly so; *lower petal* with a straight claw or slightly saccate in the middle. *Spur* (9-)11-12 mm, usually rather straight, with nectary one half to two thirds the length of the spur. *Capsule* fusiform, 15-20 x 3-4 mm, including the short beak. Seeds 4-10. Fig. 15c-e.

DISTRIBUTION. Korea, SE Manchuria. Deciduous woods. March-April. Map 11.

Very variable in the division of its leaves and in the size and form of corolla and fruits, especially in the border mountains between Manchuria and Korea. White streaks on the leaves frequently are found and the corolla is usually straight. It is close to *C. kiaotschouensis*.

Probably not in cultivation.

28. *C. kiaotschouensis* Poelln. in Repert. Spec. nov. Regni veg. 45: 103 (1938). Type: E China, Shandong: Jiaozhou, island of Arkona, 24.4.1901, *E. Zimmerman* 311 (B; BM; E; K; S).

DESCRIPTION. *Stems* ascending, to 15 cm. *Leaves* bi- to triternate with leaflets entire to deeply divided into broad or narrow obovate lobes. *Racemes* 3-10-flowered, lax. *Bracts* obovate, entire or usually flabellate-divided, enlarging in fruit. *Pedicels* slender, 10-20(-25) mm long, twice as long as bracts. *Corolla* purple (or blue?); outer petals broadly winged the limb with entire margin, emarginate, without a mucro in the notch; inner petals 9-10 mm long, with the dorsal wings extending far beyond the apex, acute; lower petal 11-14 mm long, straight or slightly saccate, broadly winged. *Spur* upward-directed, 12-14 mm long, slightly sigmoid, with nectary about two thirds as long as the spur, shortly acuminate. *Fruit* broadly lanceolate, about 20 mm long including a 3 mm long beak and a 1 mm long style. *Seeds* 5-10, smooth, 2 mm long. Fig. 15 a-b. Map 11.

DISTRIBUTION. E China: Shandong and N Jiangsu.

This species is distinguished from *C. humilis* by the prominent extension of the dorsal wings of the inner petals, from *C. lineariloba* by the lack of axillary tubers, the broader flowers and the longer nectary, and from both by the upwardly curved spur. A similar plant from Manchuria may merit recognition but only one specimen has been seen. (Fig. 15b).

Not in cultivation.

29. *C. lineariloba* Siebold & Zucc., Fl. Jap. Fam. Nat. 1: 286 (1845); *C. bulbosa* var. *lineariloba* (Siebold & Zucc.) Makino, Tokyo Bot. Mag. 8: 227 (1894); *C. ambigua* f. *lineariloba* (Siebold & Zucc.) Kitag. (*nomen, non planta*), Rep. Inst. Sci. Res. Manshoukuo, 3: 232 (1939). Type: Japan, Honshu, near Jedo (= Tokyo), *Siebold* (not seen).
C. laxa Franch. & Sav., Enum. pl. Jap. 2: 273 (1876), non Fr. Type: Japan, *Savatier* (P).
C. bulbosa var. *capillaris* Makino, Bot. Mag. Tokyo 7: 119 (1898); *C. capillaris* (Makino) Takeda, Bot. Mag. Tokyo 24: 62 (1910); *C. bulbosa* var. *remota* f. *capillaris* (Makino) Nakai, Bot. Mag.

Tokyo 26: 94 (1912); *C. lineariloba* var. *capillaris* (Makino) Ohwi in Acta Phytotax. Geobot. 5: 146 (1936). Type: Japan, Shikoku, prov. Tosa: Mt Kuishi-yama in Tadzikawa-mura, 6.5.1893, *T. Makino* (TI, not seen).
C. lineariloba var. *ovalioblonga* Ohwi in Acta Phytotax. Geobot. 11: 263 (1942). Type: Japan, Honshu, Mt Ibuki in Omi, *M. Tagawa* 1538 (KYO).
C. lineariloba var. *lanceata* Ohwi in Acta Phytotax. Geobot. 11: 263 (1942). Type: Japan, Honshu, Kanayamamura in Iwaki, *T. Suzuki* 14 (KYO).

DESCRIPTION. *Plant* glabrous, or rarely with one-celled hairs above. *Stems* strongly geniculate at the nodes, forming an angle of almost 180 degrees with the lower leaf (cf. *C. papilligera*), 8-20 cm, nearly always with an accessory tuber in the scale-leaf. *Leaves* two to four times ternate, very variable; leaflets small to medium, entire, broadly elliptic to lanceolate or linear, sometimes more or less deeply divided, usually with acute apices. *Racemes* 2-6(-15) flowered. *Bracts* obovate to ovate with narrow acute teeth, sometimes more deeply divided into linear lobes, rarely entire. *Pedicels* longer than the bracts, (5-)10-15(-20) mm long and straight in fruit. *Corolla* greenish in bud, pale to bright blue at anthesis, rarely purple, 15-25 mm long; inner petals 7-10 mm long, excluding the protruding dorsal wings. *Spur* straight, 7-14 mm long, with nectary one third to almost one half as long, acuminate. *Fruit* fusiform, 12-18 x 4-5 mm, ovate-lanceolate, slightly dorsiventrally flattened, gradually attenuate into a beak. *Seed* 4-10, 1.9-2.4 mm, smooth, with broad, often lobed elaiosome. 2n=32 (Chichibu; Hiroshima); 48 (Ohfunad; Chichibu, plant with finely dissected leaves); 64 (Fukuhara, pers. comm.). Self-incompatible. Fig. 16; Pl. 36.

DISTRIBUTION. Japan: Honshu, Shikoku, Kyushu. 'Woods and meadows in hills and mountains'. Map 11.

A well circumscribed entity but with a very intricate pattern of variation, including a number of geographical and chromosomal races. In addition, the efficient vegetative multiplication of this species enables sterile clones to spread and survive.

This lovely dwarf species is a newcomer to western gardens, appearing as late as in the 1980s. It is easy to grow and most forms multiply rapidly by means of adventive tubers formed in the scale-leaves. The flowers are large for such a small plant and, even

Fig. 16 a-d. *Corydalis lineariloba* (a, cult. Elick, Japan, W Honshu, Hiroshima; b, cult. Fukuhara, C Honshu, Nopa, Kawaguchi-Machi, Kita-uonomagun; c, cult. Rokujo, C Honshu, Chichibu; d, cult. Rokujo, Ohfunad)

if a purplish contamination is the norm, clear blue-flowered individuals are common enough to make it a popular plant in the future. It is a bit too small and slender to become a common garden-plant but will certainly adorn the gardens of wild-flower enthusiasts.

We are growing a number of different forms and all are less than 10 cm tall in bloom. The foliage often consists of discrete leaflets borne on slender stalklets and is very graceful. The flower buds remain green almost until they are fully developed. In a collection from Mt Chichibu we have observed considerable variation, including two chromosomal races: one clone has a distinctively incised, bright green foliage, and large sky-blue flowers in a compact raceme.

Corydalis lineariloba starts early in the spring but the flower-buds take a long time to mature. A trouble-free plant for the alpine house but it also does well in our peat-walls. Out in the open it needs a cool position where it does not get forced in spring.

30. *C. ohii* Lidén in Willdenowia 26:28 (1996). Type: S Korea, Kangwon-do, Mt. Odae, 10.4.1986, *B. U.*

Oh (KU, holo; GB, iso).
C. lineariloba sensu B.U.Oh (1986).
C. ambigua sensu B.U.Oh (1986).

DESCRIPTION. *Stems* slender, geniculate, 10-20 cm, usually with an accessory tuber in the scale-leaf. *Leaves* twice ternate or almost so, with broadly lanceolate to broadly obovate leaf-lobes; petiolules comparatively shorter than in *C. lineariloba*. *Racemes* 2-6-flowered, lax. *Bracts* pectinately to flabellately dentate. *Pedicels* much longer than the bracts, 10-17 mm, remaining straight in fruit. *Corolla* large; inner petals 12-13 mm long with dorsal crests not or only slightly protruding beyond apex. *Spur* straight, 11-14 mm. *Fruit* linear-oblong, 17-22 mm, including a short beak, uni-seriate. *Seeds* 3-7, 2 mm. Fig. 17.

DISTRIBUTION. South Korea (except the SE). Deciduous woods. Map 11.

Close to *C. lineariloba* but distinguished by larger leaflets, larger flowers, by the wings of inner petals

Fig. 17a, b. *Corydalis ohii* (a, type; b, unknown collector, SW Korea, Chollapuk-do, Zenhoku, 1.5.1935, KYO)

that do not, or only slightly, protrude beyond the apex and by the narrowly oblong fruit.

Not in cultivation.

31. *C. grandicalyx* B.U.Oh & Y.S.Kim in Korean J. Pl. Taxon. 17: 21 (1987). Type: S Korea, Kangwon-do, Mt Odae, P'yongch'ang-gun, 10.4.1986, *B.U.Oh* (KU, holo; GB, iso)

?*C. turtschaninovii* var. *nonapiculata* Ohwi in Acta Phytotax. Geobot. 11: 262 (1942); *C. remota* f. *nonapiculata* (Ohwi) C.Y.Wu & Z.Y.Su, Acta Bot. Yunnanica 7:269 (1985). Type: N Korea, Fusen-Kogen in Kannan, *Toh & Shim* 6 (KYO). Similar to *C. grandicalyx* but the sepals are missing.

DESCRIPTION. *Stems* 8-20 cm, slender, weakly geniculate, slightly glaucous to green, with 1-2 branches from the scale-leaf. *Leaves* bi-ternate; leaflets shallowly to deeply cleft into obovate lobes. *Racemes* 2-7-flowered, *Bracts* flabellately to sub-pectinately

incised into several narrow acute teeth or lobes. *Pedicels* slender, 8-15 mm long, or up to 20 mm in fruit. *Sepals* large, about 5 x 8 mm, deeply fimbriate. *Corolla* blue or purplish blue, broadly winged; lower petal straight, with a pronounced angular base, and broad limb with a broad triangular notch; inner petals 10-11 mm long with triangular dorsal wings that do not reach beyond the apex. *Spur* straight broad-based, tapering, 11-14 mm long, pointing slightly upwards; nectary narrowly acuminate, one third the length of the spur. *Capsule* oblong, 5-14 x 3-4 mm. *Seeds* 3-7, smooth, 2-2.2 mm. Fig. 18; Pl. 38.

DISTRIBUTION. NW South Korea: Odaesan. March-April. Map 11.

Similar to the sympatric *C. ohii* but distinguished at a glance by the large fimbriate sepals, thinner and more divided leaves and the shorter and comparatively broader flowers.

Not in cultivation.

32. *C. hallaisanensis* Levl. in Repert. Spec. nov. Regni veg. 10: 349 (1912). Type: Korea, Quelpart (Cheju-do), Mt Hallaisan, forest, 17.5.1907, *U. Faurie* 1766 (E; LE; P).

DESCRIPTION. *Stems* weak and slender, geniculate at the nodes, 9-19 cm, with 1-4 branches from the scale leaf. *Leaves* bi- to triternate with entire to deeply divided leaflets. *Racemes* 4-10-flowered. *Bracts* pectinately to flabellately divided into narrow acute teeth or lobes. *Pedicels* longer than bracts, thin, straight, 6-13 mm long. *Corolla* (pale) purplish red, or bi-coloured with purple front and whitish to bluish spur; inner petals 10-12 mm long, with dorsal wings that protrude slightly beyond the apex. *Spur* 10-14 mm long, slightly upwardly directed, narrowly triangular in shape with a shortly acuminate nectary reaching halfway. *Fruit* fusiform, 11-16 x 3 mm, with several small *seeds*, about 1.5 mm. Fig. 19; Pl. 39.

DISTRIBUTION. The island of Cheju-do (Quelpart) S of Korea, and SE Korea (at least three localities known). Deciduous woods. March-April. Map 11.

Quite variable in flower-size and degree of division of the foliage. Similar to *C. lineariloba*, but with longer nectary, no axillary tubers, differently coloured flowers, more upwardly directed and more triangular spur, less pronounced dorsal wings on the inner

Fig. 18. *Corydalis grandicalyx* (type)

petals and smaller seeds. Plants from the mainland are usually more stout and large-flowered and may be at least subspecifically distinct.

Not known in cultivation.

33. C. repens Mandl & Mühld. in Bot. Közlem. 19: 90 (1921). Type: SE Siberia, near Nikolsk-Ussurisk, *Mandl & Mühldorf* (LE).

C. turtschaninovii var. *papillata* Ohwi in J. Jap. Bot. 12: 333 (1936); *C. lineariloba* var. *papillata* (Ohwi) Ohwi in Acta Phytotax. Geobot. 11: 263 (1942). Type: Korea, near Ranan, *Saito* 430, 431 (KYO).

C. lineariloba var. *micrantha* Ohwi in Acta Phytotax. Geobot. 11: 263 (1942). Type: Manchuria, Bujun, *J. Sato* 5185 (KYO).

C. watanabei Kitag. in Rep. Inst. Sci. Res. Mansh. 6: 122 (1942); *C. repens* var. *watanabei* (Kitag.) Y.H.Chou in Fl. herb. Chin. Bor.-or. 4: 23 (1980). Type: not seen.

C. ivaschkeviczii Aparina in Novosti Sist. 7:165 (1971). Type: NW China, Czzhan-ghuan-tsaj-lin, Padinka, 1.5.1912, *B. A. Ivaschkevicz* 340 (LE).

DESCRIPTION. *Stems* weak and slender, ascending, branched from the scale, 8-14(-19) cm, glabrous or papillose-scabrid along the leaf margin. *Leaves* not or slightly glaucous above, biternate with broadly lanceolate to obovate obtuse leaflets, entire, or sometimes much divided into small narrow acute segments. *Racemes* (3-)6-14-flowered. *Bracts* variable, lanceolate to ovate, entire or apically

Fig. 19a-c. *Corydalis hallaisanensis* (a, Pak, J-H s.n., SE Korea, Yong-il-gun N of Po-hang, 810 m, 9.5.1980, KYO; b, NN 1167, S Korea, SE Chollanam-do, KYO; c, Oh s.n., Cheju-do, Konulack, 15.4.1985, GB)

divided. *Pedicels* thin and slender, longer than bracts, 6-11 mm long in flower, up to 20 mm in fruit, sometimes papillose-hairy. *Corolla* white, pale bluish, or pale purple; outer petals broadly winged with a smooth margin, usually with a deep emargination; inner petals (5)7-8 mm long, excluding the dorsal wings which protrude conspicuously beyond the apex. *Spur* straight or curved, 7-9 mm long, with an acuminate nectary about half as long. *Fruit* broadly elliptic, 8-10 mm, incl. short beak (1 mm) and style 1 mm. *Seeds* 4-6, 1.5 mm. Fig. 20.

DISTRIBUTION. E Russia (Vladivostok area), Manchuria and Korea. Damp deciduous forests. April-May. Map 12.

A variable species, especially the division of leaves and bracts and size of flowers. Frequently the dorsal crests of the inner petals are prolonged much beyond the apex in two acute appendages: this form has been segregated as *C. watanabei* but there does not seem to be any correlation with other characters.

The plants appearing under this name in the trade from the late 1980s all had their origin from Janis Ruksans and have turned out to be *C. turtschaninovii*. The true plant is in cultivation but very rarely grown (one or two Baltic collectors only). It is a plant of weak constitution and of little garden merit.

34. C. orthoceras Siebold & Zucc. in Abh. Math.-Phys. Cl. Königl. Bayer Akad. Wiss. 4(2): 175 (1843). Type: Japan, *Siebold* (TI).

C. senanensis Franch. & Sav., Enum. pl. Jap. 2: 273 (1876); *C. orthoceras* var. *angustifoliolata* Nakai in Acta Phytotax. Geobot. 15: 416 (1954). Type: Japan, Honshu, Sinano Mt, *Itiro Saba* 3372 (P).

C. capillipes Franch. in Bull. Soc. Phil. Paris ser. 7, 10: 439 (1886); *C. orthoceras* var. *latifoliolata* Nakai in Acta Phytotax. Geobot. 15: 416 (1954). Type: Japan, Honshu, prov. Mutu: Kominato, *Faurie* 259 (KYO; P).

DESCRIPTION. *Stems* 6-20 cm, sub-erect, weak and slender, slightly flexuous, with axillary tubers in the

Fig. 20a-c. *Corydalis repens* (a, Oh s.n., NE S Korea, Mt Odae, 10.4.1986, GB; b, Webster 132, K; c, Mills 221A, N Korea, Kangkai, K)

scale-leaves. *Leaves* bi- to tri-ternate (rarely more) with entire to more or less deeply divided leaflets; leaf-lobes elliptic to narrowly oblong acute. *Racemes* 3-15(-22 in cult.)-flowered. *Bracts* apically divided into a few acute teeth, rarely entire and lanceolate. *Pedicels* capillary, 5-20 mm long, equalling or longer than the bracts. *Corolla* 8-15 mm long, whitish with blue and pink shades towards the apex; outer petals broadly winged with broadly and shallowly emarginate limbs; inner petals 5-6 mm long, with broad rounded dorsal wings that slightly overtop the apex; lower petal with a broad limb and a short claw with a distinct diminutive spur at base, into a which a rudimentary nectary fits. *Spur* (of upper petal) narrow, straight, oblong, 2-6 mm long. *Capsule* ovoid, attenuate into short beak, (5-)9-13 x 4 mm, including a 1 mm long style. *Seeds* (1)4-8, 2-2.2 mm, with a straight elaiosome. 2n=16 (Echigo; Niigata); 32 (Fukuhara, *pers. comm.*). Self-incompatible. Fig. 21; Pl. 20.

DISTRIBUTION. Japan: N and WC Honshu; Oki islands. Map 12.

A very variable species as regards size, degree of division of the leaves and length of the spur. Some plants from the Niigata province are exceedingly dainty, with few flowers, entire bracts, biternate leaves with entire leaflets and flowers with very short

Fig. 21a-c. *Corydalis orthoceras* (a, cult. Rokujo, Japan, NW Honshu, Niigata-ken, Katsugi; b, cult. Fukuhara, Echigo-kawaguchi; c, cult. Rokujo, NW Honshu, Yamagata-ken, Mt Onkai-dake)

spurs, whereas the 'typical' form is taller with more divided leaves and bracts and longer spurs; however, intermediates are found. The presence of a nectary on the lower stamen is unique in the genus.

A graceful but inconspicuous species, with a strong honey fragrance. With us it is the earliest of the eastern woodlanders to appear each spring, sometimes flowering in early February. Its earliness and frail habit, combined with the small flowers, makes it quite useless in the open garden. It must be viewed and adored at close quarters in order to have its charm revealed and thus is a perfect plant for the alpine house. The shades of the floral parts in sky-blue, sea-green and pink are fascinating meditation mantras for the true enthusiast.

35. *C. papilligera* Ohwi in Acta Phytotax. Geobot. 11: 264 (1942); *C. lineariloba* var. *papilligera* (Ohwi) Ohwi. Type: Japan; Honshu, Yunowara, Minamikuwadagun in Tamba, *Y. Araki* (KYO, fruiting specimens only)

DESCRIPTION. *Tuber* with a firm and persistent tunic. *Stems* slender, 10-17 cm, with 1-3 branches and an accessory tuber in the axil of the scale-leaf, strongly geniculate at the nodes, forming a wide angle with the lower leaf. *Leaves* tri-ternate, not or slightly glaucous; leaflets obovate to elliptic, entire or divided into 2-3 lobes, the ultimate lobes acute to subobtuse. *Racemes* 4-5-flowered, long-stalked. *Bracts* divided into acute lobules. *Pedicels* much longer than the bracts, 10-20 mm long, remaining straight in fruit and elongating to 20-30 mm long. *Sepals* minute or up to 1.5 mm, deeply dentate. *Corolla* blue or pinkish blue with pale inner petals; outer petals broadly winged; lower usually with a distinct sub-basal pouch, a very short claw dilated into a rhombic limb with a large rounded apical notch; inner petals 7 mm long, with very broad dorsal wings that protrude beyond the apex. *Spur* 10-12 mm, straight, attenuate, obtuse. *Style* 1-1.5 mm. *Fruit* very broadly elliptic, strongly dorsiventrally flattened with thick valves, 11-18 x 6-10 mm, abruptly contracted into a short but distinct beak. *Seeds* 2-7, 1.8-2 mm, spinulose, with a cauliflower-like elaiosome; hilum with a thick collar. 2n=48. Self-incompatible. Fig. 22a, b; Pl. 35, 37.

DISTRIBUTION. Japan: W Honshu. Map 10.

Easily distinguished from the other species in the series by its strongly gibbous lower petal, comparatively short inner petals, broad flat fruit, papillose seeds and by its tough persistent tuber-coat.

There are two rather different forms of this species. The description above corresponds to the hexaploid large-flowered form. Around Chichibu and the Kyoto area there can be found a much more inconspicuous tetraploid race in which the spur is only about 7-10 mm long, the inner petals c. 6 mm long and the limbs of the outer petals much narrower. The relationship between chromosome number and flower-size seems, not absolute, however (T. Fukuhara, *pers. comm.*), and a formal subdivision of the species will have to await the result of his studies. It is probable that the type specimen is a tetraploid..

It is given the same conditions as *C. lineariloba* in the garden at Gothenburg.

36. C. maculata B.U.Oh & Y.S.Kim in Korean J. Pl. Taxon. 17: 26 (1987). Type: S Korea, Kyonggi-

Fig. 22a-b. *Corydalis papilligera* (a, tetraploid race, cult. Rokujo, EC Honshu, Saitama, Tuge, Shumaru-Tuge; b, hexaploid race, cult. Fukuhara, WC Honshu, Fukui)

do, Namyangju-gun, Ch'onmasan, 2.5.1984, *B.U. Oh* (KU, holo; GB, iso)

DESCRIPTION. *Plant* glaucous. *Stems* geniculate at the nodes, ascending, 8-15(-25) cm. *Leaves* rather fleshy, sometimes with white spots, biternate with entire to divided leaflets; lobes narrowly oblong, subacute. *Racemes* dense, 4-8-flowered. *Bracts* flabellately much divided into narrow acute lobes. *Pedicels* rather thick but probably soft, 6-13 mm long, equalling or longer than the bracts. *Corolla* blue to purple; inner petals 10-13 mm long, with dorsal wings not overtopping the apex; lower petal with very broad and strongly auriculate claw, and shallowly emarginate limb. *Spur* 14-17 mm long, with a shortly acuminate nectary reaching at least halfway along the spur. *Capsule* ovate-elliptic, about 15 x 4 mm (9-28 x 4-5 mm, Oh 1986). *Seeds* 5-10. Fig. 23.

Fig. 23. *Corydalis maculata* (type)

DISTRIBUTION. South Korea (except the SW). March-April. Map 10.

Readily distinguished from all other species by the strongly auriculate lower petal. Probably not in cultivation.

Series Raphanituber (Khokhr.) Lidén
Willdenowia 26:25 (1996); Sect. *Raphanituber* Khokhr., Novosti Sist. Vyssh. Rast. 10: 154 (1973). Type species: *C. magadanica* Khokhr.

Tuber usually somewhat oblong. *Stems* often with buds in the axils of cauline leaves. *Bracts* small, entire, ovate to ovate-lanceolate. *Flowers* of a firm texture. *Fruits* oblong, squarish in cross-section, sub-pendent from patent to slightly arcuate pedicels. *Nectary* acute. *Elaiosome* not twisted. 3 species; East Siberia.

37. ***C. gorodkovii* Karav.** in Bot. Mater. Gerb. Bot. Inst. Komarova Akad. Nauk SSSR. 18: 7 (1957). Type: E Siberia, Jacutia, distr. Tompon, mountains

above the upper Aditschi river, stony montane tundra, 11.6.1936, *Jarovoi* (LE, holo).

DESCRIPTION. *Tuber* rounded or often oblong. *Stems* erect, 8-20 cm, unbranched. *Leaves* 2, very glaucous, purplish-tinged below; lamina rather long-stalked, rounded in outline, ternate to sub-biternate with sessile leaflets divided into oblong segments. *Racemes* dense, 4-8-flowered. *Bracts* entire, rhombic-ovate, acute, 5 mm long. *Pedicels* straight, 7-10 mm long, more or less erect in fruit. *Corolla* white or yellow; lower petal with subacute to rounded or slightly emarginate limb; inner petals 10-12 mm long. *Spur* of upper petal 8-10(-12) mm long, with an acuminate nectary one third to one half as long. *Stigma* rounded. *Fruit* oblong, slightly pendent on erect pedicels, 15-20 x 3 mm with short style. *Seeds* 6-15, smooth, almost 2 mm. Fig. 24a.

DISTRIBUTION. East Siberia, Suntar-Khayata, Cherskogo, and Kolymskiy Khrebet. Map 13.

Similar to *C. magadanica* in details but a very different species in habit. In nature it is said to remain in growth until August. This might be due to the fact that it grows at rather high altitudes (subalpine zone) on rocky slopes, in open forest, or mountain-tundra, whereas *C. magadanica* is a coastal species. The distribution is limited to the mountain-ranges north of Magadan. It can grow up to a height of 20 cm but is generally dwarfer. How it will perform in cultivation remains to be seen but it is eagerly awaited!

38. ***C. magadanica* A. P. Khokhrjakov** in Tr. sev.-vost. kompl. inst. (Magadan) 42: 175 (1971). Type: E Siberia, prov. Magadan, distr. Ola, between Novaia Vesselaia and Zniuchlia, S-facing schistaceous stony slopes by the sea, *Khokhrjakov* (MHA, holo).

DESCRIPTION. *Stems* suberect to ascending, 10-20 cm, much-branched from the scale-leaf, and from the cauline leaves; two scale-leaves are occasionally present. *Leaves* 2 to 4, somewhat fleshy, triangular in outline, biternate with stalked leaflets once to twice deeply divided into narrow lobes, slightly glaucous above, strongly below. *Racemes* 7-16-flowered, rather dense. *Bracts* 4-10 mm long. *Pedicels* 10-20(-30) mm, slightly arcuate in fruit. *Corolla* white (sometimes pale greenish yellow in bud), often slightly suffused with dirty pink; inner petals 10-12 mm long; lower petal

Fig. 24. a, *Corydalis gorodkovii* (Jurtzov s.n., E Siberia, Jacutia, Distr. Ojmakonsk, Suntar Chajata, fl. Petruschka, 7.7.1958, C); **b**, *C. magadanica* (cult. S. & V. 176, *locus classicus*); **c**, *C. gorinensis* (cult. Seisums & Veerus 100, *locus classicus*)

abruptly widened to a rounded lamina 7-8 mm broad, usually emarginate. *Spur* of upper petal thick and straight, obtuse at apex, 9-12(-16) mm long; nectary almost half as long as the spur, tapering to a slender apex. *Fruit* oblong, squarish in cross-section, 15-30 (-35) x 4 mm. *Seeds* 4-15, 2 mm in diameter, with a strap-shaped elaiosome pressed to the seed. Self-incompatible. Fig. 24b; Pl. 41.

DISTRIBUTION. E Siberia: Magadan. Map 13.

Corydalis magadanica has a dense raceme that is made up of large, thick-spurred, white to pale pink or pale greenish-yellow flowers, which in combination with the very glaucous much divided leaves, the stout constitution and the branched stem, makes it a highly desirable plant.

It is apparently a very rare plant in the wild, being found in only a few suitable places near Magadan. It must be realised, however, that this is not an area of easy access and is particularly hostile when *C.*

magadanica is in bloom. The distribution of this species may therefore be wider than we know it today.

It was introduced into cultivation by a Baltic expedition in 1993. The area in which it grows is cold and humid and most of the region is a vast spaghnum moorland with low amounts of soluble nutrients, favouring plants like *Pinus pumila*, *Rhododendron aureum*, *Phyllodoce* and *Cassiope redowskii*. On a few rocky outcrops the nutrition-level is slightly higher so *Betula ermanii* can gain a foothold and enrich the soil with its leaves. At the margin of these groves plants like *Fritillaria camschatcensis*, *Clematis ochotensis* and *Pulsatilla* are to be found.

However, *C. magadanica* is even more particular in its needs. It is entirely confined to shelves of cliff-faces where a richer black soil has been formed by birch-leaves and grass. The stock that is in cultivation was collected on cliffs facing the Sea of Ochotsk at altitudes between 3 and 20 meters above sea-level; a narrow altitudinal range indeed!

The cool climate has affected the typical tuberous

growth-cycle and we find the species to have a very short dormancy. Rooting starts in July so it is best replanted in June soon after it has died down. Some plants come into leaf in the autumn but the bulk start in the early spring. They are subjected to hard frosts and often take a flat position on the ground and look like boiled vegetables. However, they never fail to surprise us when they rise during the next mild period, as if nothing had happened, and grow stronger each year. We grow it in a peaty but rich humus-soil and the best plants develop in a rather open position.

39. *C. gorinensis* Van in Bot. Zhurn. (Moscow & Leningrad) 69: 544 (1984). Type: E Siberia, Chabarovsk, distr. Komsomolsk, river Gorin, second 'Byk', 20.5.1982, *V. Van* (VLA, holo).

DESCRIPTION. *Stems* 15-20 cm, suberect to ascending, branched from the scale-leaf and with axillary branches from the cauline leaves in well-fed individuals. *Leaves* glaucous below, triangular, tri-ternatifid into narrowly oblong to linear segments, glabrous or papillose-puberulent below. *Racemes* 5-25-flowered, rather long-stalked. *Bracts* ovate to ovate-lanceolate, subacute. Pedicels sub-erect, straight, 10-20 mm long, twice as long as the bracts. *Corolla* bright yellow; lower petal abruptly dilated into a rounded (rarely subacute) limb 5-8 mm broad; inner petals 9-12 mm long. *Spur* straight or slightly curved downwards, 8-15 mm long, with an acute nectary one third to half as long. *Capsule* oblong-acute, squarish in cross-section, 15-20 x 4 mm. *Seeds* 6-15, smooth, c. 2 mm long, with a strap-shaped elaiosome. Self-incompatible. Fig. 24c; Pl. 42.

DISTRIBUTION. Only known from the type locality. Map 13.

From what is presently known this must be one of the rarest species in the genus. It is only known from one rocky outcrop by the Gorin River, a tributary to the Amur River, and the whole population may amount to only a few hundred plants.

It was introduced by the same expedition that brought us *C. magadanica*. In this road-less country small boats are the only means of transport. It took several days of travel (with a skipper charging the fee in vodka) to get to the type locality through the country of the cannabis-smoking Nanai tribe. The Gorin is flanked by the taiga and the bedrock only surfaces in three cliff-faces ('Byk') that provide

suitable environs for *C. gorinensis*. As far as we know, only the second 'Byk', about 70 km east of Komsomolsk, has been botanised.

Corydalis gorinensis is confined to crannies, cracks and shelves on this granite hillock, where it grows together with a juniper. Here the higher temperature and the drier ground enables the birch-leaves and other organic matter to decompose quickly and produce a more fertile black soil. On top of the knoll there is a mixed birch-oak forest edged by *Spaghnum* moss. In this forest a bluish-purple form of *C. turtschaninovii* was found together with *Fritillaria maximowiczii*.

It is a precious introduction, the golden *Corydalis*, which is much more yellow than *C. bracteata* but with smaller flowers. Closely related to *C. magadanica*, it has, however, a more continental origin. In the garden it appears earlier than the former. The olive-green foliage is a perfect foil for the golden flowers. Cultivation is the same as for *C. magadanica*.

Series Adianta Lidén

M. Lidén, Willdenowia 26:25 (1996). Type species: *C. henrikii* Lidén.

Inner petals tipped with dark brownish purple. *Spur* long and slender. *Nectary* very short, acute. *Stigma* rectangular with four rather large apical papillae.

This series shows some similarities to subsection Brevinectaria (dark-tipped inner petals; very short nectary), and should perhaps be distinguished as a separate subsection. 2 species.

40. *C. triternata* J. G. Zuccarini in Abh. Math.-Phys. Cl. Königl. Bayer Akad. Wiss. 3: 251 (1843); *C. solida* var. *brachyloba* Boiss., Fl. Or. 1: 129 (1867). Type: Lebanon, Mt Lebanon, amongst cedars, *Roth & Erdl* (not seen).

DESCRIPTION. *Stems* 10-20 cm, usually slender, with two to three branches from the scale-leaf. *Leaves* bi- to tri-ternate with leaflets deeply divided into obovate to narrowly oblong lobes. *Racemes* long and lax, 3-10(-19)-flowered. *Bracts* flabellate-divided into acute lobes, usually with larger median lobe. *Pedicels* equalling or longer than the bracts, very slender, recurved in fruit, c. 5-10 (-15) mm long in flower (or more in greenhouse-grown plants), 10-20 mm long in fruit. *Corolla* nodding, white to pale pink, with greenish-lilac keels and dark purple tips to the

42

43

44

45

Plate 42. *Corydalis gorinensis*
Plate 43. *Corydalis henrikii*
Plate 44. *Corydalis nudicaulis*
Plate 45. *Corydalis nudicaulis*, close up of flowers

46

48

47

50

49

Plate 46. *Corydalis ruksansii*
Plate 47. *Corydalis schanginii* subsp. *schanginii*
Plate 48. *Corydalis schanginii* subsp. *ainae*
Plate 49. *Corydalis glaucescens*
Plate 50. *Corydalis turtschaninovii*, early form

Fig. 25. a, *Corydalis triternata* (cult. W. Kletzing, Turkey, S Vil. Hatay, Yayladagi); **b**, *C. henrikii* (cult. type)

inner petals; inner petal 8-9 mm long; lower petal with a minute cornute spur-like protuberance at the very base, and with a narrow claw gradually dilated to an emarginate limb 6-8 mm broad. *Spur* of upper petal 13-20 mm long, straight to often sigmoidally curved, obtuse at apex, with a shortly acute nectary 2-3 mm long. *Fruit* lanceolate-oblong, 13-19 mm long, including a beak 2.5 mm long and a 2.5 mm long style. *Seeds* 2-6, smooth, 2 mm long, without a protruding beak. 2n=16. Self-incompatible. Fig. 25a; Pl. 40.

DISTRIBUTION. Lebanon; Israel; Syria; extreme S of Turkey (Vil. Hatay). Map 14.

In some individuals the spur is rather thin, although not as delicate as in *C. henrikii*. A specimen from Rachaya (herb. Paris) is extremely robust.

In 1965 H.L. Crook mentions this species in an article in the *Bulletin Alpine Garden Society* as a *C. solida* from Mt Lebanon with 'white or cream flowers just tipped with dark brown'. A Turkish accession was the first to gain a foothold in cultivation. This

was collected in 1990 near Yayladag in the Hatay area, growing in evergreen oak-scrub together with *Cyclamen coum, Sternbergia fischeriana, Galanthus fosteri* and *Fritillaria alfredae* subsp. *platyptera*. Lately it has been introduced from the Syria by Bob and Rannveig Wallis. It is an elegant, graceful species with flowers of the palest pink with dark-tipped inner petals. A welcome addition to the alpine house and eventually, we hope, the rock-garden.

41. *C. henrikii* Lidén in Willdenowia 21: 175 (1991). Type: Turkey, Vil. Gaziantep: Kartal Dagh 45 km before Gaziantep from Nur Dagh, N-facing calcareous slope, on rocks, 1050 m, 6.4.1990, *Kammerlander, Pasche, Persson & Zetterlund* 9099 (GB, holo).

DESCRIPTION. *Stems* 15-18 cm high (or much more in greenhouse-grown plants), with 1-2 branches from the scale-leaf axil. *Leaves* slightly glaucous, long-stalked, three to four times ternately divided with deeply cleft leaflets; ultimate leaf-lobes narrowly lanceolate to oblong or narrowly obovate. *Raceme* 7-13-flowered, rather dense and subsecund in the type specimen (10-20-flowered, long and lax in cultivated plants). *Bracts* sessile or often clearly stalked, flabellate-divided into c. 5 segments which are often again divided or dentate, enlarging in fruit. *Pedicels* thin, 5-11 mm long in flower (up to 30 mm long in cultivated plants), slightly elongating and recurved in fruit. *Sepals* minute. *Corolla* whitish or usually pale purplish pink with the tips of the inner petals dark-tipped, less commonly rich purple; outer petals with rather narrow limbs, 4-6 mm broad; upper petal abruptly dilated into an obtriangular truncate apex; lower petal straight or with a prominently saccate base, slightly dilated towards the truncate or slightly emarginate apex; inner petals 10 mm long. *Spur* 15-22 mm long, straight to sigmoidally curved, very slender, tapering; nectary shortly acuminate, 3-4 mm long. *Stigma* with lateral papillae very small or absent. *Capsule* lanceolate, sub-biseriate, 15-22 x 4 mm, including a beak 2-3 mm and a distinct style 2.5 mm. *Seeds* 6-10, rather large, 2.2 mm, smooth, with a small hilum-area on a short beak and with a narrow, straight elaiosome. 2n=16. Self-incompatible. Fig. 25b; Pl. 43.

DISTRIBUTION. Turkey; Anatolia, prov. Gaziantep, Kartal Dagh. Limestone mountains, 1000-1100 m. Map 14.

Similar to *C. triternata* in the short nectary, divided bracts and rectangular stigma with four large apical papillae but readily distinguished by its finely dissected leaves, non-nodding flowers, the lack of prominent lateral stigma-papillae, the elegant long and thin spurs, the much narrower and less emarginate outer petals and the beaked seeds.

Found as late as 1990 when it was discovered by Kammerlander, Pasche, Persson and Zetterlund in the Gaziantep province in S Turkey (KPPZ 90-99, 90-109, 90-113). It was abundant in the Kartal Dagh range and was first encountered on a north-facing limestone scree at an altitude around 1000 m. Later it was found scattered on limestone outcrops in cultivated areas, associated with other interesting geophytes such as the peculiar *Helleborus vesicarius*, *Bongardia*, *Iris sari* and *I. histrio*.

Its long slender flowers and finely divided glaucous leaves make it a most elegant plant. So far it has taken well to cultivation. It is one of the earliest species to flower in our alpine-house and has, to date, done well on the rock-garden.

SUBSECTION BREVINECTARIA

Subsection Brevinectaria Lidén & Zetterlund in Willdenowia 26-25 (1996). Type species: *C. schanginii* (Pall.) B. Fedtsch.

Tuber dark, rounded to oblong; daughter-tubers usually coherent (*C. glaucescens* excepted). *Nectary* very short, obtuse at apex; elaiosome with brownish uneven base. 4 species, distributed in central Asia.

42. *C. nudicaulis* Regel in Acta Horti Petrop. 8: 695 (1884). Type: Tadjikistan, Darwaz, *A. Regel* (LE; S).

DESCRIPTION. *Stem* erect, (10-)15-20 cm (up to 40 cm in cultivation), with two alternate leaves and a translucent membranous scale-leaf close to the tuber. *Leaves* bi-(rarely tri-)ternate, sessile or stalked, with lanceolate to obovate leaflets with a clear reddish apex. *Racemes* subsessile, long and lax, 10-20-flowered (up to 40-flowered in cultivation). *Bracts* ovate-oblong, entire. *Pedicels* equalling or longer than the bracts, straight, erecto-patent, slender, 5-15(-20) mm long. *Sepals* rounded, slightly dentate, to 1 mm. *Corolla* white to creamy white with a dark brown coloration towards the front and purple-tipped inner petals; outer petals with a narrow, often undulate rim; lower petal subobtuse to subacute without a basal pouch; inner petals 9-11 mm. *Spur* upwardly directed, tapering, 11-15 mm long, sometimes slightly bent downward; nectary very short (2.5 mm), obtuse. *Stigma* small, squarish, with prominent basal lobes, four apical papillae, and a geminate papillae on each side. *Fruit* sub-pendent on thin pedicels, lanceolate, thin-walled and easily dehiscing, 18-22 x 3-4 mm. Seeds about 20, 1.3-1.4 x 1.2 mm, with long to short elaiosomes. 2n = ca 16. Self-incompatible. Fig. 26b, c; Pl. 44, 45.

DISTRIBUTION. Tadjikistan, W Pamir-Alai. 1000-2000 m. Map 15.

A recent introduction to horticulture and a plant of great promise. It is most elegant and distinct with average-sized, white flowers with a coffee-brown front third. Pale violet forms have been reported but are probably referable to the next species.

Arnis Seisums tells us that he found it in humusy soils near streams and among shrubs, always seeking the moisture of north-facing slopes. In the 'Flora of the USSR' its natural habitat is described as 'clayey slopes in snow or among rocks, benches'.

Fig. 26. a, *Corydalis ruksansii* (cult. type); **b, c**, *C. nudicaulis* (b, cult. Mikulastik, Tadjikistan, Hissar Range; c, cult. Seisums, Tadjikistan, N Dushanbe, Varzob Pass)

In this Flora it is placed in the section Radix-cava but regarded as a transition to section Corydalis. This is because herbarium-specimens usually lack the scale-leaf so typical of section Corydalis, whereas the other characters fit in well. A close examination in early spring, however, discloses a typical *C. solida* scale developed right above the tuber. The stem thus pushes its way up through the soil naked and the emergence of the flowering stems above ground is strikingly similar to that of *C. cava*.

The short obtuse nectary, the well-marked dark purple tip to the inner petals, the brownish base on the elaiosomes, and a certain similarity in tuber and habit indicates that it belongs in subsection *Brevinectaria*, but the low-down situated scale-leaf, the small seeds and the coffee-brown coloration of parts of the outer petals, indicate the rather isolated position of *C. nudicaulis*.

Presently we are growing material from four different localities and the intraspecific variation seems to be small. We first received it in 1987 and so far it has been a trouble-free plant in the alpine-house as well as on the rock-garden.

43. *C. ruksansii* Lidén in Willdenowia 21: 177 (1991). Type: NW Tadjikistan, 150 km NW Dushanbe, fourth lake on the river Shink, *J. Ruksans, A. Krumins & M. Kitts* 8229, cultivated in Gothenburg Botanic Garden (GB, holo; B iso; LE iso).

C. glaucescens subsp. *pamiroalaica* Soskov, Fl. Tadzhikskoi SSR 4: 536 (1975). Type: (LE, holo).

DESCRIPTION. *Stems* 10-20 cm, suberect to ascending, with a quickly deteriorating scale-leaf. *Leaves* stalked to almost sessile, biternate (rarely three times ternate) with deeply divided leaflets; ultimate leaf-lobes often markedly unequal in size, elliptic to obovate, acute to obtuse. *Racemes* 7-20-flowered, lax. *Bracts* ovate to lanceolate, entire, enlarging in fruit. Pedicels equalling or longer than the bracts, straight, erecto-patent, slender, 7-14(-22) mm long. *Sepals* small, lanceolate. *Corolla* narrow, whitish, with purplish-pink mid-veins to the outer petals; lower petal narrowly oblong, 11-12 mm long, without a sub-basal pouch; inner petals 10 mm long, tipped with dark purple. *Spur* curved upwards, straight or slightly recurved at tip, 12-13 mm long, the nectary very short

Fig. 27. a, *Corydalis schanginii* subsp. *schanginii* (a, cult. Ruksans, Kighizia, Frunze; **b**, Schrenk, *Pl. Songariae*, GB)

(2.5 mm), obtuse. *Stigma* as in *C. nudicaulis* but more rounded. *Fruit* linear, 12-17 x 2-3 mm. *Seeds* 2-5, 2.3-2.7 x 1.5 mm with long elaiosome with brownish scabrid base. 2n= ca 16. Self-incompatible. Fig. 26a; Pl. 46.

DISTRIBUTION. N Tadjikistan: C Zeravschan range and northwards to Chimgan area, scattered, 1500-2500 m. Humusy soils. Map 15.

This odd species came into cultivation in the early 1980s and was tentatively determined as *C. nudicaulis* but turned out to be a different species once the type specimen had been examined. Popov (1937), in discussing *C. nudicaulis*, emphasised its likeness to *C. glaucescens* and remarked that transitional forms existed; this remark probably referred to *C. ruksansii*.

It is somewhat similar to *C. nudicaulis* but can be distinguished by the shorter ascending stems, the less ephemeral scale-leaf, the differently coloured flowers and the few and larger seeds.

The first verified introduction was made by Janis Ruksans, who called it *C. glaucescens* 'C.D. Brickell'. He had found it in Tadjikistan, above the village of Shink (appr. 150 km NW of Dushanbe) at the fourth lake of the Shink River.

It is a rather inconspicuous species, first described as a subspecies of *C. glaucescens* but possibly more closely related to *C. schanginii*. The small flowers are white with a pinkish-violet hue with contrasting dark-purple tipped inner petals, while the midvein of the upper petal forms a thin pinkish-purple line. It is quite attractive in a pot when admired from close quarters. A mild winter will make it suffer under glass; the leaves become chlorotic and the flowers deformed.

In the open it is more compact and can be very attractive.

44. *C. schanginii* (Pall.) B.Fedtsch. in Acta Horti Petrop. 23: 372 (1904); *Fumaria schanginii* Pall. in Acta Horti Petrop. 6: 267 (1779); *F. longiflora* Willd., Sp. Pl. 3: 860 (1800); *Corydalis longiflora* (Willd.)

Pers., Syn. 2: 269 (1807). Type: Siberia, Altai (B (WILLD) 12915; LE; P (DC))

DESCRIPTION. Mature *tuber* large, often up to 3 or 4 cm, rounded to oblong. *Stem* 10-40 cm, ascending to suberect, rather robust. *Leaves* glaucous, rather thick in texture; petiole about one third as long as lamina; lamina twice ternate with entire or deeply incised leaflets, the ultimate lobes ovate to lanceolate, usually acute. *Racemes* long, 5-25-flowered (to 30-flowered in cultivation), rising high above the leaves, rather dense at first in subsp. *schanginii*, very lax in subsp. *ainae*. *Bracts* ovate-lanceolate to linear-lanceolate, entire. *Pedicels* equalling the bracts, 5-15 mm, elongating to 10-20 mm in fruit. *Sepals* minute. *Corolla* rose-purple or yellow, long and narrow; outer petals narrow and acute; lower petal without a pouch; inner petals narrowly crested, dark-tipped, 14-16(-18) mm long. *Spur* 21-28 mm long, tapering, (30 mm long in the subspecific cross), straight or usually curved downwards at apex; nectary short, obtuse. *Stigma* rectangular with prominent basal lobes. *Fruit* linear, 18-25 x 2-3 mm. *Seed* 4-8, smooth, almost 2.5 mm long and slightly narrower, with a long elaiosome with narrow brownish base.

The two subspecies give fertile intermediate hybrids but it is not known whether this hybrid ever occurs in nature.

44a. subsp. *schanginii*

DESCRIPTION. *Tuber* greyish. *Stem* 10-30 cm, ascending to suberect. *Racemes* rather dense at first, becoming laxer. *Corolla* rosy purple, often with darker veins, especially prominent on the keels of the outer petals; lower petal with a narrow but distinct rim. 2n=16. Self-incompatible. Fig. 27a, b; Pl. 47.

DISTRIBUTION. S Russia, Kazakhstan, N Kirghizia, China (Xinjiang), W Mongolia; widely distributed from the SE bend of the river Ural to Kirghizia, Altai and Tienshan, 500-2000 m. Map 16.

The most noble and largest-flowered species in the section. The flesh-pink dark-veined flowers with dark purple-tipped inner petals, are 4 cm long or more, and produced in long racemes. It is recorded in cultivation as early as 1833, when pictured in *Curtis's Botanical Magazine* (tab. 3230) as *C. longiflora*. This material had been sent to Edinburgh from Berlin

(probably a Ledebour collection) and had its origin in the Altai Mountains. Today's cultivated material derives from a Janis Ruksans collection made in Kirghizia near Frunze (Bishkek) in 1975, where it was growing in deciduous scrub at an altitude of 2000 m.

In Gothenburg it has been grown in the open garden for a number of years. The best situation, however, has been in the bulb-frame, where the tubers grow to an astonishing size. It survived the hostile winters of the mid 1980s untouched. Bearing in mind that in January and February the temperatures stayed between -15°C and -25°C for several weeks, it may be considered wholly frost-hardy.

In nature it is found in 'slightly saline consolidated sands, clayey deserts and stony dry slopes of the lower montane zone' ('Flora of the USSR'). It is also found under shrubs and in humusy pockets in screes on north-facing slopes, always in rather arid areas, so a summer-dry spot is recommended in the garden.

44b. subsp. *ainae* Ruksans ex Lidén in Willdenowia 21: 178 as '*ainii*'. Type: Kazakhstan, Kara Tau Mts., near Berkara, 1700-2000 m., 26.4.1977, *J. Ruksans*, cultivated in Gothenburg Botanic Garden (GB, holo).

DESCRIPTION. *Tuber* yellowish. *Stems* 20-40 cm, weaker and laxer than in subsp. *schanginii*. *Leaves* more divided with longer petioles and petiolules. *Racemes* long and lax, to 20-flowered. *Corolla* with a yellow front half, the rest white or pink; lower petal without a marginal rim. *Spur* thinner and more curved. *Fruit* and seeds as in subsp. *schanginii*. 2n=16. Self-incompatible. Pl. 48.

DISTRIBUTION. Kazakhstan, known from two localities in the Kara-Tau mountains, within the area of subsp. *schanginii*. A yellow-flowered *schanginii* has also been spotted between Emba and Chelkar (NE Aral sea) by A. Seisums (oral communication). If it is the same taxon it has a remarkably sporadic distribution. Map 16.

The yellow counterpart to the above and a gem in the genus. It was revealed to science on the 26th of April 1977, when it was discovered by Janis Ruksans in the Kara-Tau Range, in the Berkara (Black Stream) Gorge, which cuts through a black schistaceous mountain south of the road 50 km from the town of Djambul towards Janatas. Here it was growing in the shade of *Crataegus, Cerasus, Amygdalus, Fraxinus* and *Salix* on moist slopes at 1700-2000 m altitude.

Fig. 28. a, *Corydalis caudata* (Ssu Ho, Harry Smith 5520, C China, S Shanxi, Yün-ch'eng, 600 m, UPS); **b**, *C. glaucescens* (cult. Ruksans, Kirghizia, S Frunze = Bishkek)

This gorge retains moisture throughout the year; search in the side gorges, which dry out in summer, proved fruitless.

It is of a weaker and laxer constitution than plain *C. schanginii* and has a more slender flower with a soft pink spur and an intensely yellow front-half. The inner petals are tipped with dark chocolate-purple, which makes a striking contrast. When grown under glass the pink is lost.

Judging from its natural habitat it should do better in the open garden than subsp. *schanginii* and this has, so far, proved to be the case.

It was awarded a Preliminary Commendation (P.C.) in 1995 by the Royal Horticultural Society.

45. *C. glaucescens* Regel in Bull. Soc. Imp. Naturalistes Moscov. 43: 253 (1870). Type: Kazakhstan/Kirgizia, sources of river Almatinka, *Sewerzow* (LE).

C. kolpakovskiana Regel in Acta Horti Petrop. 5: 633 (1877). Type: Kazakhstan/Kirgizia, Wernoje, river Almatinka, Altigimel, *A. Regel* 1877 (LE).

C. kolpakovskiana var. *hennigii* Fedde in Repert. Spec. nov. Regni veg. 21: 47 (1919). Type: Kazakhstan/Kirgizia, 21.4.1885 *P. Hennig* (B).

DESCRIPTION. *Tuber* more akin to the 'normal' form in the section *Corydalis*. *Stems* ascending to erect, 10-25 cm, usually with several branches from the large broadly ovate scale-leaf, giving this species a very distinctive appearance. *Leaves* glaucous, thinner than in the preceding species, rather long-stalked, twice ternate with stalked leaflets; ultimate leaf-lobes entire, ovate to narrowly ovate, acute or obtuse. *Racemes* long and lax, 5-12(-22)-flowered. *Bracts* entire, narrowly rhombic-ovate to lanceolate. *Pedicels* equalling or longer than the bracts, 5-15 mm long, very thin (up to 25 mm in cultivation). *Flowers* gracefully nodding. *Sepals* minute. *Corolla* pale pink to white with dark purple to greenish keels, broadly winged and emarginate at apex; lower petal with a broad limb and a short claw with a pronounced gibbosity; inner petals 7-9 mm, with pale, rather broad dorsal wings. *Spur* straight or somewhat recurved, tapering towards the apex, 10-14(-17) mm long, the nectary very short, only about 1.5 mm long, clavate-obtuse. *Fruit* broadly lanceolate, 11-17 x 4 mm. *Seeds* 1.7-2 mm with a long narrow elaiosome with brownish uneven base. 2n= 16. Self-incompatible. Fig. 28b; Pl. 49.

DISTRIBUTION. Central Asia from Bogdo Ola (Chinese Tienshan, Xinjiang) to Kirghizia and SE Kazakhstan, Dzungarskiy Alatau, Tarbagatai, (Fergana district?); shady places and north-facing slopes to 1800 m. Map 16.

This species differs from the others in the subsection by its different tuber, the broad flowers with a distinct pouch to the lower petal, as well as by the broad pale apical dorsal wings of the inner petals.

It is an elegant species that produce an abundance of racemes with white or, more usually, pink flowers. These are rather small but the overall effect is charming; it is a most garden-worthy plant. In 1887 it was pictured in *Curtis's Botanical Magazine* as *C. kolpakovskiana* (tab. 6925) from plants 'found in 1877 by Albert Regel in W. Turkestan, near the town of Wernoje, near the river Almatinka'; it has been in cultivation, intermittently, over a long period. In 1978 we were surprised to find a large patch in the Copenhagen Botanic Garden which 'had been there for ages'. It is a good-doer in the rock-garden, apparently, but it is even better in a bulb-frame.

It hails from central Asia where it grows in the shade of scrub, woods, or, at higher levels, on open slopes in meadows up to 2000 m altitude. A great number of collections have found their way into cultivation during the last decade.

Recently it appeared in the trade as *C. kashgarica*, but this is a completely different, non-tuberous, species.

'Cream Beauty'. Collected amongst dwarf juniper in the vicinity of Frunze by Janis Ruksans. It is a nice compact plant and quite distinct with a touch of yellow on the white flowers.

SUBSECTION NUMMULLARIA

Subsection Nummullaria Liden in Willdenowia 26:25 (1996). Type species: *C. caudata* (Lam.) Pers.

Plants much-branched with weak ascending stems. *Leaves* vaginate at base; leaflets rounded; petioles and petiolules long. *Pedicels* long and slender.

Flowers broadly winged with short inner petals. *Nectary* long, clavate-obtuse at apex. 2 species, distributed in E China.

46. *C. caudata* (Lam.) Pers., Syn. 2: 269 (1806); *Fumaria caudata* Lam., Encycl. 2: 569 (1786); *Corydalis longiflora* var. *caudata* (Lam.) DC., Syst. 2: 117 (1821). Type: E China, near Beijing, *Incarville* (P (JUSSIEU) 10.894).
C. repens auct, non Mandl & Mühld.
C. repens var. *humosoides* Y.H.Zhang in Acta Bot. Yunnanica 12: 37 (1990). Type: E China, Jiangsu: Xuzhou, Tongshan, in forest, 9.5.1983, *Y. Lian & L. L. Guo* (PE, holo).

DESCRIPTION. *Plant* glabrous weak, much-branched, often with two scale-leaves. *Leaves* usually vaginate at base, often with axillary branches, (bi-) tri-ternate with long and thin petioles and petiolules; leaflets rounded to elliptic, sometimes shallowly cleft, glaucous below. *Racemes* lax, 3-8-flowered. *Bracts* obovate, acute. *Pedicels* much longer than the bracts, (5-) 15-25(-40) mm long, filiform. *Sepals* minute. *Corolla* in various shades of blue or purplish blue, rarely white; upper petal broadly winged; inner petals 7-8 mm long only; lower petal with a large sub-basal gibbosity and a broad emarginate limb. *Spur* upward-curved 12-14 mm long, the nectary reaching about three quarters along the spur, obtuse at the apex. *Capsule* ovoid to ellipsoid, 8-15 mm including a beak 1-2 mm and a 1.5 mm long style. *Seeds* 4-9, smooth, about 2 mm, with long narrow elaiosomes. Fig. 28a.

DISTRIBUTION. East-central China: Henan; Jiangsu; Anhui; Shandong; Hebei; Shanxi; Hubei. In forests, April-May, 400-1200 m. Map 17.

Corydalis caudata is a very distinct species, easily recognised by the peculiar foliage, the broad corolla with its long upward-curving spur and the long obtuse nectary. The specific name *caudata* was previously considered synonymous with the central Asiatic *C. schanginii* which lacks even the slightest similarity.

Not in cultivation, as far as we know.

47. *C. humosa* Migo in J. Shanghai Sci. Inst. sect. 3, 4: 146 (1939). Type: E China, Zhejiang, Hsi-tienmu-shan, 23.4.1936, *Migo* (TI).

DESCRIPTION. *Stems* 9-20 cm, weak and slender, usually with 1-3 branches from the scale-leaf. *Leaves* biternate with long petioles and petiolules; leaflets elliptic to ovate, entire, or sometimes deeply lobed into obovate segments. *Raceme* lax, 1-3-flowered. *Bracts* ovate to ovate-lanceolate. *Pedicels* slender, 7-15 mm long. *Corolla* white, similar to that of *C. caudata* but much smaller; inner petals ca. 4 mm long. *Spur* 5-7 mm long. According to Zhang (1990) the seeds are covered with conical obtuse tubercles and the accompanying photo resembles those of *C. racemosa*. We believe that this is a mistake.

DISTRIBUTION. China: Zhejiang (Tianmushan; Anji; Changhua). 600-1700 m. Map 17.

Similar to *C. caudata*, but smaller in all parts and with much smaller white flowers. It has a very restricted distribution. Not in cultivation.

SUBSECTION OFFICINALES

Subsection Officinales Lidén in Willdenowia 26:25 (1996). Type species: *C. turtschaninovii* Besser

Stems sometimes with an axillary tuber in the scale-leaf. *Leaves* more or less glaucous, somewhat fleshy, finely and densely papillose below (difficult to see on herbarium material); lower leaf vaginate at base, sometimes with an axillary branch (especially in *C. gamosepala* and *yanhusuo*). *Corolla* blue to purple, rarely white; outer petals with emarginate, usually more or less dentate limbs, usually with a conspicuous mucro in the notch; dorsal wings of inner petals angular, rather broad, sometimes prolonged slightly beyond the apex. *Nectary* about one third to two thirds as long as the spur (very short in *C. ornata*, rather long in *C. turtschaninovii* subsp. *vernyi* and in *C. yanhusuo*), subobtuse at apex (subacute in *C. ornata*). *Fruit* linear, straight, smooth to subtorulose, 5-13-seeded, 16-26 x 2 mm with style (1.5-)2 mm, uniseriate with rather small seeds, 1.4-1.7 x 1.1-1.5 mm, smooth, with a long narrow elaiosome. 4 species in east Russia, Korea, C, E, and NE China (Japan).

A complex group with a clear-cut geographical variation, here considered to comprise four species.

48. *C. turtschaninovii* Besser, Flora 17, Beibl. 1: 6 (1834); *C. remota* Fisch. ex. Maxim., Prim. fl. Amur.: 37 (1859); *C. solida* subsp. *remota* (Maxim.) Korsh., Pl. Amur.: 306 (1892); *C. bulbosa* var. *remota* (Maxim.) Nakai in Bot. Mag. (Tokyo) 26: 91 (1912).

Type: Siberia, Dahuria, Nerczinsk, *Turczaninov* (K; LE).

The description is omitted here as it would be largely a repeat of the information in the description of the subsection.

48a. subsp. *turtschaninovii*

C. remota var. *lineariloba* Maxim., Prim. fl. Amur.: 38 (1859); *C. turtschaninovii* f. *lineariloba* (Maxim.) Kitag. in Rep. Inst. Sci. Res. Manchoukuo 3: 234 (1939); *C. remota* f. *lineariloba* (Maxim.) C.Y.Wu & Z.Y.Su in Acta Bot. Yunnanica 7: 268 (1985). Type: none designated, *Fischer* (LE) fits the description.

C. remota var. *rotundiloba* Maxim, Prim. fl. Amur.: 38 (1859); *C. remota* f. *rotundiloba* (Maxim.) C.Y.Wu & Z.Y.Su in Acta Bot. Yunnanica 7: 268 (1985). Type: none designated.

C. turtschaninovii var. *papillosa* Kitag. in Rep. Inst. Sci. Res. Manchoukuo 2: 294 (1938); *C. remota* f. *papillosa* (Kitag) C.Y.Wu & Z.Y.Su in Acta Bot. Yunnanica 7: 269 (1985). Type: Manchuria, prov. Feng-t'ien, Ling-shuei-szü, 3.5.1932, *Kitagawa* (TI).

DESCRIPTION. *Stems* more or less erect, with only one scale-leaf present (a few exceptions noted), sometimes with an axillary tuber; branches usually absent from the axil of the lower leaf, rarely present in well-fed individuals, not uncommon in cultivated plants. *Leaves* triternate or biternate with coarsely dentate to more or less deeply divided leaflets, somewhat fleshy; ultimate leaf-lobes broadly elliptic to oblanceolate or linear, obtuse or usually acute. *Racemes* rather dense at anthesis, 6-20(-30)-flowered. *Bracts* divided into few to several acute lobes. *Pedicels* equalling the bracts, 5-10 mm long in flower, 10-20 mm long in fruit. *Corolla* blue or purplish blue (rarely white?); inner petals 9-12 mm long. *Spur* rather straight, slightly recurved at apex, 10-14 mm long, with the nectary one third to half as long, obtuse to subobtuse. *Capsule* 16-26 mm, somewhat torulose. 2n=16. Self-incompatible. Fig. 29a, b; Pl. 50, 54.

DISTRIBUTION. Manchuria, SE Russia (Dahuria, Amur, and Ussuri regions). Forests, forest margins, clearings, and shrubs. Map 18.

Considerable variation in leaf-shape is often found within a single local population of subsp. *turtschaninovii*.

Plate 51. *Corydalis fumariifolia* subsp. *fumariifolia*, narrow-leaved form
Plate 52. *Corydalis ornata*, white form
Plate 53. *Corydalis ornata*, colour variants
Plate 54. *Corydalis turtschaninovii*, late form
Plate 55. *Corydalis blanda* subsp. *parnassica*, from Mt Ghiona

56

57

59

60

58

Plate 56. *Corydalis cava*, white form
Plate 57. *Corydalis cava*, yellow form
Plate 58. *Corydalis cava*, form with purple bracts
Plate 59. *Corydalis blanda* subsp. *olympica*
Plate 60. *Corydalis blanda* subsp. *parnassica*, from Mt Ghiona

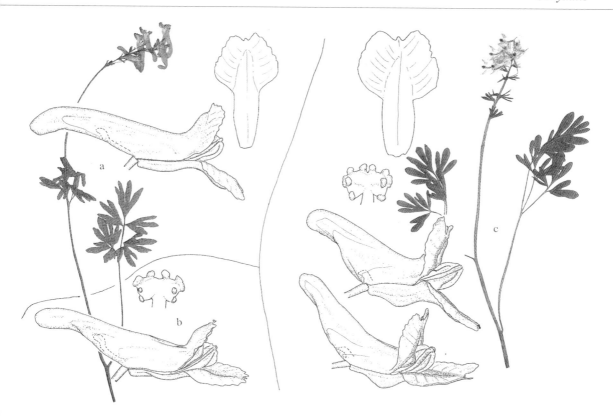

Fig. 29. a, b, *Corydalis turtschaninovii* subsp. *turtschaninovii* (a, S. & V. 58 *pro parte*, SE Siberia, Chasan distr., Kedrovaja Padj, *ussuriensis-locus*; b, cult. S. & V. 99, *gorinensis-locus*); **c**, *C. ornata* (cult. type)

This outstanding plant has recently been introduced to cultivation. It was first offered in Michael Hoog's catalogue of 1991 (as *C. remota* and *C. repens*), at a price of 75 Dutch Guilders per tuber. All cultivated material seems to have originated from Janis Ruksans who received it from a Russian friend in the 1980s. In his Latvian garden, Janis has worked up stock of some really gorgeous forms.

Most plants have clear-blue flowers borne on 15-20 cm stems. A truly striking variation can be seen in the leaves; some plants having a broad round-lobed foliage with a coppery hue, others are more sharply incised, thin and have a bright emerald lustre. To the horticulturist they may appear very different, but we consider them to be forms of the same subspecies.

In Latvia they are grown outside in a fertile, humus-rich soil, shaded by deciduous trees. In Gothenburg it is proving to be much later appearing than its 'blues-competitor', *C. fumariifolia*, and is therefore safe from late frosts and will probably be the more favoured garden-plant in the long run.

So far only one cultivar has appeared in the trade but there is room for many more:

'Eric the Red'. Bright blue flowers and red-tinted foliage; named in honour of a great Swedish Viking.

48b. subsp. *vernyi* (Franch. & Sav.) Lidén in Willdenowia 26:28 (1996); *C. vernyi* Franch. & Sav., Enum. pl. Jap. 2: 273 (1876). Type: Japan, Honshu, near Yedo (= Tokyo), *Savatier* (P).

C. turtschaninovii v. *ternata* Ohwi in Acta Phytotax. Geobot. 11: 262 (1942). Type: Korea, Hakusen in Kokaido, *Boku* 692 (TI).

DESCRIPTION. Differs from subsp. *turtschaninovii* by: *Leaves* less divided, with rather distant broad dentate leaflets. *Racemes* few-flowered. *Spur* comparatively longer, with nectary about two thirds as long (in subsp. *turtschaninovii* up to half as long). *Stigma* larger and more squarish. Fig. 30a.

DISTRIBUTION. Korea, Japan (?). The type specimen of *C. vernyi* is the only record so far from Japan and may possibly be mislabelled. Map 18.

49. *C. ornata* **Lidén & Zetterlund** in M. Lidén, Willdenowia 26:29 (1996). Type: SE Russia, Primorskij Kray, C. Arsen'yev, *leg. Kirsanova, ex J. Ruksans,* cultivated in Gothenburg Botanic Garden (GB, holo).

DESCRIPTION. Like *C. turtschaninovii* but: *Leaves* more divided with narrower lobes. *Racemes* laxer. *Bracts* smaller and more divided. *Corolla* white, blue, or greyish purple with the mouth lined with a thin blue lipstick; outer petals with broad dentate limbs, emarginate at apex with a distinct mucro in the notch; inner petals 11-12 mm long. *Spur* rather triangular in shape, somewhat upwardly directed (usually oblong and horizontal in *C. turtschaninovii*), 9-11 mm long, with a subacute nectary only 2 mm long. *Capsule* narrower with smaller seeds. 2n=32. Perhaps self-compatible to a certain degree. Fig. 29c; Pl. 52, 53.

DISTRIBUTION. SE Russia; so far only known from the original collection, which included several different clones. Map 18.

Very similar to *C. turtschaninovii* but a tetraploid with a very short subacute nectary and more triangular and more upwardly directed spur. Its flowering period in cultivation is also markedly earlier.

Yet another plant introduced via Janis Ruksans. The one collection in cultivation is variable in flower-colour which ranges from a pale lilac to clear blue. The most fabulous variant, however, is a pure white one with a crenulate lip thinly lined with blue; it is one of the most beautiful plants in existence!

It is earlier appearing than *C. turtschaninovii* but grows to perfection in Janis' Latvian garden. Horticultural needs are as for the former species.

50. *C. gamosepala* **Maxim.**, Prim. fl. Amur: 38 (1859). Type: near Peking (LE).
C. remota var. *heteroclita* K.T.Fu, Fl. Tsinglingensis 1: 605 (1974); *C. remota* f. *heteroclita* (K.T.Fu) C.Y.Wu & Z.Y.Su in Acta Bot. Yunnanica 7: 269 (1985). Type: C China, Taipaishan, Ti-tze-yai-kow, forested slopes, 1200 m, *C. P. Wei* 4199 (not seen).
C. turtschaninovii f. *haitaoensis* Y.H.Chou & C.Q.Xu, Fl. pl. herb. Chin. bor.-or. 4: 229 (1980); *C. remota* f. *haitaoensis* (Y.H.Chou & C.Q.Xu) C.Y.Wu & Z.Y.Su in Acta Bot. Yunnanica 7: 269 (1985). Type: NE China, Liaoning: Changhai island, 27.6.1927, *Zhourong Han* 2387 (Inst.

Forest & Soil Res., Acad. Sin., holo; not seen but the accompanying illustration suggests that it should be placed here).

DESCRIPTION. Like *C. turtschaninovii* but: *Stems* sub-erect, or even decumbent, (7-)12-22 cm, frequently with two scale-leaves and often with three cauline leaves. Axillary tuber absent. *Leaves* as in subsp. *turtschaninovii*, or sometimes clearly anisophyllous, especially in the west of its range (i. e. upper leaves with small obovate lobes, lower ones with lanceolate acute lobes); lower leaf usually broadly vaginate at base, frequently with axillary branches. *Racemes* 7-13-flowered. *Bracts, lower,* with coarse acute teeth, upper entire or with 1-2 teeth. *Pedicels* 5-13 mm long in flower, 10-15 mm in fruit, thin, equalling or longer than bracts. *Corolla* pink to purple, rarely blue; inner petals (8-)9-10 mm.. *Spur* (8-)10-13 mm long, slightly upwardly directed, and usually slightly recurved at tip, with nectary a half to two thirds as long. Fig. 30b.

DISTRIBUTION. China: Inner Mongolia; Hubei; Shanxi; Shaanxi; Ningxia; Gansu; Shandong, SW Liaoning. Map 18.

Plants from inner Mongolia (*David* 2610, P; Daqingshan, *Wu & Ma* 9, HIMC) deviate in their short decumbent stems, small pale rosy flowers and small fruits, 14-17 mm long, and may be worthy of formal recognition. A probable hybrid with *C. kiaotsch-ouensis* is known (*Zimmerman* 534, K).

Not in cultivation.

51. C. yanhusuo (Y.H.Chou & C.C.Xu) W.T.Wang ex Z.Y.Su & C.Y.Wu in Acta Bot. Yunnanica 7: 267 (1985); *C. yanhusuo* W.T.Wang, Illustrated Flora of the Vascular Plants of China 2(12): no 1754 (1972) *nomen nudum*; *C. turtschaninovii* f. *yanhusuo* Y.H.Chou & C.C.Xu in Acta Phytotax. Sin. 15: 82 (1977). Type: E China, Zhejiang: Hangzhou, cultivated in Lang-gu-oh medical experimental laboratory (Shenyang medicinal institute, holo). Note: Wu & Su give 'Chu Xian, 14.4.1951, *JSBI* 1514 (JSBI)' as the type but the name is automatically typified by reference to *C. turtschaninovii* f. *yanhusuo*.

DESCRIPTION. *Stems* very slender, 12-29 cm, rather branched, with an axillary tuber in the lowermost

Fig. 30. a, *Corydalis turtschaninovii* subsp. *vernyi* (Oh, NW S Korea, Kangning, Kyonggi-do, 28.4.1983, GB); **b**, *C. gamosepala* (Lao Chin, H. Smith 8100, China, C Shanxi, Lu Yah shan, UPS); **c**, *C. yanhusuo* (Tsu L.-F., 1078, China, Anhui, Chuchow, K)

scale-leaf, sometimes with a second scale-leaf, or with a third cauline leaf low down the stem with a broadly vaginate petiole-base. *Leaves* biternate to sub-triternate with entire lanceolate leaf-lobes; petioles and petiolules of lower leaves often very long. *Racemes* long and lax, 5-15-flowered. *Bracts* lanceolate, acute, entire or the lowermost slightly divided. *Pedicels* slender, about 10 mm long in flower, up to 20 mm long in fruit. *Corolla* purple, curved, with upwardly directed mouth; inner petals 8-9 mm; outer petals with limbs dentate, emarginate, mucronate; lower petal with a short claw, gradually widened into a spreading limb. *Spur* upward-directed, 11-13 mm long. *Stigma* with papillae longer than those in *CC. turtschaninovii* and *gamosepala*. *Fruit* 28-23 mm, linear. 2n=48 (Zhang 1996). Fig. 30c.

DISTRIBUTION. China: probably native in Anhui, Jiangsu, and Zhejiang but cultivated also elsewhere in eastern China. Grassland. Map 18.

Closely related to *C. gamosepala* but distinguishable by the accessory tuber, the entire leaf-lobes and the strongly curved corolla.

An important drug in China, containing more than 20 alkaloids. It is said to relieve pain by invigorating blood-circulation, but is especially important for postpartum treatment ('inhibits aldose reductase; anti-inflammatoric; can treat chi and blood associated pricking pain').

Commonly cultivated in eastern China and recently introduced in Japan and Sweden.

SUBSECTION MONSTRUOSA

Subsection Monstruosa Lidén in Willdenowia 26:26 (1996). Type species: *C. filistipes* Nakai.

52. *C. filistipes* Nakai in Bot. Mag. (Tokyo) 32: 104 (1918). Type: S Korea, Ullung-do (Kyongbuk-do), Mt Jöhö, 600 m, 31.5.1917, *Nakai* (TI, holo, B, iso).

DESCRIPTION. *Stem* very robust, 15-30(-50) cm, never branched, scale-leaf large. *Leaves* 3-4 times ternate (or primary and secondary leaflets sub-pinnate) with deeply divided leaflets; ultimate lobes narrowly

oblong to ob-lanceolate. *Racemes* dense in flower, very lax in fruit, 4-5-flowered. *Bracts* oblong, entire to dentate, or sometimes more divided, about 10 mm. *Pedicels* 8-20 mm, elongating considerably in fruit up to 55 mm. *Corolla* 11-13 mm long, white to pale yellowish, very inconspicuous; inner petals, at least sometimes, not apically coherent, 8-9 mm long, with dorsal wings overtopping the apex. *Spur* 3 mm long with a very short and narrow obtuse nectary.*Capsule* oblong, 15-25(-40?) x 3-4 mm, uniseriate. *Seeds* 1-6, large, 2.5-2.7 mm. Fig. 31.

DISTRIBUTION. The island of Ullûng-Do east of Korea in the Japanese sea. April-May. Map 10.

A very peculiar species, not similar to anything else. Also anatomically it differs from the rest of the section (Oh 1987, Oh & al. 1993).

Fig. 31. *Corydalis filistipes* (Oh s.n., S Korea, Ullung-do,10.5.1986, GB)

SECTION RADIX-CAVA

This is a small and easily circumscribed assemblage but with an intricate pattern of variation, making it one of the taxonomically more difficult groups in the genus. It is the only *Corydalis* section with its main distribution in Europe, stretching as it does from Portugal to northern Iran. Due to the reticulate pattern of variability we have chosen to adopt a wider circumscription of the species than has appeared in other recent treatments, including our own. The two species recognised here are morphologically quite distinct. *C. blanda* is compact with glaucous somewhat fleshy leaves with usually lanceolate and acute leaflets. In addition, it flowers considerably later than *C. cava*, the pedicels are stouter and red-coloured, the corolla is pale (with the pigmentation usually appearing 'freckled'), the capsule is short and broad and the seeds are larger. All of these characteristics are maintained in greenhouse-grown plants.

NOTE: *Corydalis nudicaulis,* which is sometimes misplaced here, belongs in section *Corydalis*.

CULTIVATION The species in this group are good, reliable garden-plants, some with outstanding qualities. *C. cava* is a classical garden-plant that will flourish in any decent position. The woodland garden suits it particularly well but it will be at home in the herba-ceous border, the peat-wall and the north-facing rock-garden. The needs of the various subspecies of *C. blanda* have not ben fully explored but they seem to enjoy a gritty soil in the cooler parts of the rock-garden.

Horticulturally they hold a position between section *Corydalis* and section *Leonticoides*, sharing with the former a preference for humus-rich, cool soils that do not dry out completely and, with the latter, a perennial deep-seated tuber and lack of a scale enclosing the shoot.

When planted in the open garden *C. cava* should be buried at least 20 cm deep. The soil should be open, rich in humus and nutrition if one wants maximum development. Planting is best carried out in August - September. The tubers of this section do not appreciate desiccation and should be packed in slightly moist peat when handled by nurseries (or whenevever they are lifted and stored). Dry tubers are best left in the nursery or the garden-centre, for they are unlikely to grow and their purchase will be a waste of money.

IN POTS They are easily grown in pots and should be planted in the same compost as for the Western Woodlanders of section *Corydalis*. On the other hand they require a deep planting and spacing similar to the species of section *Leonticoides* but there is no need to play around with sand; just fill the pot with one third of compost, plant the cleaned tuber and fill up with compost, finally top-dressing with one centimetre of grit.

Repotting is done in September, at the latest, and the plants can be immediately activated by a watering. From now on they are cared for in a similar way as the Western Woodlanders of Section Corydalis.

They are among the last of the tuberous corydalis to come into growth, lengthening the greenhouse season well into April. When dormant they should be plunged and kept slightly moist throughout the summer.

PROPAGATION Species in this section have the largest seeds of any of the tuberous species and produce flowering plants in three or four years. The seeds should be sown and treated as for section Leonticoides. Since the small perennial tubers readjust to their final position the first year they do need deep pots. The compost and watering-regime, however, should be similar to that for the Western Woodlanders.

Plants can also be increased by division. Older tubers tend to become irregularly disintegrated and are easily broken apart into rather small fragments. As early as 1822 Parkinson had noted the ease with which the parts recovered and built up healthy individuals. Even if there is no sign of shoot-production, adventive buds will arise during the first winter.

Corydalis Section Radix-cava Irmisch in Abh. Naturf. Ges. Halle 6: 273 (1867). Type species: *C. cava* (L.) Schweigg. & Körte

Seedlings with one cotyledon. *Tuber* perennial, with roots scattered over the surface, becoming hollow, and eventually disintegrating in old individuals, monopodial in growth. *Stems* formed axillary to scale-leaves or radical leaves, one to several from each tuber, simple, each with two alternate leaves, often with long root hairs on the subterranean part (cf. Sect. Leonticoides). *Bracts* rather large, entire, ovate. *Sepals* minute. *Outer petals* broadly winged, emarginate. *Nectary* obtuse at apex, fused to the spur for most of its length. *Stigma* rounded with several papillae, the basal pair (and usually the lateral ones) geminate. *Fruit* oblong to ellipsoid.

KEY TO SPECIES OF SECTION RADIX-CAVA

1. Leaves not or slightly glaucous above; corolla red, purple, yellow, or white, with pigment evenly distributed. Spur of upper petal 10-14 mm; capsule 18-23 x 4 mm; seeds 2.5 mm long   **1. C. cava**
1. Leaves glaucous on both sides; corolla white, often minutely freckled with bluish purple; spur of upper petal 7-10(-12) mm; capsule 10-18 x 5 mm; seeds 3-3.5 mm long   **2. C. blanda**

1. *Corydalis cava* (L.) Schweigg. & Körte, Fl. Erl. 2: 44 (1811); *Fumaria bulbosa* α *cava* L., Sp. Pl.: 699 (1753); *F. cava* (L.) Mill., Gard. dict. ed 8 (1768). *F. bulbosa* Mill., Gard. abr. dict. ed. 6: 110 (1771), non Mill. 1768; *F. major* Roth, Tent. Fl. Germ. 1: 300 (1788); *Corydalis tuberosa* DC., Fl. Fr. ed 3 (4): 637 (1805); *C. bulbosa* auct., non DC. Type: Burser Hortus Siccus VII(1)99 (UPS, lecto).
Corydalis marschalliana Pers., Syn. 2: 269 (1807); *Fumaria marschalliana* Pall. ex. Willd., Sp. pl. 3: 860 (1800); Pallas in Nov. Act. Petrop. 10: 315 (1797), nomen. Type: Ukraine, Crimea (B (WILLD)).
C. albiflora Kit. ex Schult., Österr. Fl. ed. 2, 2: 305 (1814). Type: none designated.
C. marschalliana var. *purpureo-lilacina* Rupr., Fl. Cauc.: 55 (1869). Type: numerous syntypes from Transcaucasus.
?*C. pseudocava* Pant. in Verh. Vereins Natur.-Heilk. Presburg 2: 88 (1872). Type: Montenegro, Mt Kom, *Pantocsek* (not seen).
C. stummeri Pant. in Magyar Növényt Lapok 5: 150 (1888). Type: 'Viragzik Aprilhoban Serajevo Körül Bozniaban', *Stummer Agoston* (not seen).

DESCRIPTION. *Tuber* rounded, becoming hollow with age, with the basal parts eventually disintegrating (especially in plants from Central and North Europe the tuber then attains a conical form). *Stems* 10-30 cm (subterranean part excluded), erect, glabrous, very rarely papillose. *Leaves* twice ternate, with leaflets deeply to shallowly cut; ultimate lobes usually obovate-obtuse. *Racemes* 6-16(-23)-flowered, elongate. *Bracts* entire, ovate, 10-20(-30) mm long. *Pedicels* 3-10 mm, erecto-patent, slightly recurved in fruit. *Corolla* white, pink, purple-red or red to pale yellow. *Fruit* oblong, 18-24 x 4 (-5) mm. *Seeds* 5-10, 2.5 mm, with long strap-shaped elaiosome. 2n=16 (Caucasus; Gothenburg; Moravia; Greece: several

Fig. 32. a, *Corydalis cava* (*marschalliana sensu stricto*, tetraploid, cult. Ruksans, Crimea); **b**, *C. cava* (*cava sensu stricto*, diploid, cult., Georgia, near Tblisi)

places) 2n=24 (*Zetterlund* 88-85); 2n=32 (*Ruksans*: N Caucasus, Crimea). Fig. 32a, b; Pl. 56-58.

DISTRIBUTION. Widespread in the euxine region from Portugal to N Iran, with its northernmost populations in southern Sweden. Mainly in deciduous forests (notably *Fagus*) but growing with *Abies* for example in Greece; rarely in damp subalpine pastures. 0-1800 m. April-early June. Map 19.

The complex variation in this species is partly geographical with distinct types (for example in Caucasus (var. *purpureo-lilacina* Rupr.), Crimea and N Caucasus (the tetraploid *C. marschalliana sensu stricto*) and southern Greece, whereas in the northern Balkans there is a complete intergradation between *marschalliana*- and *cava*-like forms. More research is needed to clarify the pattern of variation but it seems at present impossible to uphold two distinct species.

Corydalis marschalliana was described from the Crimea but has been regarded as being distributed from the northern Balkans and the Ukraine through

the Caucasus to northern Iran. Its main distinguishing characters are said to be the entire obovate to elliptic leaf-lobes (apically dentate in *C. cava*), a small solid rounded tuber (becoming conical, large and concave in *C. cava*), yellow flowers (purple, red, or white in *C. cava*) and a tetraploid chromosome number (diploid in *C. cava*).

Over the whole distribution area, however, these characters are not, or only weakly correlated. In 'true' tetraploid *C. marschalliana* from the Crimea, purple-flowered plants are to be found. Diploid plants, with tubers and leaves like '*cava*', can have yellow flowers. The white-flowered Macedonian '*marschalliana*' may be diploid as well as tetraploid. '*C. marschalliana* var. *purpureo-lilacina*' from the Tblisi area is a diploid race, distinguished by a white corolla with a long purple spur, in which the foliage corresponds to the *C. cava* type. Plants from Iran, generally attributed to *C. marschalliana*, also have most characters pertaining to the '*cava*' syndrome.

Corydalis cava has been cultivated, at least, since the 15th century. Primarily it was used as an

Fig. 33. a, *Corydalis blanda* subsp. *oxelmannii* (cult. type); **b**, *C. blanda* subsp. *blanda* (cult. Ek 15, Greece, Ep. Artis, Mt Tzoumerka); **c**, *C. blanda* subsp. *parnassica* (cult. Ek 9, Greece, Ep. Doridos, Mt Ghiona); **d**, *C. blanda* subsp. *olympica* (cult. type)

adulteration for *Aristolochia rotunda* root (*Radix Aristolochiae cavae*), a highly praised medical drug. For this reason it is still frequently found growing around old monastaries and castles.

The common plant in cultivation is the north and central European form which produces a variable mix of white and purple-red individuals. If kept isolated from the purple one, the white form will produce a clean, white-flowered seed-strain, which looks particularly lovely in a dusky woodland garden.

There are other forms in cultivation but these are still rare. In the Balkans, uniformly white- or pale yellow-flowered populations are common. These vary in flower-size and number of flowers per raceme and some are very attractive.

In some population of mixed colours one can find intermediate colours: a plant from Kabardino Balchar in Georgia, cultivated in Gothenburg, has a strange mixed yellow-purple tone.

For garden use we favour the extreme colour-variations; the darkest purples, the purest whites and the deepest yellows. Still, in a semi-wild area of the garden the normal mixture is quite at home.

2. *C. blanda* Schott in Österr. Bot. Wochenbl. 7: 149 (1857). Type: Montenegro, *Maly* (S).

DESCRIPTION. *Tuber* more flat and irregular and growing to a larger ultimate size. *Stems* usually low, 4-15 cm, erect to ascending, rather stout, glabrous. *Leaves* glaucous, slightly to strongly fleshy, (once to) twice ternately to sub-pinnately divided with deeply lobed or dentate leaflets; ultimate lobes narrowly to broadly lanceolate, usually acute. *Racemes* 5-10(-13)-flowered, very dense to rather lax. *Pedicels* red (at least in sunny locations), 3-6 mm long, somewhat reflexed in fruits. *Corolla* white, often minutely freckled with bluish purple. *Fruits* short and broad, very glaucous, 10-18 mm long. *Seeds* 1-5, large, at least 3 x 3 mm.

DISTRIBUTION. W Balkan Peninsula from Montenegro to N Peloponnese (Chelmos) with an isolated outlier on Mt Olympus. Alpine meadows and screes, often where snow has lingered. May to early July. Map 20.

The Mt Olympus and more especially the Mt Chelmos populations are very distinct, while the difference between subsp. *blanda* and subsp. *parnassica* is less pronounced.

Corydalis blanda subsp. *blanda* (N Pindus, Albania, Montenegro) is often less condensed than the other subspecies and stands out in the tetraploid chromosome number, although this has only been recorded from the northern Pindus Mountains. Subsp. *parnassica* (Parnassus area) is close to subsp. *blanda*. Subsp. *olympica* from Mt Olympus differs from subsp. *blanda* and subsp. *parnassica* by its very compact growth, the very glaucous fleshy and stiff leaves which are cut into several small narrow leaf-lobes, the denser racemes and by a somewhat different stigma. Subsp. *oxelmannii* from Mt Chelmos has very distinctive leaves, laxer racemes and more slender flowers. On all of these mountains, *C. cava* is found in deeper soil at lower altitudes and in more shady situations. The alpine taxa rarely hybridise with *C. cava* at intermediate altitudes; for example on Chelmos where a small patch of intermediate, apparently fertile, plants was noted by Niclas Ek and brought into cultivation.

KEY TO SUBSPECIES

1. Leaf-lamina at least as long as broad, with 60-100 ultimate lobes or teeth   **2d subsp. *oxelmannii***
1. Leaf-lamina broader than long, with 15-60 ultimate lobes or teeth   **2**

2. Racemes very dense, almost capitate; lamina with 45-60 ultimate lobes or teeth **2c subsp. *olympica***
2. Racemes dense to rather lax; lamina with 15-40 ultimate lobes or teeth   **3**

3. Leaf-lamina 2-5 cm long; 2n=16
     2a subsp. *parnassica*
3. Lamina 3-10 cm long; 2n=32   **2b subsp. *blanda***

2a. subsp. *parnassica* (Orph. & Heldr.) Lidén in Willdenowia 26:29 (1996); *C. parnassica* Orph. & Heldr. in Boiss., Diagn. ser. 6: 9 (1859). Type: Greece, Sterea Ellas, Parnassus, *Orphanides* (G, lecto; S, iso).

DESCRIPTION. *Stems* 5-15 cm. *Leaves* glaucous, triangular in outline, very variable with broad to narrow, acute or obtuse ultimate leaf-lobes; ultimate lobes or teeth 15-30(-40). *Racemes* 3-12-flowered, rather dense. *Flowers* short and broad. *Spur* 7-10 mm long. 2n=16 (*Ek* 6; *Ek* 9). Fig. 33c; Pl. 55, 60.

DISTRIBUTION. Mt Parnassus and neighbouring mountain areas. Alpine meadows and screes, 1800-2250 m.

The plant referred to as *C. parnassica* in the *Bulletin Alpine Garden Society* (61: 49) is *C. cava*, possibly with some introgression of *C. blanda* subsp. *parnassica*. The true plant has fewer and paler flowers in the raceme and quite different leaves .

2b. subsp. *blanda* Schott
? C. pseudocava Pant. in Verh. Vereins Natur.-Heilk. Presburg 2: 88 (1872). Type: Montenegro, Mt Kom, *Pantocsek* (not seen).

DESCRIPTION. Very similar to subsp. *parnassica*. *Leaves* (3-)5-10 cm broad, cut into elliptic to lanceolate acute leaf-lobes; number of ultimate lobes or teeth 17-30(-40). *Racemes* 5-12-flowered, rather dense. *Spur* 8-12 mm long. 2n=32 (*Ek* 14; *Ek* 15). Fig. 33b; Pl. 61.

DISTRIBUTION. Mountains in Montenegro, W Macedonia, Albania, and NW Greece (Pindus). Alpine meadows, 1800-2250 m.

We have at present plants from Montenegro and Pindus in cultivation at Gothenburg. The Montenegro one differs in its creamy white corolla from all other *C. blanda* plants that we have seen. The tetraploid chromosome number (at least of the Pindus plants) is worth noting.

2c. subsp. *olympica* Lidén in Willdenowia 26:29 (1996). Type: Greece, Nomos Pierias, Mt Olympus, SE of the Kakavrakos peak, 2200 m.s.m., damp stony alpine pasture, south-facing slope, 4.6.1992, *N. Ek 19* (GB, holo; C iso; Patras, iso).

DESCRIPTION. *Plant* 4-10 cm high. *Leaves* rather fleshy, cut into several linear to lanceolate lobes, with about 45-60 ultimate lobes or teeth. *Racemes* very dense, 7-10-flowered. *Spur* 7-10 mm long. 2n=16 (*Ek* 19; *Strid* s.n.). Fig. 33d; Pl. 59.

DISTRIBUTION. Greece: Mt Olympus. Alpine meadows and screes, 2000-2400 m.

A very glaucous and compact plant with dense racemes of short-spurred flowers. The pygmy of the 'blanda-tribe'. This Mt Olympus endemic has been cultivated for years as *C. parnassica*. It remains compact in cultivation and is a delightful pot-plant in the alpine-house. Its habit once fooled us into treating it like the section *Leonticoides* species, resulting in a rapid loss of the plants. It cannot take a dust-dry summer dormancy.

It does well in the rock-garden when planted in a gritty soil in a cool but light position.

2d. subsp. *oxelmannii* Lidén in Willdenowia 26:29 (1996). Type: Greece, Peloponnese, Nomos Achaïas, Mt Chelmos, Vrisi, 1800-1950 m, stony alpine pasture, 17.6.1991, *B. Oxelman 1928* (GB, holo).

DESCRIPTION. *Plant* 6-12 cm high with racemes least as long as broad (in the other subspecies broader much overtopping the leaves than long). *Leaves* with lamina at than long), cut into several small, usually obtuse and overlapping, segments; number of ultimate lobes or teeth 60-100. *Racemes* 4-10-flowered, rather dense to rather lax, especially in shady situations. *Flowers* comparatively more slender. *Spur* 10-12 mm. *Seeds* slightly smaller than in the other subspecies, about 3 mm. 2n=16 (*Ek 1*; *Oxelman* 1928). Fig. 33a.

DISTRIBUTION. Greece: N Peloponnese: Mt Chelmos. Alpine meadows and screes, 1800-2000 m.

In cultivation this subspecies is strikingly different, with its long lax racemes and quite different leaves. It is very elegant with its large pale pink to purple flowers and finely dissected, glaucous foliage with overlapping segments. The best subspecies within *C. blanda* !

SECTION LEONTICOIDES

This section provides some of the most beautiful as well as the most bizarre species in the genus. In the wild most of them are confined to rocky habitats (or, more rarely, steep meadows or forest-slopes) at mid- to high elevations of mountainous areas from Turkey to Central Asia with outposts in Crete, Cyprus and the western Himalaya. Map 21.

In order to withstand the harsh environment and climate they have deep-seated tubers (15-50 cm below the surface) protected by a corky 'skin', and very glaucous foliage nesting amongst the protecting rocks. The shoots spread widely and irregularly before emerging above the ground, thus making the tuber very difficult to locate. The underground parts of the stems and petioles are covered by a felt of hairs, which probably have the same function as proper root-hairs. This may help to support the final ripening of the seeds, should the stem be prematurely detached from the tuber. Besides *Corydalis* section Radix-cava, we know of no other example of this structure.

The annual race with nature necessitates a rapid growth-cycle. In the wild cool and humid autumnal weather serves to revive the plants, with roots and shoots growing through the winter under a protective snow-cover. As the snow melts in early spring the shoots lie folded just below the ground, ready to sprout. Flowering, setting seed and building up the tuber for the following season has to be carried out within a time-span of four to eight weeks before the ground is too dry and the temperature too high.

CULTIVATION. In a 'normal' season hardiness is not a problem; they survive the cold of Scandinavia. However, a mild winter followed by a cold spell in February-March, can kill off one year's growth. With the plants of this section this is by no means fatal, since the tubers will take more frost than the shoots.

In pots. The species of this section are not perfect pot plants, although they are not at all difficult to maintain but their early appearance in spring can cause problems. In a mild winter they start unfolding as early as January or even December. With the poor light of winter they tend to elongate in a most untidy manner, the flowers become smaller and do not colour as brightly as they might otherwise. Their growth-habit makes the shoots collide with the inner surface of the pot and they follow this to the surface, giving the impression of Medusa's head with a tonsure as they sprawl over the edge of the pot.

This, of course, applies to areas with an Atlantic (oceanic) climate like Britain and the west coast of Sweden. In areas with a more continental climate, like Central Europe, there is no such problem.

Still, since they will not survive for many years in the open garden and few people have access to bulb-frames, pot-culture may often be the only way to keep them. 'Long Tom' pots are recommended; no doubt, these species will grow in pots of ordinary design, but to delay their appearance in spring the tubers should be planted as deeply as possible.

In Gothenburg we are using 18 cm rose-pots for adult corms (4-10 cm diameter). The compost is a gritty one into which a little bone-meal has been added (2 parts sterilised loam, 1 part neutralised peat, 2 parts sand and 2 parts grit (2-5 mm) + 1/2 litre bone-meal to each 70 litres of compost). We fill the pot to one third of its depth with compost. On top of this we place the tuber after it has been carefully cleaned from any loose remnants of old growth but do not clean it too thoroughly! It is very easy to penetrate the skin and open up the juicy, fleshy tissues to treacherous fungi. On top of the tuber we do not use any compost but fill the pot almost to the rim with clean sharp sand. This reduces the moisture, gives the tuber a hygienic surrounding and the shoots a clean run, factors that reduce the risk of fungal infections. The pot is then mulched with a 3 cm layer of grit that keeps the substrate airy, reduces evaporation and gives the pot a tidier look.

These species are best kept dry well into late autumn so repotting can wait until October if necessary (and possibly longer, see below!). However, if the autumn is very humid and cool, root- and shoot-formation can start earlier, so be alert. In order to delay them we try to water them as late as possible. If they have not started growing when they are repotted, we keep them dry until late November or early December. Remember, once you have given them the first drink you must not let them dry out again!

They should then be kept slightly moist through the winter. As the leaf-lamina unfolds and the buds start swelling (January to March) they require more water. When the leaves are fully developed they need a lot of water; at this point in the season there is no risk from over-watering. After flowering and seed-set the plants will announce their forth-coming dormancy and watering should be reduced as the leaves turn yellow, withholding water altogether when they whither. The dormancy should be on the dry side, perhaps with some moistening of the plunge during the hottest weather if you live in a dry area. These are the most drought-tolerant corydalis.

Timing. Breaking of dormancy is induced by a combination of time, temperature and air-humidity. Once we found a corm of *C. oppositifolia* in a corner of the potting-shed. It had been forgotten in a plastic bag at a temperature around 18°C. It was found in January, healthy but with no sign of growth. Directly planted and placed in a cold frame, the leaves appeared in May. By that time there was plenty of light so the plant remained very compact. It did not flower but if this was due to the treatment is not for us to say. This encouraged us to experiment with more tubers the following year with good results. Adult corms were stored in dry peat at 18-20°C and planted just before Christmas and plunged in a cold greenhouse. These gave nice compact flowering plants in the second half of April.

In bulb-frames. This is undoubtedly the best way to keep them. An environment where you can control the watering and provide a dry summer rest will ensure long-lived healthy plants. A gritty mix as recommended above, deep planting (30-50 cm) and a late initial watering have given splendid results. Some years they look as attractive as they do in their native screes, compact and brightly coloured, surrounded by small juno-irises, Mediterranean crocuses and dwarf tulips.

In the open garden. Unfortunately, they will not be permanent in the garden if grown without protection. They will make it through the winter and look good in the spring but they will not stand moisture during their summer dormancy. We once tried *C. chionophila* in the rock garden: it looked marvellous the first year, pathetic the second and then it disappeared. Possibly a few species like *C. diphylla*, *C. ledebouriana* and *C. maracandica* can survive for a longer period if given perfect positions.

One solution is to lift the tubers just as the foliage starts to wither and store them in sand or dry peat in a shady cool spot under a roof. This method is successfully practised by Janis Ruksans and other commercial growers.

PROPAGATION. The tuber will not divide naturally, so seed is the best mean of propagation. For ripening, dispersal and collecting see under Section Corydalis. Seed sown the moment it is ripe gives excellent germination the following spring. Sown before August they will still germinate well: the autumn is crucial for the development of the embryo. We have experienced sporadic germination with seeds sown in February the year after ripening.

First year seedlings have a typical monocot-look. The new tuber is formed deep down in the ground in the final position (15-50 cm under the surface). Since the tubers are perennial and lack contractile roots they cannot change position during their life-span. When sown in pots the tubers will always be located crowded at the bottom.

Since young seedlings are extremely vulnerable, particularly to fungal infection, we prefer to use clay-pots for sowing. These are better ventilated and it is easier to control watering. We sow the seeds directly when ripe, using the same mix that we use for the adults, cover them with 1/2 cm of clean sand and top with a one centimetre layer of grit. Then we plunge the pots in sand, water them and keep them slightly moist by watering the plunge now and then during the summer. In August they are properly watered and kept moist until they germinate the following spring. When they die back, water should be drastically reduced but they should not be kept as dry during dormancy as is recommended for adult plants. Water the plunge every week or every second week, depending on the weather. The seed-pots can be left for one or two more seasons before the tubers need to be spaced out. During this period a liquid fertiliser will encourage tuber build-up. Apply this as a weak dose in late autumn and a stronger one as the leaves unfold in the spring.

Division. The tubers can live for a long time and tend to become irregular with age. Sometimes the tubers divide 'naturally' as some parts deteriorate. Others remain weakly connected by living tissue and can easily be broken apart without harm.

The most drastic way to divide them is to cut the tuber in parts with a sharp knife. This procedure has its risks! A tuber with a diameter of 7-8 cm should not be cut into more than four parts. The operation is best carried out in late August and the parts should then be left in a dry airy room until the wound is dry. After a few days they should be placed in a cooler place (alpine-house) so they do not become too dehydrated. Keep them uncovered, unless the atmosphere is too dry, in which case a propagator-box or something similar is preferable. Do not pot them before late October and water with care. Even

if the cuts have been made so that some segments seem to lack visible growing-points, buds will normally arise on each of them.

Corydalis Section Leonticoides DC. Syst. 2:114 (1821); Section *Radix-cava* subsect. *Leonticoides* (DC.) Fedde (1936); Subgenus *Corydalium* Koch, Linnaea 15: 252 (1841); Genus *Cryptoceras* Schott, Österr. Bot. Wochenbl. 4: 121 (1854). Type species: *C. verticillaris* DC.

DESCRIPTION. *Tuber* perennial, enlarging outwards each year, old tubers decaying in the middle and often becoming rather irregular, sometimes forming a ring, or disintegrating into separate parts, run through by a cambial mantle with the potential to produce shoots everywhere; growth-points usually few, surrounded by several scale leaves or withered petiole-bases from previous years, monopodial, with flowering stems arising axillary from radical leaves or scale leaves. *Roots* produced in fascicles from few to several points. *Stem*: underground part gradually tapering towards the point of attachment and equipped with one-celled roothairs; aerial stem with two opposite leaves (rarely with a third leaf above). *Leaves* usually sessile or sub-sessile, glaucous , the lamina once to three times ternately divided, long-stalked primary leaflets, sometimes giving the impression of six verticillate leaves. *Bracts* usually entire (divided in *C. macrocentra*). *Corolla*: outer petals usually ecristate, but in *CC. nariniana, seisumsiana* and *darwasica* a narrow crest is usually present; lower petal strongly reflexed. *Nectary* usually very long, reaching almost to the tip of the spur, clavate-obtuse at apex.

This section has a chiefly Irano-Turanian distribution, with most species found in central Asia. The westernmost representative is *C. uniflora*, which is endemic to Crete, and in the east *C. diphylla* reaches western Nepal. It is a very homogenous section, here divided into 5 series:

Series Coronatae (*CC. cyrtocentra, ledebouriana, maracandica, popovii, sewerzowii, darwasica*)
Series Elegantes (*CC. afghanica, podlechii, griffithii*)
Series Leonticoides (*CC. aitchisonii, chionophila, rutifolia, uniflora, lydica, oppositifolia, erdelii, nariniana, verticillaris, seisumsiana*)
Series Macrocentra (*C. macrocentra*)
Series Petiolatae (*C. diphylla*)

KEY TO SPECIES OF SECTION LEONTICOIDES

The key is designed for quick determination of both herbarium specimens and live plants. Some aberrant forms may fall outside the parameters given. Fortunately, species that are difficult to distinguish with simple key-characters grow in different areas and geographic distribution has been included in some cases as an aid to correct determination.

1. Leaves distinctly stalked (W Himalaya) **1. *C. diphylla***
1. Leaves sessile or almost so (petiole less than 5 mm) **2**

2. Bracts divided, stems branched **11. *C. macrocentra***
2. Bracts entire, stems simple **3**

3. Inner petals with a conspicuous triangular notch **5. *C. popovii***
3. Inner petals not or very slightly notched **4**

4. Flowers yellow, sometimes suffused with reddish or brownish **5**
4. Flowers white or in various shades of pink or purple **8**

5. Spur 10-12 mm, very broad at apex **4. *C. maracandica***
5. Spur 15-35 mm long, tapering towards the apex **6**

6. Spur 15-18 mm long **13b. *C. chionophila* subsp. *firouzii***
6. Spur 23-35 mm long **7**

7. Leaves ternate to biternate with entire leaflets, pedicels 10-40 mm long **12. *C. aitchisonii***
7. Leaves biternate with divided leaflets, pedicels 5-10(-15) mm long **6. *C. sewerzowii***

8. Spur more than 20 mm long **9**
8. Spur 20 mm long or less **13**

9. Pedicels 2-5 mm long **2. *C. cyrtocentra***
9. Pedicels longer **10**

10. Leaves ternate to biternate with entire leaflets **13b. *C. aitchisonii* subsp. *kamelinii***
10. Leaves more divided **11**

11. Outer petals subacute, not broadly winged (Iran) **21. *C. verticillaris***
11. Outer petals with broad rounded to emarginate apex (Afghanistan) **12**

12. Corolla strongly curved upwards, fruit linear **9. *C. podlechii***
12. Corolla slightly sigmoidally curved, fruit broadly ovoid to broadly elliptic **10. *C. afghanica***

13. Nectary much shorter than spur, pedicels 2-10 mm **3. *C. ledebouriana***
13. Nectary almost as long as spur, pedicels usually longer **14**

14. Racemes 1-3-flowered (Crete) **15. *C. uniflora***
14. Racemes 2-15-flowered **15**

15. Spur very broad at apex; pedicels 2-10 mm long **4. *C. maracandica***
15. Spur not broader at apex, pedicels usually longer **16**

16. Outer petals lacking a marginal rim, spur 9-12 mm long **18. *C. erdelii***
16. Outer petals with a marginal rim or wing **17**

17. Lower petal with a dark purple blotch across the limb; outer petals with narrow dorsal crests **18**
17. Lower petal often with a dark keel, but not with a dark blotch across the limb **19**

18. Spur 10-13 mm long (C Asia) **7. *C. darwasica***
18. Spur 13-19 mm long (Armenia, Nakhichevan) **20. *C. seisumsiana***

19. Leaves ternate, or at most biternate with entire leaf-lobes **20**
19. Leaves more divided **23**

20. Pedicels 6-15 mm long (Cyprus) **14. *C. rutifolia***
20. Pedicels 10-25 mm long **21**

21. Lateral stigma-papillae very small (E Anatolia) **16. *C. oppositifolia***
21. Lateral stigma papillae conspicuous **22**

22. Flowers (usually?) creamy white, without dark keels; spur 11-14 mm long, cylindrical (W Anatolia) **17. *C. lydica***

22. Flowers pale pink to purplish, rarely white, with darker keels; spur (13-)15-20 mm long, sigmoidally curved, usually tapering towards the apex (N Iran, Turkmenistan, Afghanistan) **13. *C. chionophila***

23. Corolla with white front with dark keels, and carmine to purple spur; outer petals with a dorsal crest **19. *C. nariniana***
23. Corolla without contrasting spur; outer petals not crested **24**

24. Terminal leaflets very much larger than the lateral, rounded **8. *C. griffithii***
24. Leaf-lobes not markedly unequal, usually acute **25**

25. Leaves c. tripinnate with small acute ultimate lobes **21. *C. verticillaris***
25. Leaves less divided **26**

26. Spur 19-25 mm long (N Iran, Azarbaijan) **21b. *C. verticillaris* subsp. *boissieri***
26. Spur 13-18 mm long (E Anatolia, Iraq, W Iran) **16. *C. oppositifolia***

In the following accounts the description of leaves always refer to the two cauline ones, the radical (basal) leaves often being larger and less divided. The figure for plant height excludes more or less the underground part of the stem.

Series Petiolatae Lidén
Willdenowia 26:30 (1996). Type species: *C. diphylla* Wall.

1. *C. diphylla* Wall., Tent. fl. Nap.: 54 (1826). Type: N India, Kumaon, Serinagur, *Blinkworth*, *Wall. cat.* 1430 (K).

DESCRIPTION. *Stem* erect, 6-15 cm. *Leaves* stalked, slightly glaucous, bi- to triternate (rarely once or four times ternate); petiole 5-50 mm. Leaf-lobes very unequal in size, the median one large, narrowly obovate to ovate-lanceolate. *Racemes* 3-11-flowered, lax. *Bracts* 6-12 mm long, enlarging in fruit, broadly lanceolate. *Pedicels* 5-30 mm long in flower, 10-35(-50) mm long and strongly reflexed in fruit. *Sepals* very variable in size, 0-2.5 mm, entire to laciniate. *Corolla* white or cream with the tips of the inner petals and the wings of the outer petals purple; outer petals widely divergent, exposing the purple limbs. *Spur* broad at base, curved upwards, 8-13 mm long, recurved at apex. *Fruit* flattened, elliptical. *Seeds* 2-2.5 mm with large elaiosomes.

DISTRIBUTION. Himalaya, eastwards to W Nepal. 2000-4100 m, slopes, woods, forest, often near melting snow. Map 22.

A very variable species, here divided into three subspecies. Subsp. *occidentalis* and *murreana* are, however, not geographically disjunct and it is possible that they are, despite the substantial differences, extremes of a continuous variation.

1. Stems branched; Sepals 1-2.5 mm long **1a subsp. *diphylla***
1. Stems simple; Sepals up to 1 mm long **2**
2. Corolla about 10 mm broad at apex, white to pale pink with purple front **1b subsp. *occidentalis***
2. Corolla about 5 mm broad at apex, cream with purple front **1c subsp. *murreana***

1a. subsp. *diphylla*
C. pauciflora Edgew. in Trans. Linn. Soc. London 20:30 (1851), non (Steph.) Pers. Type: India, Simla, 2150 m, April 1849, *Edgeworth* (K).

DESCRIPTION. *Stems* nearly always branched. *Leaves* usually triternate. *Racemes* 3-6-flowered. *Bracts* much enlarging in fruit. *Sepals* rather large, 1-2.5 mm. Fig. 34a.

DISTRIBUTION. From Simla in N India eastwards to West Nepal, 2000-4000 m. Map 22.

Probably not in cultivation.

1b. subsp. *occidentalis* Lidén in Willdenowia 26:30 (1996). Type: Pakistan, Swat: E Kalam, 3000 m, 6.6.1965, *Lamond (Rechinger) 30851* (S, holo; C, iso, photo in Wendelbo, P., Fumariaceae, in Rechinger, K. H. (ed.) Fl. Iranica 110 (1974), tab. 5:2).

DESCRIPTION. *Stems* not branched. *Racemes* usually more floriferous. *Corolla* broader, white or rarely pale pink with contrasting purple front. *Sepals* small or up to 1 mm. *Lower petal* 9-13 mm long and up to 12 mm wide. *Spur* 8-13 mm long. 2n=16. Self-incompatible. Fig. 34b; Pl. 62.

Fig. 34. a, *Corydalis diphylla* subsp. *murreana* (cult. SEP 348, N Pakistan, Kalam, Ushu Valley, Mahodan, 3-3350 m); **b**, *C. diphylla* subsp. *occidentalis* (cult. Kohli, *sine loco*)

DISTRIBUTION. Kashmir, locally common, preferring rich soil on shady banks, shrubberies and forests, 2000-4000 m. Map 22.

One of the few members of this section that will grow in the open garden. It has been regularly available in the trade for a long time as stock imported from Kashmir. It has elegant, distinct foliage that makes it easy to recognise. The flowers vary in size and colour but some forms are rather boring. At its best the broad lips can be deep purple and the thick spur pure white, a very attractive combination.

It received a Preliminary Commendation (P.C.) in 1978 when exhibited by the Royal Botanic Gardens Kew.

1c. subsp. *murreana* (Jafri) Lidén in Willdenowia 26:30 (1996); *C. murreana* Jafri, Fl. Pak. 73. (Fumariaceae): 7 (1980). Type: N Pakistan, Murree

hills, 2000 m, 20.4.1917, *R. R. Stewart & I. D. Stewart* 1647 (RAW, holo; S, iso).

DESCRIPTION. *Stems* not branched. *Racemes* usually denser and more floriferous. *Corolla* much narrower, cream-coloured. *Sepals* small or up to 1 mm. *Lower petal* 8-10 mm long and up to 4 mm wide. *Spur* 8-11 mm long. 2n=16. Self-incompatible. Pl. 63.

DISTRIBUTION. NW India, Murree hills; Hazara, Swat 1500-2000 m. Map 22.

We are growing a collection of this subspecies in Gothenburg from the westernmost area of its distribution (SEP 348). It is very elegant in the combination of small creamy white flowers with red lower lips and its beautiful, glaucous leaves.

Series Coronatae Lidén

Willdenowia 26:30 (1996). Type species: *C. ledebouriana*.

Pedicels short, 2-15 mm. *Elaiosome* thick, rounded, closely capping the funicular region like a minute fur cap. Central Asia.

2. *C. cyrtocentra* Prain in J. As. Soc. Bengal. 65: 20 (1896); *C. diphylla* var. *cyrtocentra* (Prain) Jafri, Fl. Pak. 73 (Fumariaceae): 7 (1980). Type: N Pakistan, Chitral 1894, *Younghusband* (K).

DESCRIPTION. *Plant* low, 5-8 cm. *Leaves* sessile, irregularly triternate, glaucous; leaflets very unequal in size, rounded to obovate. *Racemes* 3-4-flowered, dense. *Bracts* ovate. *Pedicels* 2-5 mm long in flower. *Corolla* large with inner petals 13-14 mm long. *Spur* 25-30 mm long, curved upwards, rather broad. *Nectary* reaching almost to the tip of the spur. *Fruit* and *seeds* unknown. Fig. 35.

Fig. 35. *Corydalis cyrtocentra* (type)

DISTRIBUTION. NW Pakistan, Chitral; 'shale-slopes; 'damp sheltered places, loam of tree-trunk'. 1100-1400 m. Map 23.

This is perhaps one of the more striking species in the genus with its short stem, small leaves and dense raceme of large flowers. It is known from NW Pakistan and neighbouring eastern Afghanistan and has been found only four times. Not in cultivation as far as we know.

3. *C. ledebouriana* Kar. & Kir. in Bull. Soc. Imp. Naturalistes Moscov. 14: 377 (1841). Type: Kazakhstan, Tarbagatai, Tschcheharak-Assu, May 1840, *Karelin & Kir* 54 (LE; K).
C. cabulica Gilli in Repert. Spec. nov. Regni veg. 52: 99 (1955). Type: Afghanistan, 'No-Hang des Korogh bei Kabul', 2000 m, 9.4.1950, *Gilli* 878 (B, holo).

DESCRIPTION. Similar to *C. cyrtocentra* but: *Leaves* bi- to triternate and flowers smaller. *Racemes* long, 5-10 (-14)-flowered. *Pedicels* 2-9(-12) mm long, more or less erect in fruit. *Corolla* with a purplish violet apex and a pale pink or almost white spur, rarely reddish purple or white; outer petals acute to acuminate, very narrowly winged; inner petals 9-11 mm. *Spur* 9-15(-18) mm long, never apically recurved, often strongly curved upwards and inflated towards the apex, but forms with slender and/or more straight flowers also occur; nectary much shorter than spur, turned upwards. *Fruit* 10-15 x 5-6 mm. *Seeds* 5-10, 2-2.5 mm, or slightly more. 2n=32. Self-incompatible. Fig. 36c, d; Pl. 66.

DISTRIBUTION. Mountains of Central Asia from Tarbagatai in the NE to C Afghanistan in the south; NW Xinjiang close to the border (Tarbagatai, Huocheng, N Tienshan), (700)1000-3000(-3600) m, '*Platanus-Acer* woods in deep clay-leafmould soil', 'sticky clay-slopes; rocky slopes', 'clayey and stony slopes of the central zone in patches of melting snow' (Fl. USSR). Map 23.

An extremely variable species especially as regards colour, size and form of corolla, but easily recognisable by the characteristic short nectary. Each population is usually homogeneous but substantial differences, both in morphology and habitat preferences (for example altitude), are found between different populations. Plants from the W Zerawshan

range are notable for their upwardly directed inflated spurs and long-acuminate outer petals.

Natural hybrids with *C. maracandica* and *C. popovii* are known.

Lax-growing and small-flowered, it is not among the more attractive of this group but is still rather common in cultivation. One form has flowers so deeply coloured that they appear almost black while another has pale grayish-lilac flowers. No doubt any corydalis-fan will be able to find a form to his fancy.

It caused excitement in Britain in the 1880s when introduced by A. Regel of St. Petersburg.

4. *C. maracandica* Michajlova in Novosti Sist. Vyssh. Rast. 24: 100 (1987). Type: Uzbekistan, Mt Zerawshan, Tachta Karacza S Samarkand, 13.4.1971, *Kamelin, Michajlova, Mischenkova & Solovjev* 210 (LE, holo).
C. maracandica var. *diffusa* Michajlova in Novosti Sist. Vyssh. Rast. 24: 103 (1987). Type: Uzbekistan, Tachta Karacza, 14.4.1971, *Kamelin et al.* 230 (LE, holo).

DESCRIPTION. Similar to *C. ledebouriana* vegetatively. *Stems* 6-15 cm long above the leaves. *Leaves* bi- to tri-ternate (very rarely simply ternate) with very unequal lobules. *Racemes* rather lax, 3-14-flowered. *Bracts* obovate-acute, longer than the short erect pedicels which are 2-6(-12) mm long. *Sepals* minute. *Corolla* pale yellow, often suffused with reddish purple, especially towards the end of anthesis but pure pale pink forms are also found; outer petals obtuse to acute, more broadly winged than in *C. ledebouriana*; inner petals 11-13 mm long. *Spur* rather broad, slightly recurved at apex, 10-12 mm long; nectary fitting into the recurved apex, almost as long as the spur. *Fruit* about 12 x 4 mm with a 4-5 mm long style. *Seeds* almost 3 mm in diameter. 2n=32. Self-incompatible. Fig. 36b; Pl. 64, 65.

DISTRIBUTION. Tadjikstan, W Zerawshan range (several collections, GB, LE, K, P, S). A collection by S. Husak, (35-55 km SW Alma Ata', herb. Graz) is probably mislabelled, as Husak also collected on Mt Amankutan during the same expedition. '*Platanus-Acer* woods in deep clay/leaf mould soil', (1000-)1500-2500 m. Map 23.

This has been referred to as a yellow form of *C. ledebouriana* and was actually diagnosed as such in the type description. However, recently a pink form

Fig. 36. a, *Corydalis rutifolia* (cult. from KEW, Cyprus, summit of Mt Tripylos); **b**, *C. maracandica* (cult. Mikulastik, locus classicus); **c, d**, *C. ledebouriana* (c, cult. Halda 9209124, Tadjikistan, Hissar Range, 3800 m; d, cult. Seisums, Tadjikistan, N Dushanbe, Varzob Pass); **e**, *C. uniflora* (cult. J. Persson 85-14, Crete); **f**, *C. macrocentra* (cult. Seisums, Tadjikistan, N Dushanbe, between Luchob and Varzob rivers); **g**, *C. sewerzowii* (cult. Seisums, N Tadjikistan, Mogul Tou hills, Mt Spa); **h**, *C. popovii* (cult. Ruksans, Tadjikistan, Hissar Range, Shaglau); **i**, *C. darwasica* (cult. from E. Pasche 87, *sine coll.*, Uzbekistan, Çhimgan, 2500 m); **j**, *C. afghanica* subsp. *elegans* (cult. type)

has been discovered. It is still readily distinguished from its sister-species by the different spur and nectary; no intermediates are known. In the type locality it is found at higher altitudes than *C. ledebouriana* but hybridises with it in zones of overlap, creating a beautiful and varied hybrid swarm.

Recently introduced to cultivation. In 1989 it was awarded a Preliminary Commendation (P.C.) when shown by Norman Stevens at the Royal Horticultural Society.

5. *C. popovii* Nevski ex Popov in Trudy Sredne-Aziatsk. Gosud. Univ. ser. 8b, Bot. 17: 87 (1934). Type: N Tadjikistan, Hissar range, Kuhitang, *Nevski* (LE).

DESCRIPTION. *Stems* 8-15 cm (-25 cm in cult.), erect. *Leaves* close to the ground, usually glaucous,

bi- to triternate, sessile; leaf-lobes obovate to lanceolate, with the terminal lobes much larger, usually acute. *Racemes* 2-7-flowered, long and lax, rising high above the leaves, basipetally developing. *Pedicels* erect in flower, erect to patent in fruit, (3-)5-10(-25) mm long. *Sepals* minute. *Corolla* medium to large, (30-)40-45(-50) mm long, pale pink to purplish pink (rarely white) with dark purple apical parts; outer petals with apices laterally compressed, truncate in profile, but with a distinct mucro; inner petals 14-16(-18) mm long, with a broad conspicuous triangular notch. *Spur* 18-30(-34) mm long, straight for most of its length, but often strongly curved, or almost coiled, at apex. *Fruit* ovate-elliptic, 18-28 x 5-6 mm, including a short beak and a 2 mm long style. *Seeds* 10-20, rather small, 1.75-2 mm, smooth, with a small elaiosome similar to a fur cap. 2n=32. Self-incompatible. Fig. 36h; Pl. 69.

61
62
64

63
65

Plate 61. *Corydalis blanda* subsp. *blanda*
Plate 62. *Corydalis diphylla* subsp. *occidentalis*
Plate 63. *Corydalis diphylla* subsp. *murreana*
Plate 64. *Corydalis maracandica*, from the Amankhutan Valley
Plate 65. *Corydalis maracandica*

66

67

69

70

71

68

Plate 66. *Corydalis ledebouriana*, in the Chimgan Valley, Tien Shan
Plate 67. *Corydalis darwasica*
Plate 68. *Corydalis darwasica*, close up of flower
Plate 69. *Corydalis popovii*
Plate 70. *Corydalis macrocentra*
Plate 71. *Corydalis sewerzowii*

DISTRIBUTION. Western Pamir-Alai (W Tadjikistan, SE Turkmenistan, SE Uzbekistan), 600-1500(-1900) m, on clayey slopes. Map 24.

The flowers have a very peculiar odour; a nauseous heavy perfume with an additional component of manure and, unlike all other species of *Corydalis*, it flowers from the top of the raceme downwards. It is also unique in the section in its many-seeded fruits.

Corydalis popovii is usually found growing at lower altitudes than *C. ledebouriana* but hybridises with it where the two overlap in the wild. Due to the rather high fertility of the hybrids, extensive introgression occurs in some places north of Dushanbe, creating a whole spectrum of forms, including *popovii*-type flowers with short nectaries and upwardly curved spurs and *ledebouriana*-type flowers with pink spurs and pale fronts.

The most striking species in the group and one of the largest flowered in the entire genus. The fascinating flowers, combined with a sturdy growth, makes it qualify for a selected spot in the alpine-house where it is trouble-free and long-lived. Although a fairly uniform species, one collection from the Susistan Range in Tadjikistan stands out as being particularly compact with a pure white spur.

It was awarded a P.C. in 1979 and an A.M. in 1983, both times exhibited at the Royal Horticultural Society by the Royal Botanic Gardens Kew.

6. C. sewerzowii Regel in Bull. Soc. Imp. Naturalistes Moscov. 63: 252 (1870). Type: SE Kazakhstan, Turlan in Karatau, 900 m, *Sewerzow* (LE). Note: several different spellings of the specific name occur, the original being *sewerzowi*.

DESCRIPTION. *Stems* ascending to erect, often several from each tuber, 5-10(-15) cm. *Leaves* glaucous, bi- to triternate with entire to shallowly incised leaflets; lobes obovate to broadly lanceolate, acute or obtuse. *Racemes* erect, conspicuous, 4-10-flowered, rather dense. *Bracts* obovate, entire, 10-15 mm long, longer than the pedicels. *Pedicels* 5-10(-15) mm long, erecto-patent in flower, erect or rarely slightly recurved in fruit. *Sepals* minute or up to 1 mm. *Corolla* golden yellow, rather straight, with the spur directed downwards and the corolla mouth upwards; outer petals subacute to obtuse at apex, with a distinct rim, ecristate. *Inner petals* 13-15 mm. *Spur* 23-30 mm long, often flushed brownish red, straight but recurved at apex. *Stigma* longer than broad, with long apical and small lateral papillae. *Capsule* narrowly ovate-elliptic, 15-27 x 4-7 mm including a beak 4-7 mm and a 3-4 mm long style. *Seeds* 3-7, 3 x 2.5 mm, colliculate, with a small cap-like elaiosome. 2n=16. Self-incompatible. Fig. 36g; Pl. 71.

DISTRIBUTION. SE Kazakhstan (Chimkent area); NW Tadjikistan, E Uzbekistan.'Steep banks, loess-covered hills, foot of rocks, clayey slopes, mountain foothills, semideserts (Fl. USSR)', 500-1700 m. Map 26.

A conspicuous species with its dense racemes of almost vertically held flowers. The flower shows a superficial similarity to *C. aitchisonii* but the short pedicels and the cap-like elaiosome suggest a more distant relationship to that species.

The one form that we grow was collected at Mogul Tou in N Tadjikistan and cannot be too highly prized. it has a compact habit with huge, vibrantly golden flowers in dense racemes just over-topping the intensely glaucous foliage.

It was first introduced to cultivation in 1880 by Dr. A. Regel who collected in the Angren Mountains in E Uzbekistan. In the 1880s it was repeatedly written up in British horticultural magazines but seems to have vanished from cultivation before 1890.

7. C. darwasica Regel ex. Prain in J. As. Soc. Bengal. 65: 20 (1896). Type: Tadjikistan, Darwaz, Tevildara, 1500-1850 m, 11.3.1883, *Regel* (BM; C; E; Graz; K; LE; P, S).

DESCRIPTION. *Plant* rather small, firm and erect, (2.5-)4-6(-10) cm (to 18 in cult.). *Leaves* ternate, primary leaflets pinnate, secondary leaflets sub-pinnatisect to deeply 3-6-fid with oblanceolate to elliptic, overlapping very glaucous lobes. *Racemes* dense, 4-10 (-13)-flowered. *Pedicels* stout, 10-15(20) mm long, reflexed in fruit. *Sepals* about 2 mm, subentire. *Corolla* white to cream, or with a pinkish suffusion, and with the limb of the reflexed part of the lower petal with a contrasting dark purple blotch; outer petals with rather broad limbs, slightly emarginate; upper petal often with a narrow dorsal rim towards the apex; inner petals 10 mm. *Spur* 10-12 mm long. *Fruit* ovoid, 12-15 x 5 mm, with a 4-5 mm long style. *Seeds* (2.5-)3 mm. 2n=16 (erroneously recorded as 2n=32 by Lidén 1986). Self-incompatible. Fig. 36i; Pl. 67, 68.

DISTRIBUTION. NE Uzbekistan, SE Kazakhstan: W Tienshan, Pamir-Alai, Tashkent area. 1000-3200 m, 'marble and granite scree'. Map 24.

The dainty flowers together with the much dissected, glaucous foliage give this species a decorative appearance. It was introduced into cultivation quite recently but is now firmly established. In 1987 it was awarded a Preliminary Commendation (P.C.) when exhibited by the Royal Botanic Gardens Kew.

Series *Elegantes* Lidén

Willdenowia 26:30 (1996). Type species: *C. afghanica* Gilli.

An exclusive group of three Afghan species with very elegant white, broad-lipped, flowers borne in lax racemes. The foliage is much-divided, usually with the median ultimate leaf-lobes much larger than the lateral ones.

8. *C. griffithii* Boiss., Diagn. ser. 2, I: 15 (1853). Type: Afghanistan/Pakistan: Bharawul, Nuristan, Mt Sikaram, *Griffith* 1417 (CAL; K).

DESCRIPTION. *Stems* 2-10 cm above the leaves. *Leaves* rather fleshy, sessile to shortly stalked (-14 mm), bi- to triternate to sub-pinnatisect; leaflets entire to deeply ternatisect, very unequal, rounded. *Racemes* short, 4-10-flowered, elongating in fruit. *Bracts* small, rounded-obovate, obtuse, shorter than pedicels. *Pedicels* 5-10(-20 in cult.) mm long, reflexed in fruit and elongating to 10-20(-30) mm long. *Sepals* less than 0.5 mm. *Corolla* pale pink to white, darker towards the apex; outer petals obtuse to slightly emarginate at apex, not or very narrowly crested; inner petals 8-9 mm long. *Spur* 10-14 mm long, rather stout, with broad base, more or less upwardly directed, sometimes with recurved apex. *Fruit* elliptic, 6-10 x 4 mm, with or without a short beak, and with a style 2-3 mm long. *Seeds* about 2.5 mm with broad spreading elaiosome. Fig. 37d.

DISTRIBUTION. Pakistan/Afghanistan, Sikaram range, E Hindu Kush; Chitral. Limestone. (1000) 2000-4200 m. Map 25.

A rather variable species. Plants from the Sikaram-range are smaller with less divided leaves, smaller flowers and few-seeded fruits. In the northern populations the outer petals are broader and slightly emarginate with a mucro in the sinus and may carry a narrow dorsal rim. *C. griffithi* grows together with *C. diphylla* in some localities in Chitral.

One of the rarest species in cultivation. As far as we know, only represented by one clone that came as an unidentified tuber with *Lilium polyphyllum* from the Hedge & Wendelbo Afghanistan Expedition in 1969. It has been easy to grow and has now divided into several plants.

9. *C. podlechii* Lidén in Willdenowia 26:30 (1996). Type: Afghanistan, Laghman: Alishang valley, Manangor in Darrah-i-Manangor, W Dawlatshah, 2060 m, 25.3.1971, *Podlech* 17630 (Herb. Podlech, holo).

DESCRIPTION. *Leaves* sessile, very rarely with a petiole up to 25 mm, triternate with long petiolules; leaflets entire to deeply ternatisect, the median divisions always much larger than the lateral ones; lobes rounded-obtuse, obovate. *Racemes* 7-9-flowered, lax. *Bracts* rhombic to ovate, entire to slightly crenulate, rarely 3-cleft, 7-10 mm long, enlarging to 13-17 mm long, in fruit. *Pedicels* 5-10 mm long in flower, elongating to 10-25(-40) mm long and reflexed in fruit. *Corolla* similar to that of *C. afghanica*; inner petals 12-13 mm, very narrow with comparatively longer claw. *Spur* strongly curved upwards, about 25 mm. *Fruit* linear-oblong, 18-26 mm long (including a narrow seedless portion 3-5 mm), with a 4-5 mm long style. *Seeds* 6-11, faintly reticulate, 3.5 mm. Fig. 37c.

DISTRIBUTION. E Afghanistan; prov. Laghman and Panjshir. 1400-1900 m. Map 25.

Similar to *CC. afghanica* and *griffithii* but fruit very different and corolla strongly curved. Probably not in cultivation. Previously recorded as *C. afghanica*.

10. *C. afghanica* Gilli in Repert. Spec. nov. Regni veg. 57: 99 (1955). Type: Afghanistan, 'W-hange des Scher Darwasah bei Kabul', 1840 m, 31.3.1950 *Gilli* 877 (not seen).

DESCRIPTION. Similar to *C. griffithii* but: *Leaves* usually more divided. *Racemes* very lax, 2-10(-14)-flowered. *Pedicels* 15-25 mm long in flower, 20-60 mm long in fruit, much longer than the rather small

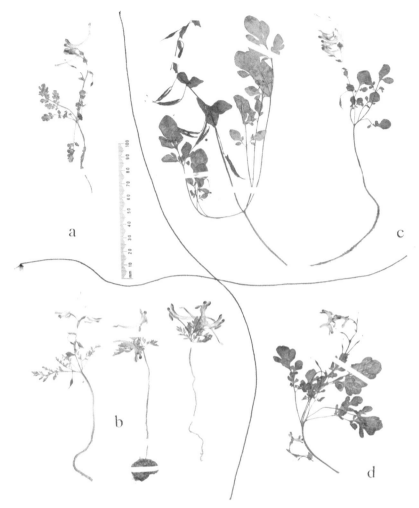

Fig. 37. a, *Corydalis afghanica* subsp. *afghanica* (Wendelbo 2916, Afghanistan, Kabul, Sher Darwasah, GB); **b**, *C. afghanica* subsp. *tenuis* (type); **c**, *C. podlechii* (type); **d**, *C. griffithii* (Wendelbo 895b, E Afghanistan, Sikaram Range)

rounded bracts. *Sepals* up to 1 mm. *Corolla* white; outer petals emarginate at apex with rather broad spreading margins; *inner petals* 13-14 mm. *Spur* (15-) 20-30 mm. *Capsule* broadly elliptic, 10-15 x 5-6 mm with 4-6 mm long style. *Seeds* 2. 5 mm with a broad spreading elaiosome.

Distinguished from *C. griffithii* by the larger flowers, from *C. podlechii* by the ovate to elliptic fruit, and from both by the long pedicels. Three vicariant subspecies can be distinguished.

10a. subsp. *tenuis* **Lidén** in Willldenowia 26:31 (1996). Type: Afghanistan, Zabul: Qalaat-i-Ghilzai, 'W-hange des Passes an der Straße nach Shenkay,

2000-2200 m, 10.4.1970, *Podlech* 20088 (Herb. Podlech, holo).

DESCRIPTION. *Tubers* small in specimens seen. *Leaflets* pinnatisect into several small narrowly lanceolate lobules, very glaucous. *Racemes* 2-6-flowered. *Spur* of upper petal 22-30 mm. Fig. 37b.

DISTRIBUTION. E Afghanistan: known from two localities in the Zabul province S of Kabul. 2000-2200 m. Map 25.

10b. subsp. *afghanica*
C. griffithii sensu Wendelbo, (1974), *pro parte*.

DESCRIPTION. Rather similar to a large-flowered *C. griffithii. Leaves* with median primary leaflet triangular in outline, sub-bipinnate with ultimate leaflets cut into overlapping lobules. *Racemes* 2-9-flowered. *Corolla* sometimes with a pinkish suffusion. *Spur* of upper petal 15-25 mm long. Fig. 37a.

DISTRIBUTION. E Afghanistan: Kabul area. (1200)1700-2400(-3000) m, 'base of sandy hornblende-slate boulders.' Map 25.

10c. subsp. *elegans* **Lidén** in Willdenowia 26:31 (1996). Type: Afghanistan: Tob Darreh, 3 km SW Charikar, 24.8.1969, *Wendelbo 7369* (GB, holo).

DESCRIPTION. *Leaves* with median primary leaflet ovate-oblong, pinnate, with ternatisect secondary leaflets which are cut into several overlapping lobules, very unequal in size. *Racemes* 6-10(-14)-flowered. *Corolla* pure white. *Spur* of upper petal 23-26 mm long. 2n=32. Self-incompatible. Fig. 36j; Pl. 72.

DISTRIBUTION. CE Afghanistan: Salang pass area. Map 25.

An extremely graceful plant with beautifully curved, long-spurred flowers and a distinct, finely cut, glaucous and subordinate foliage. The flowers open in the usual horizontal position but after a while the pedicels twist to let the flowers face the sky.

Today's cultivated stock is the seed offspring from two tubers introduced by Hedge & Wendelbo from Afghanistan in 1969. Despite a long period of negligence the original tubers still survive.

NOTE. *C. griffithii* subsp. *salangensis* Wendelbo, Fl. Iranica 110: 16 (1974), described from the Salang Pass (2700-3300 m, 30. 6. 1965, *Rechinger* 31547 (Graz; L; W)), is habitually intermediate between *C. darwasica* and *C. afghanica* but differs from both in the narrow leaf-lobes. The type collection is somewhat heterogeneous and possibly represents a hybrid swarm with *C. afghanica* involved.

Series Macrocentra Popov ex Lidén

Willdenowia 26:30 (1996). Type species: *C. macrocentra* Regel.

11. *C. macrocentra* Regel in Acta Horti Petrop. 8: 694 (1884). Type: Tadjikistan, Darwaz, Diwalai above Kulab, 900-1200 m, 26.3.1883, *Regel* (BM; K; LE, S).

DESCRIPTION. *Tuber* often very large (up to 10 cm), with a lot of fragments from previous years. *Stems* short, 4-10 cm, with one to several axillary branches or racemes; glabrous or usually with inflorescence axis, petioles, petiolules and fruit papillose-scabrid by whitish papillate ridges. *Leaves* glaucous, rather fleshy, ternate, sessile; sometimes with a third leaf above the two opposite ones; leaflets bipinnate with dark red acute tips to the cuneate-oblong lobules. *Racemes* 2-6-flowered, usually more than one, slightly overtopping the leaves. *Bracts* crispate-undulate, apically divided into acute lobes. *Pedicels* longer than the bracts, erecto-patent, 12-20(-25) mm long, strongly recurved in fruit. *Sepals* whitish, 1-1.5 mm, lacerate-dentate. *Corolla* yellow with the spur flushed with reddish brown (corolla pinkish according to 'FL. USSR'); *upper petal* acute, with prominent auricles at apex; inner petals 13-14 mm, with very low dorsal crests. *Spur* very slender and tapering, 24-30 mm long, straight, or usually curved upwards, especially in bud. *Stigma* broader than long. *Fruit* oblong, 20-28 x 3-4 mm, torulose, tapering to a flattened beak, including a 6-7 mm long style. *Seed* 1-4, smooth, 3 mm long, with a dense, cap-shaped elaiosome. 2n=16. Fig. 36f; Pl. 70.

DISTRIBUTION. Tadjikistan and NC Afghanistan: rare and scattered. 700-1000(-1600?) m, sandy screes on dry hills.

Corydalis macrocentra is unique in the section with its divided bracts, branched stems, peculiar front to the upper petal, as well as the broad stigma. Due to the presence of axillary branches it has a longer flowering season than most other species. Unlike most species of the section it is found at rather lower altitudes with a preference for sandy habitats.

A superb species that remains compact in cultivation. The long-spurred flowers are bronzed in bud, golden when opened and, again, attain a bronze hue with age. The foliage is blue-green and finely cut and provides the perfect contrast to the flowers.

It is rare in cultivation as well as in nature. As it is now produced from seed in the Baltic countries there is no reason to acquire plants dug from the wild!

Series Leonticoides

12. C. *aitchisonii* Popov in Komarov (ed.), Fl. USSR 7: 750 (1937). Type: NW Afghanistan: Badghys, Paropamissus, *Aitchison* (BM; K; LE).

DESCRIPTION. *Stems* slender, weak, ascending, (5)10-15(-20) cm. *Leaves* with lateral primary *leaflets* entire; median leaflet entire or ternately divided with ovate-oblong segments. *Racemes* rather lax, 2-5(-7)-flowered. *Bracts* large, oblong-obovate, 10-30 mm long. *Pedicels* 10-45 mm long in flower, becoming slightly arcuate in fruit. *Corolla* with outer petals with a distinct marginal rim. *Spur* long, tapering, slightly sigmoidally curved to almost straight, sometimes coiled at apex. *Stigma* rectangular with large apical papillae and small lateral papillae. *Fruit* 12-18 x 5-6 mm with a 5 mm long style. *Seeds* 1-5, 2-2.5 mm with broad spreading elaiosome.

12a. subsp. *aitchisonii*

C. sewerzowii var. *simplicifolia* Fedde in Repert Sp. nov. Regni veg. 19:224 (1923). Type: Turkmenistan, mountain close to Ashkabad, 900 m, 23.3.1897, *Litwinov* 480 (E).
C. nevskii Popov, in Komarov (ed.), Fl. USSR 7: 750 (1937). Type: N Tadjikistan, Alai Mt, Kamusch, 24.4.1913, *Dessjatova* 1660 (LE). Note: in Fl. USSR, *C. nevskii* was distinguished by its 2-flowered raceme; however, the type collection includes plants with up to 5 flowers!

DESCRIPTION. *Corolla* lemon yellow to golden yellow, often streaked with greenish or brownish veins, sometimes with a purplish brown lower petal, very delicate with a long and slender tapering spur, 22-35 mm long; outer petals acute; inner petals c. 14 mm long. Fig. 38m; Fig. 75.

DISTRIBUTION. Turkmenistan (Kopet Dagh, Badghys), Tadjikistan, SE Uzbekistan, SW Kirgizia, NE Iran, N and NW Afghanistan. 'Clayey and stony slopes, lower mountain zone.' Map 26.

This species is similar to *C. sewerzowii* in its long-spurred yellow corolla but is different in the slender habit, less divided leaves, large bracts and the long-stalked acute flowers with very thin spurs; in extreme cases this is longer than in any other species in the genus. Rather variable: some plants from Alai are more robust with flowers with apical blackish markings and should perhaps be formally distinguished (described as *C. nevskii* Popov, see map 26).
Despite being a beautiful plant in its native hills, the forms that we have grown are particularly prone to etiolation and have never developed satisfactory.

It is probably best grown in a bulb-frame, and delayed by deep planting and a late start to watering.
So far it has only been grown by specialists. Awarded a Preliminary Commendation (P.C). in 1988 and an Award of Merit (A.M.) in 1989 as *C. nevskii*, when exhibited by the Royal Botanic Gardens Kew.

12b. subsp. *kamelinii* (Kurbanov) Lidén in Willdenowia 26:31 (1996); *C. kamelinii* Kurbanov in Bot. Zhurn. (Moscow & Leningrad) 70: 20 (1985). Type: Turkmenistan, Kjurendag, Kizilarvat, 28.3.1984, *Kamelin & Kurbanov* (LE).

DESCRIPTION. *Corolla* deep purple with darker keels; outer petals subobtuse, mucronulate, more broadly winged than in subsp. *aitchisonii*; inner petals 12-13 mm. *Spur* 24-27 mm long.

DISTRIBUTION. Endemic to W Turkmenistan (Kjurendag). Map 26.

Differs from subsp. *aitchisonii* by the deep pink, usually somewhat more broadly winged, corolla. It inhabits the low, barren hills of Kjurendag, an outlier of the western Kopet-Dagh. It has not, to date, been introduced into cultivation.

13. *C. chionophila* Czerniak. in Repert. Spec. nov. Regni veg. 26: 268 (1930); '*C. chionophylla*' sphalm., hort. litt. Type: Turkmenistan, Kopet Dagh: Tschapan-Dagh, 9.6.1924, *Czerniakowskaya* 149 (LE, holo).

DESCRIPTION. *Leaves* glaucous, entire, or usually once to twice ternately divided. Corolla pale pink (yellow in subsp. *firouzii*), with spur less than 20 mm long; outer petals with dark keels. *Stigma* about as broad as long with equally sized, prominent papillae.

Three vicariant subspecies are distinguished here but the subsp. *chionophila* may possibly be heterogeneous in relation to the other two.

1. Corolla yellow; leaves biternate, or ternate with terminal leaflet again ternate **13b subsp.** *firouzii*
1. Corolla pale pink; leaves usually less divided **2**

2. Spur of upper petal c. 10 mm long; leaves entire to ternate with entire leaflets **13c subsp.** *parviflora*
2. Spur of upper petal 15-20 mm long; leaves ternate to biternate **13a subsp.** *chionophila*

13a. subsp. *chionophila*

DESCRIPTION. *Stems* ascending, 5-15 cm, slender. *Leaves* glaucous, ternately divided with entire to deeply 2-cleft leaflets, rarely biternate; ultimate lobes broadly obovate. *Racemes* 3-10(-14)-flowered. *Bracts* obovate, rather large. *Pedicels* equal or shorter than the bracts, 10-20(-30) mm long, recurved in fruit. *Corolla* pale pink, rarely white; outer petals with a distinct spreading margin, rounded-obtuse at apex; inner petals 10-11 mm long. *Spur* (13-)15-20 mm long, sigmoidally curved, tapering towards the apex. *Capsule* ovate to elliptic, 15-19 x 5-6 mm. *Seeds* 4-8, about 2.5 mm with broad spreading elaiosome. 2n=16. Self-incompatible. Fig. 38i, j; Pl. 74.

DISTRIBUTION. Kopet Dagh (Turkmenistan), NE Iran, W Afghanistan, 600-2900 m. 'Limestone cliffs, forests 'stony and clayey slopes of subalpine zone (Fl. USSR).' Map 27.

This subspecies is variable in the degree of leaf-division and in the length of the spur. The largest flowered forms are found in W Afghanistan, and the smallest in Turkmenistan.

Like *C. aitchisonii,* this has proved to be a leggy, pale disappointment in the alpine-house. Some tubers were therefore planted deeply in bulb-frames and these have produced lovely, compact specimens with dense racemes of larger and better coloured flowers.

First introduced from Iran in 1978 by Per Wendelbo and later by Czech and Baltic collectors from Turkmenistan. It is now well established in specialists collections.

13b. subsp. *firouzii* **(Wendelbo) Lidén** in Willdenowia 26:31 (1996); *C. firouzii* Wendelbo in Iran. J. Bot. 1: 61 (1976). Type: Iran, Semnan: Kuh-e-Ghatri, south side, 2200 m, on broad ledges of lime-stone rock near melting snow, 3.5.1974, *Wendelbo, Foroughi, Sanii & Shirdelpur* 11162 (TARI, holo; E, iso; GB, iso; W, iso).

DESCRIPTION. Like subsp. *chionophila* but stouter and low-growing. *Leaves* ternate with terminal leaflet again ternate. *Flowers* sulphur-yellow, turning purplish with age. 2n=16. Self-incompatible. Fig. 38l; Pl. 73; Map 27.

DISTRIBUTION. N Iran; known from two localities in the E Elburz Mts; Kuh-e-Ghatri and Kuh-e-Abr.

Like subsp. *chionophila,* but with more divided leaves and denser, more floriferous, racemes of yellow flowers. Horticulturally a better plant than subsp. *chionophila* because of its more compact habit. Now well established amongst collectors as seedling off-spring from a collection made by Per Wendelbo on Kuh-e-Abr in 1978.

In 1989 it was exhibited by Norman Stevens and awarded a Preliminary Commendation (P.C.).

13c. subsp. *parviflora* **Lidén** in Willdenowia 26:31 (1996). Type: Afghanistan, Baghlan, N side of Salang pass, stony S-facing slopes, *Hedge & Wendelbo* 7548 (GB, holo; E, iso; K, iso).
C. ledebouriana sensu Wendelbo, Fl. Iran. 110:19 (1974), *pro parte*, incl. tab. 19.

DESCRIPTION. *Plant* small, 2-10 cm, glaucous and fleshy. *Leaves* small, often subopposite; lower one entire or ternate with fleshy ovate to obovate segments; upper ternate with usually entire segments. *Racemes* 5-13-flowered. *Bracts* elliptic. *Pedicels* equalling bracts, 10-20 mm long. *Corolla* with outer petals white to pale pink with reddish-purple keels, subacute to subobtuse at apex, narrowly winged; inner petals 8 mm long. *Spur* c. 10 mm long. *Fruit* smaller, seeds fewer than in subsp. *chionophila*. Fig. 38k.

DISTRIBUTION. NE Afghanistan; known only from four collections. Map 27.

14. C. rutifolia (Sm.) DC., Syst. 2: 115 (1821); *Fumaria rutifolia* Sm. in P. F. von Sibthorp & J. E. Smith, Fl. Graec. Prod. 2: 49 (1813). Type: Cyprus, *Sibthorp* (OXF).

DESCRIPTION. *Stems* 3-10(-18) cm, erect. *Leaves* small, very glaucous, usually shortly stalked, ternate to bi-ternate; leaflets broadly obovate usually with a small lobe on each side. *Racemes* 3-11-flowered, dense to rather lax. *Pedicels* 6-16 mm long in fruit (occasionally up to 30mm long in cultivated plants). *Corolla* initially white or pale pink with darker keels, often turning reddish purple after fertilisation or at the end of anthesis; inner petals 10-11 mm long. *Spur* 13-18 mm long, strongly reflexed apically. *Capsule* broadly elliptic 12-16 x 5 mm, 4-8-seeded 2n=16. Self-incompatible. Fig. 36a.

DISTRIBUTION. Endemic to Cyprus; pine-forests and open ground at high altitudes. Map 28.

Fig. 38. a, *Corydalis nariniana* (cult. Prasil, Armenia, near Lake Sewan); **b**, *C. seisumsiana* (cult. type); **c**, *C. verticillaris* subsp. *boissieri* (Wendelbo & Assadi 19297, NW Iran, Azerbaijan, Tabriz to Ahar Pass, 1700 m, GB); **d**, *C. verticillaris* subsp. *verticillaris* (Wendelbo & Assadi 16461, N Iran, Tehran, Arak area, Kuh Barf-Khaneh, 2300-2800 m, GB); **e**, *C. verticillaris* subsp. *parviflora* (type); **f**, *C. oppositifolia* subsp. *oppositifolia* (cult. KPPZ 166, Turkey, Vil. Mardin, Hop Geçidi); **g**, *C. lydica* (cult. type); *C. erdelii* (cult. Wendelbo 41a, Turkey, Vil. Antalya, Yesil Göl Dagh, 1500-1800 m); **i, j**, *C. chionophila* subsp. *chionophila* (i, cult. Wendelbo s.n., N Iran, prov. Gorgan, Khush Yailaq; j, cult. from KEW, *sine coll.*, Turkmenistan, Kopet Dagh, Dushab Mt); **k**, *C. chionophila* subsp. *firouzii* (Wendelbo 11172, N Iran, Semnan, Kuh-e-Abr, 2200 m); **m**, *C. aitchisonii* subsp. *aitchisonii* (Grey-Wilson & Hewer 464, Iran, Khorasan, 25 km NE

Similar to *C. uniflora* but racemes with 3-11 flowers, fruits larger and pedicels longer. Contrary to *C. uniflora*, it is also self-incompatible. In cultivation the two are quite different, with *C. rutifolia* forming a long raceme, rising high above the leaves.

A rather inconspicuous species of limited horticultural value.

15. C. uniflora (Sieber) Nyman, Syll. Fl. Eur.: 185 (1854); *Fumaria uniflora* Sieber, Reise in Kreta 2: 320 (1823); *C. rutifolia* var. *subuniflora* Boiss. & Heldr., Diagn. ser. 1, 8: 11 (1849); *C. rutifolia* subsp. *uniflora* (Sieber) Cullen & P.H.Davis in Notes Roy. Bot. Gard. Edinb. 25: 45 (1963). Type: Crete, Mt Dikhti, *Sieber* (not seen).

DESCRIPTION. *Stems* 2-5 cm, very glaucous. *Leaves* sessile or often shortly stalked, ternate or biternate with ovate-acute leaflets, sometimes with the lateral second-order leaflets very small. *Racemes* 1-4-flowered, very dense. *Bracts* rhombic-ovate, 10-15 mm. Pe*dicels* 3-15 mm long in fruit, rather stout, recurved. *Corolla* pale bluish pink to almost white with darker veins, rarely turning reddish purple after fertilisation; inner petals 9-11 mm long. *Spur* 13-18 mm long, strongly recurved at the very apex. *Fruit* short and broad, 8-11 mm long, with a beak 0-3 mm, and a short style ca. 2 mm. *Seeds* 3-6, (2-)2.5 mm with a large spreading elaiosome. 2n=16. Self-compatible. Fig. 36e.

DISTRIBUTION. Crete, endemic. 1600-2500 m. 'Kleine Lehmhochflächen, häufig an offene Stellen und im Gebüsch ..... in saxosis calc. ad nives deliquescentes'..... 'Felsgerölle'. Flowering from early April until the beginning of July. Map 28.

So far, a downright disappointment in cultivation. The pale muddy flowers are generally over-grown by the foliage when they open and capsules are produced in a few days due to self-fertilisation. Hardly a plant to cultivate!

16-21. *C. oppositifolia* complex

Species 16-19 form a group of vicariant taxa and could be further subdivided or, alternatively, even lumped into a single species. *C. erdelii* stands out on account of its small narrow corolla; *C. nariniana* has a bi-coloured stout corolla with reddish-purple spur and spreading pure white margins; *C. lydica* is also a homogenous taxon, uniting characters of *C. oppositifolia* and *C. erdelii*, and with some unique features; *C. oppositifolia*, is very variable with several recognisable geographical races, but the rather distinctive stigma seems to be an important uniting feature.

16. *C. oppositifolia* DC., Syst. 2: 114 (1821). Type: 'Inter Alep et Mosul', Olivier (P, holo; B, iso).

DESCRIPTION. *Corolla* with outer petals with distinct rim; inner petals 10-13 mm long. *Stigma* ovate with one or two pairs of small lateral geminate papillae. *Spur* straight to sigmoidally curved, 15-20 mm long. *Fruit* elliptic, 15-24 x 5-6 mm. *Seeds* 4-11, 2-2.5 mm with strap-shaped or broadly spreading elaiosome.

16a. subsp. *oppositifolia*

DESCRIPTION. *Leaves* once to almost three times ternate with broadly lanceolate to obovate, acute to obtuse, more or less equally sized leaf-lobes. *Corolla* rather robust. 2n=16. Fig. 38f; Pl. 76, 77.

DISTRIBUTION. Turkey: E Anatolia. 'Near melting snow',1000-2800 m. Map 28.

Generally a rather large-flowered subspecies, being compact and very attractive. The flower colour is mostly a clear pink that deepens to red with age. Some forms open white suffused with pink but they also blush considerably with age. The most deviating form hails from the Kop Dagh near Erzurum in Turkey, and has much divided leaves and very short-spurred flowers.

The subspecies is common in the mountains of Turkey above 1800 m and can be found in rocky places in oak-scrub, at the edge of forests, as well as in screes.

It was awarded a Preliminary Commendation (P.C.) in 1978 when shown at the Royal Horticultural Society by the Royal Botanic Gardens Kew.

16b. subsp. *kurdica* (Cullen & P.H.Davis) Lidén in Notes Roy. Bot. Gard. Edinb. 45: 362 (1989 [1988]); *C. rutifolia* subsp. *kurdica* Cullen & P.H.Davis in Notes Roy. Bot. Gard. Edinb. 25:45 (1963); *Pistolochia kurdica* (Cullen & P.H.Davis) Holub in Folia Geobot. Phytotax. 8: 172 (1973). Type: Turkey, Hakkari: Çilo Dagh, 10 km NW Çilo Tepe, 3300 m, by snow line, *Davis & Polunin, D. 24185* (E, holo).

DESCRIPTION. Like subsp. *oppositifolia* but: *Leaves* bi- to triternate with leaflets irregularly cut into lanceolate acute lobes, usually with the terminal lobe much larger than the lateral.

DISTRIBUTION. Kurdistan: SE Anatolia, W Iran, NE Iraq. High mountains near snowline, 1000-3500 m. Clayey, stony soil. Map 28.

This subspecies is extremely variable in the amount of leaf-division, the size of flowers and length and width of the spur. The flowers are sometimes very narrowly winged, almost as in *C. erdelii*. In the Central Zagros Mountains a few plants transitional to *C. verticillaris* have been recorded and these possibly represent introgression to some degree.

17. *C. lydica* Lidén in Willdenowia 26:32 (1996). Type: Turkey, Anatolia, Boz Dagh, 1700-1800 m. 24.4.1991, *J & K. Persson 91-66* (GB, holo).

DESCRIPTION. *Plant* glaucous with stiff erect *stems* 5-10 cm. *Leaves* ternate with the central leaflet again ternate, lateral leaflets entire or more or less deeply cleft into 2-3 lobes, petiolules short; leaf-lobes broadly elliptic. *Racemes* 8-11-flowered, dense (rather lax in cultivation). *Pedicels* 10-35 mm long, equalling or longer than bracts. *Corolla* creamy white, rarely pinkish purple (or turning pinkish purple with age?), rather broadly winged, obtuse; inner petals 10 mm. *Stigma* broad, squarish, with a single pair of distinct geminate papillae. *Capsules* ovate, 15-20 x 5-7 mm, borne on long recurved pedicels. *Seeds* 6-10, smooth, 2.5 mm, with large elaiosomes. 2n=16. Self-incompatible. Fig. 38g; Pl. 78.

72

73

75

74

76

Plate 72. *Corydalis afghanica* subsp. *elegans*
Plate 73. *Corydalis chionophila* subsp. *firouzii*
Plate 74. *Corydalis chionophila* subsp. *chionophila*
Plate 75. *Corydalis aitchisonii* subsp. *aitichisonii*
Plate 76. *Corydalis oppositifolia* subsp. *oppositifolia*

77

78

79

80

81

82

Plate 77. *Corydalis oppositifolia* subsp. *oppositifolia*
Plate 78. *Corydalis lydica*
Plate 79. *Corydalis seisumsiana*
Plate 80. *Corydalis nariniana*
Plate 81. *Corydalis alpestris*
Plate 82. *Corydalis emanueli* var. *pallidiflora*

DISTRIBUTION. Turkey: mountains of W Anatolia (Kütahya, Izmir); *C. lydica* is known from three localities only. Map 28.

Like *C. nariniana* and *C. erdelii* in the stigma, and *C. oppositifolia* and *C. nariniana* in the distinct margin of the outer petals. The compact growth, the long stiff pedicels and the usually creamy white corolla render it a distinct appearance.

This is indeed a surprising find and a lovely plant. It remains compact under glass and the fat, ivory-white flowers blush to pink in a charming way after a while.

18. *C. erdelii* Zucc. in Abh. Math.-Phys. Cl. Königl. Bayer Akad. Wiss. 3: 251 (1843dd); *C. rutifolia* subsp. *erdelii* (Zucc.) Cullen & P.H.Davis in Notes Roy. Bot. Gard. Edinb. 25: 45 (1963). Type: Lebanon, Mt Lebanon, *Roth & Erdl* (not seen).
Cryptoceras pulchellum Schott in Österr. Bot. Wochenbl. 7: 149 (1857). Type: Turkey, 'in monte Tauro' 1836, *Schott & Kotschy* 15 (S; W).
? *Cryptoceras modestum* Schott in Österr. Bot. Wochenbl. 7: 150 (1857). Type: Turkey, 'in monte Tauro' (not seen).
? *Cryptoceras purpurans* Schott in Österr. Bot. Wochenbl. 7: 150 (1857); *Corydalis 'purp-urascens'* (Schott) Boiss., Fl. Or. 1: 126 (1867). Type: Turkey 'in monte Tauro' (not seen).

DESCRIPTION. *Stems* suberect, 5-10 cm. *Leaves* rather stiff and thick, very glaucous, irregularly bi- to triternate with small lanceolate acute leaf-lobes, the lateral ones usually much smaller. *Racemes* 5-11-flowered, elongate. *Pedicels* 10-15 mm long (or longer in greenhouse-grown plants), strongly reflexed in fruit. *Corolla* 15-20(-22) mm long, lacking a distinct marginal rim at apex of outer petals, pale pink to reddish purple, with a dark purple spur and dark keels to the outer petals, or wholly purple, usually changing to dark purplish red after fertilisation; inner petals 7-9 mm long. *Spur* 9-12(-15) mm long. *Stigma* squarish with one distinct pair of geminate lateral papillae. *Fruit* elliptic, 15-18 mm long. *Seed* 3-10, as in *nariniana* or slightly larger. 2n=16. Self-incompatible. Fig. 38h.

DISTRIBUTION. Turkey: S Anatolia eastwards to 37°E; Mt Libanon, Antilibanon, Djebel Druze. A very similar distribution pattern was noted by K. Persson in the *Colchicum feinbruniae* group. (1992). Stony subalpine to alpine slopes, usually on limestone, 1300-3450 m. Map 28.

A uniform species throughout most of its distributional region. In the NE (Pinarbasi) part of its range rather large-flowered and long-spurred forms can be found and these can be attractive. However, the plant does not have a great deal of horticultural merit.

19. *C. nariniana* Fed. in Not. Syst. Geogr. Inst. Bot. Tphilis 10:60 (1941). Type: Armenia, near Gadis (Yerevan) (LE, holo).
C. alpina Koch in Linnaea 15: 252 (1841), non Gay. Type: (LE).
C. erdelii auct. ross.
C. persica auct. hort.

DESCRIPTION. *Leaves* biternate; leaflets usually again divided with unequally sized elliptic subacute leaf-lobes. *Corolla* robust, distinctly bicoloured with rich carmine or purple spur and blackish-purple narrowly crested keels towards the apices of the outer petals; inner petals and wings of outer petals pure white; rarely white all over; inner petals (9-)10-12 mm long. *Spur* broad, cylindrical, not tapering towards the obtuse apex, 12-18 mm long, straight, recurved at apex. *Stigma* as in *C. erdelii* but much larger. *Capsule* rather small, 11-15 x 5-6 mm. *Seeds* (2-)2.5 mm with broad spreading lobed elaiosome. 2n=16. Self-incompatible. Fig. 38a; Pl. 80.

DISTRIBUTION. Armenia: Yerevan area southwards to Nakhichevan; E Anatolia (Cug pass). Map 28.

Distinguished from *C. erdelii* by its broad robust flowers, the limbs of the outer petals with distinct spreading margins, from *C. oppositifolia* by the form and coloration of the corolla and stigma, and from both by the narrow dorsal crests to the outer petals. It hybridises (possibly) with *C. seisumsiana* in zones of contact (one intermediate plant has been seen!).

It was introduced to cultivation from the Sevan Lake area by Czech collectors in the 1980s as *C. persica* and has persisted. Quite variable in overall flower-size, the best forms having pure white flowers, blackish purple striped in the front third which is abruptly separated from a rich deep carmine spur.

In 1986 it was awarded a Preliminary Commendation (P.C.) when exhibited by Dr J. Cobb as *C. persica*.

20. *C. seisumsiana* Lidén in Willdenowia 26:32 (1996). Type: Nakhichevan, Zangezur range, *A.*

Seisums, cultivated in Gothenburg Botanic Garden (GB, holo).
C. persica auct. Ross.

DESCRIPTION. *Stem* 5-10(-15) cm, suberect. *Leaves* glaucous, bi-(tri-)ternate or sometimes bipinnatisect (i.e. with small lateral primary leaflets); leaflets broadly ovate, incised into broadly obovate partly overlapping lobules that are rounded or mucronate at apex. *Raceme* erect, 5-10-flowered. *Bracts* rather small, rhombic-ovate, entire or rarely slightly divided. *Pedicels* 5-10(-20) mm long. *Flowers* purple to creamy white with darker markings towards the apex, resembling those of *C. darwasica*, due to the blackish purple colouring of the apical part of the lower petal, and the narrow dorsal crests of the outer petals; inner petals 9-10 mm long. *Spur* slender, tapering, 13-20 mm long. *Fruit* ovate-elliptic, 15-19 mm, including a very short beak and a 1 mm long style. *Seeds* 3-8, rather small, c. 2 mm, with a large flat obovate elaiosome. 2n=16. Self-incompatible. Fig. 38b; Pl. 79.

DISTRIBUTION. Armenia: Nakhichevan. S-facing rocky slopes, 1500-2200 m. Map 28.

Closely related to *C. verticillaris* but readily distinguished by the shorter spur, the more unequally cut leaves and the prominent purple blotch on the lower petal. It has the crests of the outer petals in common with *C. nariniana* but is easily told from that species by its more divided leaves, thin spur and the coloration of the lower petal.

This species was introduced to cultivation by Arnis Seisums of Salaspils Botanic Garden in Latvia, from arid, rocky slopes in the Zangezur Range. It is variable in flower-size and colour; some forms are quite attractive. We are growing a short-spurred form with white, purple-blotched petals which turn pink with age, as well as longer-spurred forms with more deeply coloured flowers in well-pronounced, denser racemes. They all remain compact under glass and the finely cut foliage is very ornamental.

21. C. verticillaris DC., Syst. 2: 114 (1821). Type: Iran, Mt Elwind (Kuh-Alwand near Hamadan), *Olivier* (P).

21a. subsp. *verticillaris*
C. persica Cham. & Schltdl. in Linnaea 1: 567 (1826). Type: Gmelin (B (WILLD) 12916). The application of the epithet *persica* has caused a lot of confusion. Wendelbo (1974) used it for *C. verticillaris* subsp. *boissieri*, and in Russian floras it has been used for *C. seisumsiana*. The distribution of *C. nariniana* as *C. persica* among gardeners, has added to the confusion. The type is unfortunately in a poor state, but the shape of the leaves suggests a small-flowered *C. verticillaris*. According to Popov (1937), it was collected in N Iran, Asterabad (Gorgan) province, an area where *C. verticillaris* exists but *C. seisumsiana* and *C. nariniana* are unknown.

C. verticillaris var. *grandiflora* Bornm. & Gauba in Repert. Spec. nov. Regni veg. 39:79 (1935); *C. verticillaris* subsp. *grandiflora* (Bornm. & Gauba) Wendelbo, Fl. Iran. 110: 18 (1974). Type: Iran, Elburz, Karadj, 2600 m, 20.3.1934, *Gauba* (B, holo).

C. verticillaris subsp. *boissieri* sensu Wendelbo in Rechinger, K.H. (ed.), Fl. Iran. 110:19 (1974) *pro parte*, excl. type.

?*C. hyrcana* Wendelbo, Fl. Iran. 110: 14 (1974). Type: Iran, Mazandaran, NW Elburz, in Haraz valley above Siah Bisheh (Zardman), 1000 m, 14.4.1959, *Wendelbo* 127 (GB, holo). Note: Similar to *C. verticillaris* but leaves less divided, and corolla very broadly winged with short coarse spur only 13 mm long. Only collected once (Wendelbo's Azerbaijan citation refers to subsp. *boissieri*) mixed in with 'normal' *verticillaris* plants. An occasional abberation?

DESCRIPTION. *Leaves* ternately divided with sub-bipinnate leaflets with deeply incised leaflets, or sometimes leaves tripinnate; ultimate lobes very small, lanceolate-acute to obovate, sometimes overlapping. *Racemes* 2-8-flowered. *Pedicels* usually longer than the bracts, 10-20 mm long, strongly reflexed in fruit. *Corolla* usually quite large, broadly winged at apex. *Spur* 16-28 mm. *Inner petals* 10-12 mm. *Fruit* broadly elliptic, 15-18 x 5 mm. *Seeds* 3-8, as in *C. erdelii*. Fig. 38d.

Corydalis verticillaris is an elegant species with its long, slender, curved, white to pale pinkish corollas, with their dark purple-tipped keels and, sometimes with a purple spur; the corollas probably turn reddish all over at the end of anthesis.

This lovely plant made a brief appearance in cultivation in the 1930s. It was introduced as seed and plants by E.K. Balls who collected it in the Mt Alvand (Elwend) area south of Hamadan (N Iran) in 1932. The story relates that the tubers had been exposed by ruminating pigs (euphemism for bulb-collectors, perhaps?). Balls also found it in flower at the edge of melting snow in moist rocky granitic soils. He staged a flowering specimen in 1933 which was awarded a Preliminary Commendation (P.C.) by the Royal Horticultural Society and in 1934 it received an Award of Merit (A.M.) when exhibited by Frank Barker. It is beautifully pictured in *Curtis's Botanical Magazine* (tab. 9486), 1937.

The next introduction was by Paul Furse in the late 1960s but this did not make much impression in horticultural literature.

21b. subsp. *boissieri* **(Prain) Wendelbo,** Fl. Iran. 110: 18 (1974) *pro parte*; *C. boissieri* Prain in Bull. Herb. Boissier 7: 172 (1899). Type: Iran: Azarbaijan, near Delima, *Szovitz* 113 (LE).
C. persica sensu Wendelbo in Rechinger, K.H. (ed.) Fl. Iran. 110:14 (1974), *pro parte, non* Cham. & Schltdl.
C. hyrcana Wendelbo in Rechinger, K.H. (ed.) Fl. Iran. 110:14 (1974), *pro parte*, excluding type.

DESCRIPTION. *Plant* very glaucous, 5-10 cm. *Leaves* small, ternately or usually biternately divided with broadly oblanceolate to obovate leaflets. *Racemes* 2-9-flowered. *Pedicels* equalling or longer than the bracts, (5-)10-20 mm long, reflexed in fruit. *Spur* often very strongly curved upwards with recurved apex, 19-24 mm long. Fig. 38c.

DISTRIBUTION. NW Iran: Azerbaijan. 1300-2500 m, stony ground, N-facing stony slopes, ledges of N-facing cliff wall. Map 28.

It is rather variable in the degree of leaf-division, although the leaves are never as much divided as they are in subsp. *verticillaris*.

21c. subsp. *parviflora* **Lidén** in Willdenowia 28:32 (1996). Type: Iran, Kermanshah: Kerend, 16.4.1951, *Sharif* 6554-E (GB).

DESCRIPTION. Like subsp. *verticillaris* but: *Racemes* 7-11-flowered. *Pedicels* 10-15 mm long (to 35 mm long in fruit). *Corolla* very small; inner petals 7-8 mm long. S*pur* 8-9 mm long. *Immature capsules* with 1-2 seeds.

DISTRIBUTION. Iran; Southern Zagros Mountains.

SECTION DACTYLOTUBER

In spite of some heterogeneity regarding stigma characters, the distinctive tuber and stem-structure clearly show that Section *Dactylotuber* is a natural taxon. The section has a wide but scattered distribution from Turkey to NW Canada and southwards to Kashmir, Bhutan and NW Yunnan. Map 29.

Corydalis benecincta is similar to *C. hemidicentra* in the trifoliate leaves with rounded leaflets and Fedde segregated them as Section *Benecinctae*. Despite this the two species are widely different, however. The *C. benecincta*-group (*CC. benecincta, dajingensis, geocarpa*) is well circumscribed and is readily recognised by the peculiar, much-elongating, geocarpic pedicels and by the non-explosive fruits.

CULTIVATION. To date, few species have been tried in cultivation but we think that we are able to give some general advice based on our limited experience. We are growing seven species; *CC. alpestris, arctica, benecincta, conorhiza, emanueli* var. *pallidiflora,* hemidicentra, tianzhuensis but, unfortunately, have lost the blue *C. emanueli*.

Since all the species are of sub- to high alpine or arctic to boreal origin they cannot endure drought and excessive heat at any time.

In pots. With few exceptions, we find this a difficult group to maintain in our climate. Some will survive and flower in the alpine house if treated with extreme care. With small stocks we grow the tubers singularly in rather small clay-pots, plunged in moist sand. The compost is acid (even for species from limestone screes), sharply drained and rather rich in nutrients. We suggest a mix of equal parts peat, well-rotted manure, leaf-mould, sand and grit. The tubers are never really dormant and roots are active throughout the year. We repot in August, starting by carefully separating the dead roots from the living and using a pair of tweezers to clean off the flakes of dead tissue from the tubers. Shallow planting is crucial; the terminal bud should not be deeper than 3 cm below the surface. The pots are then plunged and watered, after which the plunge is kept moist. Some species may produce a leaf in the autumn, but this does not matter. Growth commences in April and by the end of the month the plants should be in flower. By late May they disappear for the season but must be kept slightly moist over the summer.

In the open garden. The only species that we have had enough plants of to try outside is *C. emanueli* var. *pallidiflora*. This seems to be the most vigorous taxon and it has grown well with us. Plants are grown in an open peatwall and in a north-exposed site in the rock-garden. In both situations it has proved to be a sound perennial, even seeding itself around.

Shallow planting is equally important in the open garden and the compost should be the same as that for difficult Asiatic primulas. It is important that the site is extremely well-drained, so that it can be watered frequently through the summer. For the scree species we recommend mixing a third to a half (by volume) of coarse grit into the compost.

If a species does not behave as you wish it to in the alpine house, you might just as well try it in the open garden, rather than suffer the depressing sight under glass. Good luck but please do not hold us responsible for possible losses!

PROPAGATION. A plant that performs well forms an increasing cylinder crowned by several buds. As the tuber disintegrates with age it can be carefully divided but make sure that each fragment is tipped by a bud. You must use some force while undertaking this and the small wounds that result should be dusted with a suitable fungicide. This operation is carried out in August and September.

Seed. Some species, like *CC. alpestris* and *C. emanueli* var. *pallidiflora*, set good amounts of seed. These should be sown fresh in a slightly acid soil. If treated correctly they will germinate the following spring, producing no more than a single, monocot-type cotyledon during the first year. Seedlings should be left in the seed-pot for at least another season. When you repot the seedlings after two or three seasons you will see how shallowly situated the tubers are; follow this indication. Drought will not be tolerated at any time, neither will excessive watering. Seedlings will flower in their third or fourth year of growth.

Corydalis Section Dactylotuber (Rupr.) Popov in Komarov, V.L. (ed.) Fl. USSR 7: 675 (1937);*Capnites* sect. Dactylotuber Rupr., Fl. Cauc: 58 (1869); *Pesgallinaceus* subsect. *Elongatae* Poelln. in Repert. Spec. nov. Regni. veg. 42: 101 (1937). Type species: *C. pauciflora* (Willd.) Pers.

Tuber solid, oblong, simple or often divided below and with one or a few tufts of roots at the end of each lobe. *Growth* sympodial (Ryberg 1960) with the apical meristem forming a flowering stem (in contrast to sections Leonticoides and Radix-cava). *Stems* usually few, with 2-6 leaves, simple or branched; stems and leaves with a rather firm and thickish character, frequently glaucous, sometimes strongly so. *Petioles* sheathing at base; the 1-3 lowermost leaves reduced to sheathing scales. *Bracts* conspicuous, entire or slightly divided.

KEY TO SPECIES

1.	Pedicels erect in fruit	**2**
1.	Pedicels arcuate-recurved in fruit	**15**
2.	Leaves uni- or tri-foliate with rounded to cordate leaflets	**3**
2.	Leaves more divided, with obovate to lanceolate lobes	**5**
3.	Leaves simple	**14. C. ludlowii**
3.	Leaves trifoliate	**4**
4.	Spur 12-18 mm long; peduncles straight in fruit	**13. C. hemidicentra**
4.	Spur c. 7 mm long; peduncles arcuate-recurved in fruit	**15. C. hepaticifolia**
5.	Caucasian species	**6**
5.	Asian and N American species	**8**
6.	Median primary leaflet stalked, lobes acute; sepals large, fimbriate	**4. C. conorhiza**
6.	Median leaflet subsessile, lobes obtuse; sepals usually smaller, shallowly dentate	**7**
7.	Branched scree-plant with slender stem bases; corolla horizontal; spur ± recurved at apex	**1. C. alpestris**
7.	Erect meadow-plant, not or slightly branched; corolla subvertical; spur straight	**2. C. emanueli**

8. Stems erect, not or slightly branched (Siberia, Mongolia, NW America) **9**
8. Stems branched, ascending (China, Tarbagatai, Himalaya) **11**

9. Corolla horizontal (with a right angle between pedicel and lower petal) **10**
9. Corolla vertical (with an acute angle between pedicel and lower petal) **7. C. arctica**

10. Corolla blue, lower petal gibbous but not spurred **6. C. sajanensis**
10. Corolla purple, lower petal with a diminutive spur **5. C. pauciflora**

11. Lower petal 7-8 mm broad **12. C. gyrophylla**
11. Lower petal 3-5 mm broad **12**

12. Corolla horizontal (with a right angle between pedicel and lower petal) (Helanshan) **8. C. alashanica**
12. Corolla vertical (with an acute angle between pedicel and lower petal) **13**

13. Lower petal with a small spur, stigma with six apical papillae (Tarbagatai Mt) **9. C. pseudoalpestris**
13. Lower petal straight or saccate, but not spurred; stigma with four apical papillae **14**

14. Peduncle 4-8 cm long; flowers narrowly crested; spur 10-12 mm long **10.C. hsiaowutaishanensis**
14. Peduncle 1-4 cm long; flowers usually ecristate; spur 6-10 mm long **11. C. tianzhuensis**

15. Leaves pinnate **17. C. geocarpa**
15. Leaves ternately divided **16**

16. Peduncle distinct **15. C. hepaticifolia**
16. Peduncle absent or indistinct **17**

17. Bracts divided, leaflets usually divided **18. C. dajingensis**
17. Most bracts entire, leaflets 3, rounded, entire **16. C. benecincta**

SUBSECTION DACTYLOTUBER

Pedicels erect in fruit. *Fruit* explosively dehiscent (perhaps with the exception of *C. hepaticifolia*).

1. C. alpestris C. A. Mey., Verzeichn. Pfl. Cauc.: 176 (1831); *C. pauciflora* var. *alpestris* (C.A.Mey.) Akinf., Fl. Cauc. Centr.: 55 (1894). Type: Russia, W Caucasus, Elbrus, Mt Jungusché, c. 3000-3500 m, 7.7.18xx, *C. A. Meyer* (LE).

C. nivalis Boiss. & Huet in Boiss., Diagn., ser. 2, 5: 16 (1859); *C. pauciflora* var. *nivalis* (Boiss. & Huet) Boiss., Fl. Or. 1: 130 (1867). Type: NE Turkey, Anatolia, near Gumuschka (Gumushane ?), between Trapbzon and Erzurum, near melting snow, c.2000 m, May 1853, *Huet du Pavillon* (S).

Capnites pallidiflora var. *bayerniana* Rupr., Fl. Cauc.: 58 (1869); *Corydalis pauciflora* var. *bayerniana* (Rupr.) Boiss., Fl. Or. Suppl.: 25 (1888); *C. pallidiflora* var. *bayerniana* (Rupr.) Fedde in Repert. Spec. nov. Regni veg. 44: 106 (1938). Type: Georgia, Chevsuretia, source of Archot, between Roschkioni ad Quiris-zminda, Archotis-mtba, 28.7.1861, *Bayern* (LE).

Corydalis swanetica Krasn. Enum. Pl. Nouv. Swanetiae: 15 (1891). Type: not seen.

C. glareosa Sommier & Levier in Acta Horti Petrop. 13: 27 (1893); *C. alpestris* var. *glareosa* (Sommier & Levier) Fedde in Repert. Spec. nov. Regni veg. 16:195 (1919). Type: Russia, Caucasus, Kuban, above Tjeberdinsky between the Teberda and Do-ut rivers, alpine screes, 2800-3000 m, 2.9.1890, *Sommier & Levier* 58 (LE).

C. calcarea Albov, Prodr. Fl. Colch.: 17 (1895); *C. alpestris* var. *calcarea* (Albov) N.Busch in Acta Horti Tiflis 9, suppl. (Fl. Cauc. crit. 3): 50 (1905). Typ: Georgia, Abchasia, calcareous screes of Mt. Akhalibokh et mt. Kutysh, 2200 m, 1894, *Alboff* 17 (LE).

DESCRIPTION. *Tuber* usually branched into oblong lobes, sometimes much-branched. *Stems* slender and thin at base (creeping through scree and cliffs), branched. *Leaves* 2-3, close to the base, often appearing more numerous due to axillary branches, rounded in outline, ternate with ternatisect to biternatisect leaflets, usually very glaucous; segments oblong-obovate, obtuse. *Racemes* 2-7-flowered with peduncle (1.5-)4-12 cm long. *Lower bracts* often divided. *Pedicels* 4-7 mm long in flower, equalling bracts, 8-12 mm long in fruit. *Corolla* purple to blue, rarely pale yellow, usually ecristate; inner petals 8-10 mm long. *Spur* 10-15 mm long, recurved at tip. *Capsules* pendent on erect pedicels, obovoid, 10-13 x 4 mm; style short style. *Seeds* 9-12. 2n=16. Self-

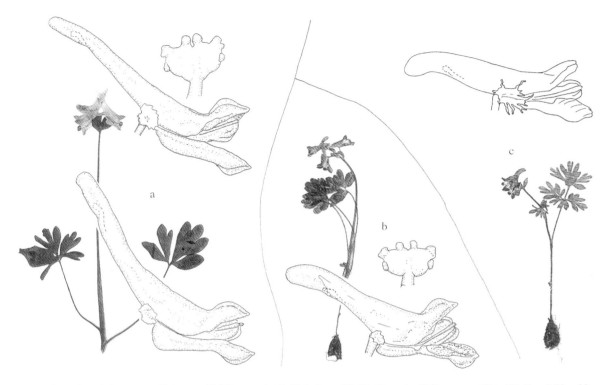

Fig. 39. a, *Corydalis emanueli* (var. *pallidiflora,* cult. R. Holmberg 88-27, Georgia, C Caucasus, Chted Valley, 15 km N Kazbegi, 1600 m); **b**, *C. alpestris* (plant, Grossheim & Schischkin 157, *legit* Kozlovsky, S Georgia, Tbilisi, distr. Gori, Tzchra-Tzkaro near Bakuriani, 2286 m, S; flower, cult. Pasche & Schacht 9102, NE Turkey, Trabzon, 2700 m); **c**, *C. conorhiza* (Desavoulay 802, NW Caucasus, between the Teberda and Kuban rivers, 2440-3050 m, S)

compatible. Fig. 39b; Pl. 81.

DISTRIBUTION. Caucasus Mountains; Turkey (E Anatolia). 'Stony slopes and taluses, rarely in grass plots of the alpine zone, 2500-3300 m.' Map 30.

A very variable species, especially its size and the coloration of flowers and it is perhaps divisible into a number of geographical entities. Plants from Anatolia usually have larger flowers.

Being native to NE Turkey makes this the most readily available species, together with *C. conorhiza.* The two grow in the same areas but *C. conorhiza* prefers peaty short-grass turf, whereas *C. alpestris* is confined to scree and rocks. Surprisingly, *C. alpestris* is the one that best accepts being abducted from its native mountains.

It is quite easy to grow in the alpine house; we are growing plants from Soganli, near Trabzon, Turkey. They have not increased vegetatively but set an annual crop of seed.

Corydalis alpestris is a nice dwarf species; our

plants have rather reduced foliage, only slightly glaucous, and white and blue flowers with a slight flush of purple. New introductions in clearer colours would make a valuable addition to collections.

2. *C. emanueli* C.A.Mey., Verzeichn. Pfl. Cauc.: 176 (1831). Type: Russia, W Caucasus, Elbrus, Mt Jungusché, c. 2300 m, 13.7.18xx, *C. A. Meyer* 261 (LE).

Capnites pallidiflora Rupr., Fl. Cauc.: 58 (1869); *Corydalis pauciflora* var. *pallidiflora* (Rupr.) Trautv. in Acta Horti Petrop. 5: 404 (1877); *C. emanueli* var. *pallidiflora* (Rupr.) Lipsky, Fl. Kauk.: 217 (1899); *C. pallidiflora* (Rupr.) N.Busch in Acta Horti Tiflis 9, suppl. (Fl. Cauc. crit. 3): 52 (1905). Type: S Russia, Dagestan, Tuschetia, Mt Kartiani, c. 3000 m, 9.8.18xx, *Ruprecht* (LE).

C. heteropetala Otschiauri in Bot. Zhurn. (Moscow & Leningrad) 79:93 (1994). Type: Georgia, Chevsuretia, Archoti, upper Assa, near Czimga,

Mt Czimgiskide, 2500 m. (LE).

DESCRIPTION. Similar to *C. alpestris* but: *Plant* less glaucous. *Stems* 10-15 (-20) cm, erect, simple or with a few late branches. *Leaves* 2-4, all towards the base of the stem, biternate, with entire to 2-3-fid segments; lobes narrowly obovate, obtuse or rarely acute. *Scale leaves* 1-3. *Peduncle* 5-12 cm long. *Racemes* dense, 2-5-flowered, much overtopping the leaves. *Pedicels* 4-5 mm long in flower, equalling the bracts. *Sepals* dentate, whitish, 1-3 mm. *Corolla* pale to bright yellow, or sometimes blue to bluish purple, jasmine-fragrant, not or narrowly cristate, vertically held according to most floras but this seems to vary; inner petals 9-11 mm; lower petal sometimes strongly bullate. *Spur* 14-20 mm long, straight. *Fruit* pendent, obovoid, 15-20 x 5 mm. Seeds 10-18. 2n=16. Self-compatible. Fig. 39a; Pl. 82.

DISTRIBUTION. Caucasus Mtns, grassy slopes, meadows, margin of shrub, 1600-3300 m. Map 30.

This species is sometimes confused with *C. alpestris*, due to its obtuse leaf-lobes, but can be distinguished by the erect stem, not or only sparsely branched, the long peduncle, the less glaucous leaves, and the larger flowers and fruits. In addition, its ecology is very different.

This taxon is usually treated as two or even three species, but the variation is reticulate and a division into two species based on flower colour alone would be unnatural. A statement in the 'Flora USSR' that the blue-flowered form is confined to the lower parts of the altitudinal range (2400-2500 m) is incorrect. Our cultivated yellow form (var. *pallidiflora*) was collected at only 1600 m and blue-flowered plants have been collected at both higher and lower altitudes than those indicated in that flora.

We do not know to what degree 'mixed' populations can be found.

This is a gem that is rather easy to grow. In its yellow form it has been the most successful species of the section at Gothenburg and it has been widely distributed by means of seedlings. We hope that it will gain a firm foothold in more general cultivation. It thrives in a cool spot in our rock-garden and is also splendid in the alpine house.

We grew the blue-flowered 'typical' form for a few years but eventually lost it; our material was collected in the Elbrus area, in birch-forest below the Tschschelda glacier, a stout large-flowered plant of the clearest sky-blue, with bright green, thin leaves,

so it was a severe loss.

3. C. conorhiza Ledeb., Fl. Ross. 1: 99 (1842). Type: SE Georgia,'ad limite Guriae in Mt. Gor-Somlia Adschariae, *Nordmann* (LE).

C. macrosepala Rupr., Fl. Cauc.: 61 (1869); *Corydalis macrosepala* (Rupr.) Trautv. in Acta Horti Petrop. 8: 71 (1883). *C. conorhiza* var. *macrosepala* (Rupr.) Boiss., Fl. Or. Suppl.: 26 (1888). Type: Georgia, Chevsuretia, summit of road between Ukanchado and lake Tanies-mtba, c. 3000 m, 21.7.18xx, *Bayern* (not seen).

Capnites ochroleuca Rupr., Fl. Cauc.: 61 (1869); *C. conorhiza* var. *ochroleuca* (Rupr.) Boiss., Fl. Or. Suppl.: 26 (1888); *C. ochroleuca* Radde, Grundz.: 341 (1899), non Koch; *C. conorhiza* var. *ruprechtii* N.Busch in Acta Horti Tiflis 9, suppl (Fl. Cauc. crit. 3: 54 (1913), *nom. illeg.* Type: Russia, Tuschetia, 'in latere Didoènse, supra regionem Zindako', c. 3000 m, 26.7.18xx, (LE).

Capnites (*macrosepala* var.) *araratica* Rupr. Fl Cauc.: 61 (1869), *nom. inval.; Corydalis conorhiza* var. *araratica* (Rupr.) Boiss., Fl. Or. Suppl.: 26 (1888); *C. araratica* Lipsky, Fl. Cauc.: 217 (1899).

C. conorhiza var. *sommieri* Fedde in Repert. Spec. nov. Regni veg. 16: 196 (1919). Type: Swanetia in jugo Latpari between Hippum and Ingur rivers, close to melting snow, 2800 m, 4.8.1890, *Sommier & Levier* 59 (not seen).

C. conorhiza var. *brotherusiorum* (Fedde) Fedde in Repert. Spec. nov. Regni veg. 16: 196 (1919). Type: Caucasus, Ossetia, Mt Brutsabseli by Didi Liachua river, July 1881, *Brotherus* 41 (S).

DESCRIPTION. *Tuber* widened and more or less divided below. *Stems* rather rigid, suberect or procumbent, 5-15 cm with (0-)1(-2) scale-leaves, simple, very rarely with a late branch. *Leaves* 2-3, scattered, not glaucous; leaflets ± deeply sub-biternatisect into acute lobules; middle primary leaflet comparatively long-stalked; uppermost leaf smaller. *Peduncle* usually short, 1.5-6 cm long (the higher figure for Turkish specimens). *Racemes* 2-10-flowered, slightly elongating in fruit. *Bracts* obovate to oblanceolate, entire, or rarely the lowermost 3-fid. *Pedicels* 4-7 mm long. *Sepals* fimbriate-dentate, about 5 mm in diameter. *Corolla* purple, rarely pale yellow, horizontally held; inner petals 9-10 mm long. *Spur* 12-14 mm long, slightly sigmoidally curved. *Fruit* pendent on erect pedicels, oblanceolate, 12-16 x 3-3.5 mm. Seeds 8-16. 2n=16. Self-compatible. Fig. 39c; Pl. 85, 86.

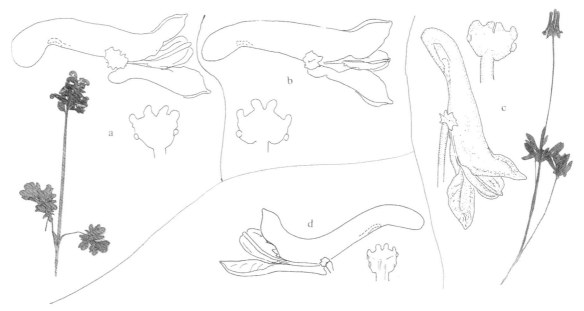

Fig.40. a, *Corydalis pauciflora* (Lisitsyn, Siberia, Altai, Baschkaus river system, 20.5, S); **b**, *C. sajanansis* (Elias 8021, Siberia, Sajan Mts, S); **c**, *C. arctica* (cult. Molau, N Alaska); **d**, *C. alaschanica* (type)

DISTRIBUTION. Caucasus; Turkey (NE Anatolia). 'Alpine meadows, grass plots near snow-patches at 2100-3150 m.' Map 31.

Unmistakable in its green somewhat fleshy leaves with stalked median leaflet, acute leaf-segments and large fimbriate sepals. Individuals with pale yellow flowers may be found together with the more common purple-flowered plants. Plants from Mt Ararat are said to differ in their strongly gibbous lower petal but similar forms are also found in NE Anatolia.

As stated under *C. alpestris*, *C. conorhiza* prefers rather peaty conditions in nature. We have seen it edging the thickets of *Rhododendron caucasicum* at alpine altitudes in the Caucasus, but also in pure mineral soil at the highest elevations. It is quite common there and several attempts have been made to introduce it into cultivation. For some reason it does not perform as well as *C. alpestris* in the alpine house; plants linger and become weaker each year and rarely flowers. Our suggestion is therefore to try it in the open garden the next time it is available. It will probably prefer a really cool spot in the peat-garden together with dwarf rhododendrons and Sino-Himalayan primulas, meconopsis and lilies. The tubers should be shallowly planted! It is not as attractive as *C. alpestris* but there is a wide variation in flower-colour so better forms could be selected.

4. *C. pauciflora* (Willd.) Pers., Syn. 2: 269 (1807). *Fumaria pauciflora* Willd., Sp. Pl. 3: 861 (1800); *F. altaica* Ledeb. in Mem. Acad. Imp. Sci. Saint-Petersb. 5: 551 (1812); *Corydalis altaica* (Ledeb.) Besser in Flora 22: 5 (1834). Type: S Siberia, Altai (B (WILLD) 12920).
Corydalis pauciflora var. aquilegifolia DC., Syst. 2: 116 (1821). Type: S Siberia, Altai, *Patrin*. (P (DC)).

DESCRIPTION. *Tuber* cylindrical, ± covered with old remnants, usually divided below. *Stems* simple, erect, 7-25 cm with 2-3 leaves. *Leaves* ± glaucous below, ternate to biternate; leaflets entire or cut into obovate obtuse lobes, the median leaflet often with a short stalk. *Peduncle* long, (4-)8-15(-18) cm long. *Racemes* dense, 3-10-flowered. *Bracts* 5-10 mm, obovate, rarely lanceolate or shortly stalked. *Pedicels* 4-12 mm long. *Corolla* ± horizontal, purple, conspicuously growing during anthesis, usually with a short distinct crest; inner petals 9-10(-11) mm; lower petal with a small spur. *Spur* apically recurved, often strongly so, 9-14 mm long. Fig. 40a.

DISTRIBUTION. S Siberia: Altai; W Mongolia. 'Moss-lichen or stony tundra in the alpine zone, moraines and banks of mountain streams.' Map 32.

We have no horticultural experience of this species but think that it requires treatment similar to that recommended for *C. conorhiza*.

5. C. sajanensis Peschkova in Bot. Zhurn. (Moscow & Leningrad) 75: 85 (1990). Type: S Siberia, E Sajan Mts near Mondy, 15.6.1953, *Popov & Bardunov* (LE, holo; NS, iso).

DESCRIPTION. *Stems* erect, 7-15 cm in flower (up to 30 cm in fruit), with 2-3(-4) scale-leaves and 2-4 leaves. *Leaves* bi- to triternate with median leaflet stalked (3-7(-12) mm); leaflets entire or cut into ovate obtuse lobes. *Racemes* dense, (3-)5-9(-13)-flowered. *Bracts* ovate, with violet veins. *Corolla* (17-)20-25 mm long, blue to bluish violet, rarely purple (?), with an obtuse spur, straight or usually apically slightly recurved; lower petal saccate at base, but not spurred, apically with a narrow dorsal crest. Fig. 40b.

DISTRIBUTION. S Siberia: Sajan Mts; Central Mongolia. Map 32.

Very similar to *C. pauciflora* but the corolla is usually blue (usually purple in *C. pauciflora*) with more acute outer petals, the lower petal saccate but not spurred. In addition, there are perhaps also minor differences in the stigmas. The two taxa keep distinct on the Siberian side of the border, but the variation found in Mongolia is not yet fully understood and, according to Marina Mikhailova (pers. comm.), the two should be held conspecific.

Probably not in cultivation.

6. C. arctica Popov in Komarov (ed.), Fl. USSR 7: 751 (1937). Type: NE Siberia, Jacutia, between Olenek and lower Lena by Atyrkan river, 3-4.8.1876, *Czekanowski* (LE, holo).
C. pauciflora var. *sibirica* Regel in Bull. Soc. Imp. Naturalistes Moscov. 34:135 (1861). Type: E Siberia, Ajan, *Tilling* 1859: 44 no 29 (LE, S, UPS).
C. pauciflora var. *parviflora* Regel in Bull. Soc. Imp. Naturalistes Moscov. 34: 136 (1861). Type: 'Russisches Amerika', fl. Krich Pak, *Sagoskin* (LE, S; UPS).
C. pauciflora var. *chamissonis* Fedde in Repert. Spec. nov. Regni veg. 16: 48 (1919). Type: Bering Straight, St Lawrence Is, *Chamisso* 1816 (UPS).
C. udokanica Peschkova in Bot. Zhurn. (Moscow & Leningrad) 75: 87 (1990). Type: E Russia, Udokani, upper Neminga river, 1350 m,

26.6.1969, *Malyschev & Petroczenko* 338 (LE, holo).

DESCRIPTION. *Stems* (4-)10-15(-27) cm, erect, simple or with late branches. *Scale-leaves* (1-)2(-3). *Leaves* 2-4, ternate, glaucous; leaflets sessile or very shortly stalked, deeply divided into 3-5 obtuse to acute lanceolate segments, rarely entire in dwarf specimens. *Racemes* 2-7-flowered, dense. *Peduncle* (1.5)3-10(-13) cm long. *Bracts* obovate, ± acute. *Pedicels* erect, 3-5 mm long in flower, 6-16 mm long in fruit. *Corolla* rather straight, vertically held, white, pale blue, pale purple, purplish violet, etc; outer petals acute, often with a short dorsal crest at apex; inner petals usually dark-tipped but with pale dorsal wings, (7-)8-10 mm long; lower petal acute at apex, not gibbous at the very base, but often sub-basally more or less saccate. *Spur* almost straight or slightly recurved at apex, 8-15 mm long. *Fruit* elliptic, 8-15 x 3-4 mm, with style c. 1.5 mm. *Seed* 5-13, smooth, 1.8 x 1.6 mm with very small elaiosome. 2n=16. Fig. 40c.

DISTRIBUTION. Siberia from 93°E eastwards to the Mackenzie district in West Canada, between 55°N and 73°N. 'Blades and shores of seas and rivers'. 0-2000 m. Map 32.

Like the two previous species, but tubers smaller, racemes more few-flowered, spur ± erect, and lower petal not strongly gibbous. Quite variable. The north-western populations have larger flowers and broader stigmas. *C. udokanica* was segregated on the more strongly saccate lower petal, but intermediates occur.

Together with *C. solida*, this is the most widely spread of all species of *Corydalis*.

We are growing some plants originally collected in Alaska. It is remarkably early sprouting, appearing in early January in the alpine house. Probably best in a peat-wall in the open garden.

7. C. alaschanica (Maxim.) Peschkova in Bot. Zhurn. (Moscow & Leningrad) 75: 86 (1990); *C. pauciflora* var. *alaschanica* Maxim., Mongol.: 37 (1889). Type: China, Inner Mongolia, Helanshan *Potanin?* (LE, holo).
C. pauciflora var. *holanschanica* Fedde in Repert. Spec. nov. Regni veg. 22: 221 (1926). Type: Helan-shan.

DESCRIPTION. *Stems* branched, 5-15 cm. *Leaves* green above, strongly glaucous below, ternately divided with shortly stalked median leaflet; leaflets deeply cut into 3-5 broadly obovate obtuse lobes. *Racemes* about 5-flowered. *Bracts* ovate, subacute, 4-5 mm long. *Pedicels* 5-9 mm long. *Sepals* small, 0.5-1 mm, shallowly dentate. *Corolla* purple or blue, horizontally held, with reflexed, rather broad wings, shortly cristate; inner petals 9-11 mm with prominent processions near the joint; lower petal straight or with a distinct narrow pouch at the very base, subacute, with rather narrow claw. *Spur* rather narrowly cylindrical, straight to subsigmoidally curved, 9-11 mm long, with nectary half to two thirds as long. *Stigma* squarish with two pairs of lateral geminate papillae. *Fruit* obovoid, 10-12 x 3 mm. Seeds c.10. Fig. 40d.

DISTRIBUTION. N China: Inner Mongolia and Ningxia (Helan-shan), 2300 to 3100 m. Map 33.

A somewhat isolated species, not closely related to the other Chinese taxa and not in cultivation.

8. *C. pseudoalpestris* Popov, in Komarov, V.L. (ed.) Fl. USSR 7: 677 (1937). Type: Kazakhstan, Tarbagatai Mustau, source of Ulkun-Ulasty, 28.7.1914, *Saposchnikov* (LE).

DESCRIPTION. *Stems* 5-10 cm, with 2-4 long-stalked leaves, branched; petioles long, vaginate. *Leaves* more or less glaucous, rather thick, ternately divided; leaflets sessile or the median one usually shortly stalked, more or less deeply divided into 2-3 lobes which are shallowly 2-3-fid; ultimate lobes obovate to elliptic or oblong, subobtuse to acute. *Racemes* not overtopping leaves, 1-4-flowered, dense. *Peduncles* 2-4 cm long. *Bracts* obovate, obtuse, 4-6 mm. *Pedicels* (2-)4-5 mm long, erect. *Sepals* 1 mm long. *Corolla* '17 mm longa, albida v. coerulescentes, apice azureo-violacea; petalum inferum basi calcarato-dentatum; calcar petali superioris tenue rectum horizontale apice ipsa sursum incurvum, petalo infero 2-plo longius' (Popov). *Stigma* with small geminate lateral papillae and six apical papillae. *Capsule* 10-12 x 4 mm. Seeds c. 10.

DISTRIBUTION. Kazakhstan; NW China (Xinjiang): endemic to Tarbagatai. 'Rock streams and rocks in the alpine zone.' Map 33.

Very similar to *C. tianzhuensis* in vegetative characters (no flowers remained on the type), but

differs, according to Popov, in the long-spurred upper petal, and the small spur-like procession at the base of the lower petal. The area is far removed from that of *C. tianzhuensis*.

Not in cultivation.

9. *C. hsiaowutaishanensis* T.P.Wang in Contr. Inst. Bot. Natl. Acad. Peiping 2: 301 (1934). Type: China, Shanxi: near Tangch'ihsze, above 2000 m, 2.6.1930, 'weedy slope', *Kung, H.-W.* 220 (BEI, holo).

DESCRIPTION. *Tuber* small, 5-10 x 5 mm. *Stems* weak, 4-10 cm, with 1-3 scale leaves. *Leaves* (cauline) 2-3, long-stalked, sheathing at base, with axillary branches, ternately divided, green or glaucous above, strongly glaucous beneath; leaflets sessile, deeply divided into 2-3 obovate segments, which are sometimes again shallowly cut into overlapping lobules. *Racemes* very dense (1-)2-5-flowered, borne on long (3-8 cm) peduncles. *Bracts* 5-8 mm, broadly obovate. *Pedicels* 3-5 mm long, erect in fruit. *Corolla* pale purple, almost vertically held; outer petals acute, narrowly cristate; inner petals 7-8 mm long; lower petal broadly and shallowly saccate. *Spur* straight or slightly curved, 10-12 mm long, with nectary about two thirds as long. *Stigma* with small lateral geminate papillae and four apical papillae. *Capsule* pendent on erect pedicels, obovoid, 8-10 x 3 mm with 1.5 mm long style. *Seeds* 4-10. Fig. 41e.

DISTRIBUTION. China, Shanxi: Wu-tai-shan, Xiao-wu-tai-shan, Pei-tai-shan; Chili (Hubei): Po-chua-shan. 2000-3000 m. Map 33.

Not in cultivation but it really should be looked for. 'Do you want to see my *hsiaowutaishanensis*?' is evidently the perfect phrase for picking up a date at the disco.

10. *C. tianzhuensis* M.S.Yan & C.J.Wang in Bull. Bot. Res. Harbin 9(3): 21 (1989). Type: China, Gansu, Tian-zhu (photo seen).

DESCRIPTION. *Plant* similar to *C. hsiaowutaishanensis* but: *Plant* more compact. *Leaves* thicker with the median leaflet usually shortly stalked, and ultimate lobes often acute at apex; petioles shorter and peduncles 0.5-3 cm long. *Corolla* pale blue to purple (rarely yellow: Tianzhu; SE Qinghai, *Yan & Wang* 1989), usually ecristate (narrowly cristate in some specimens from Nan-shan); inner petals 6-7 mm long.

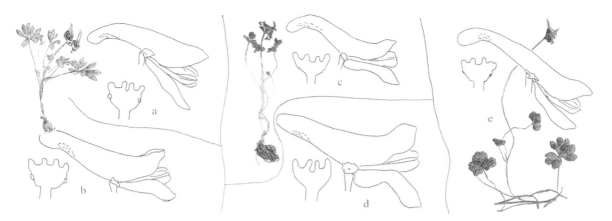

Fig. 41. a, b, *Corydalis tianzhuensis* subsp. *tianzhuensis* (a, Hummel 4452, China, Gansu, Shimen, S; b, Friis-Johansen 2803, Gansu, Nan Shan, Richthofen, 3700 m, S); **c, d,** *C. tianzhuensis* subsp. *bullata* (c, KGB 357, China, NW Yunnan, Beimashan, 4400 m, GB; d, Bowes-Lyon 9024, Bhutan, E); **e,** *C. hsiaowutaishanensis* (Chanet & Serre 497, China, Shanxi, Wutaishan, N peak, P)

Spur 6-10 mm long with nectary reaching at least three quartres of the distance through the spur. *Capsule* pendent, on erect pedicels, obovoid, 8-10 x 3-4 mm with 1.5 mm long style. *Seeds* 6-14, 1.3 mm with small elaiosome, somewhat flattened with slightly convex testa cells.

Two distinct vicariant subspecies are recognised here:

10a. subsp. *tianzhuensis*
C. pauciflora var. latiloba Maxim., Fl. Tangut.: 38 (1889); *C. tangutica* Peschkova in Bot. Zhurn. (Moscow & Leningrad) 75: 87 (1990). Type: China, Qinghai, Amdo (LE).

DESCRIPTION. *Lower petal* slightly saccate. *Spur* straight. *Stigma* nearly always with small but distinct lateral geminate papillae. Fig. 41a, b.

DISTRIBUTION. China: Qinghai, Amdo; Gansu: Schimen, Tian-zhu, Nan-shan (Richthofen); N Sichuan, Dongrergro. 3700-4900 m. Map 33.

10b. subsp. *bullata* Lidén in Willldenowia 26:33 (1996). Type: SE Tibet, Kam, Yang-tse basin, banks of small river Go-rin-chou, 4300 m, 17.5.1901, *Ladigin 50* (LE, holo).
C. alpestris auct.

DESCRIPTION. Differs from subsp. *tianzhuensis* by: *Style* slightly longer and stigma without lateral papillae. *Lower petal* usually strongly gibbous. *Spur*

often more slender and sigmoidally curved. 2n=16. Self-compatible. Fig. 41c, d.

DISTRIBUTION. SE Tibet (Xizang) to Bhutan and NW Yunnan, with an isolated occurrence in Kashmir. 4000-5800 m. Snow-ledges. Map 33.

An inconspicuous species, found by the KGB Expedition in short grass patches beside the late-lying snow at 4500 m at Shu La on the border between Tibet and NW Yunnan. The collection KGB 360 is grown in Gothenburg and treated just as the Caucasian representatives of the section. Unfortunately, it has no horticultural merits. The tiny flowers, which are a clouded sky-blue. are produced early in the season and are completely hidden within the low, green foliage.

11. C. gyrophylla Lidén in Willdenowia 26:33 (1996). Type: China, NW Sichuan, Dege, 4500 m., 18.6.1991, *Yang jin-zen* 91-362 (KUN, holo).

DESCRIPTION. *Tuber* rounded with a crown of scales on top. *Stem* about 10 cm, without or perhaps with ephemeral scale-leaves, with three leaves (on the main stem), all with axillary branches. *Leaves* fleshy and glaucous, especially below, long-stalked with small ovate lamina twice cut into threes; leaflets crowded, subsessile, almost orbicular, entire or slightly lobed. *Peduncle* 3 cm long. *Raceme* corymbose, 2-3-flowered. *Bracts* ovate, 3-4 mm long. *Pedicels* thin, 10 mm long, probably straight in fruit.

Fig. 42. a, *Corydalis gyrophylla* (type); **b**, *C. hepaticifolia* (based on type, with kind permission from Kunming); **c**, *C. ludlowii* (based on type, with kind permission from Kunming)

Sepals 1 mm, shallowly dentate. *Corolla* apparently purple; outer petals without or with very narrow crest, rather broadly winged apically; lower petal with a cornute basal appendage and broad shallow pouch, distally widened into a shallowly emarginate limb 7-8 mm broad; inner petals 6-7 mm long, with short claw. *Spur* straight or slightly curved downwards, gradually attenuate towards the tip; nectary a little more than half as long as the spur. *Stigma* obtriangular like in *C. tianzhuensis* but with two pairs of geminate papillae present. *Fruit* unknown.

Only known from the type collection. Map 33.

A rather isolated species, easily recognised by the comparatively broad outer petals. Not in cultivation.

12. *C. hemidicentra* Hand.-Mazz. in Sitzungsanz. Akad. Wiss. Wien, Math. Nat. 57: 86 (1920). Type: China, Yunnan: Chungtien (Zhongdian), Mt Piepun, 4300-4650 m, 11.8.1914, *Handel-Mazzetti* 4686 (E).

DESCRIPTION. *Tuber* long, cylindrical. *Stems* and leaves often with long slender underground parts; stems with 2-3 scale-leaves at base, branched. *Leaves* trifoliolate with large rounded variegated leaflets, often reddish brown in colour; petioles sheathing. *Peduncle* conspicuous, 3-10 cm long. *Racemes* simple, very condensed, ± umbellate, 3-9-flowered; flowers strongly fragrant. *Bracts* (3-) 5-15 mm, rounded-

obovate, obtuse, small. *Pedicels* 7-30 mm long, stout, erect. *Sepals* 1.5 mm long, dentate. *Corolla* blue to bluish purple with acute, usually conspicuously crested, outer petals; lower petal gibbous; inner petal 10-13 mm long. *Spur* attenuate, straight or often upwardly curved, sometimes slightly recurved at the very apex, 12-18 mm long; nectary two thirds to three quartres as long as the spur. *Stigma* wider than long, with four prominent papillae. *Capsule* pendent on erect pedicels, 7-12 x 3-4.5 mm, obovoid, with style 2-3 mm long, including a very narrow part immediately below the stigma. Seeds 5-10. Self-incompatible. Fig. 43a-c; Pl. 84.

DISTRIBUTION. China: NW Yunnan. Rough alpine screes, usually on limestone. 3500-4900 m. Map 34.

The colour of the leaves varies from a peculiar greyish green to reddish brown, with paler and darker spots and streaks, thus presumably camouflaging the plant from predators. Similar, though less extreme, patterns are found in *C. benecincta* and *C. crassifolia*.

The combination of the strangely coloured, hepatica-like, succulent leaves and the boldly presented, sky-blue flowers is striking. It is a truly one of the most breathtaking of all *Corydalis*. However, we doubt that it will ever be common in cultivation. It has been introduced from Yunnan by the KGB and the ACE expeditions and has flowered in cultivation. During the coming years we will see if it becomes firmly established and amenable to cultivation.

In its native screes, the tuber is seated in a pure mineral-soil; clay, silt, and sand formed by the limestone. The foliage and flowers have to find their way up through a deep loose layer of moving limestone rocks and pebbles. In the same screes one can find *CC. benecincta, calcicola, melanochlora* and *Fritillaria delavayi*.

13. *C. ludlowii* Stearn in F. Ludlow & W. T. Stern, Bull. Brit. Mus. (Nat. Hist.) Bot. 5. Type: SE Tibet, Nambu La, Tongyuk river, Pome, 3650 m, 11.6.1947, plentiful in sandy march, *Ludlow, Sherriff & Elliott* 13881 (BM, holo).

DESCRIPTION. Similar to *C. hemidicentra* but: *Leaves* simple. *Sepals* 1 mm, dentate. *Petals:* outer petals obtuse with straight spur 11 mm long; lower petal gibbous at base; inner petals 10 mm long. *Stigma*-papillae several, basal ones geminate. *Fruit* lanceolate, 15 x 3 mm with 2 mm long style (including 1 mm narrow part). Seeds c. 10-seeded. Fig. 42c.

Only known from the type-collection. Map 34.

This species is unique in its entire leaves. Not in cultivation.

14. *C. hepaticifolia* C.Y.Wu & Z.Y.Su in Acta Bot. Yunnanica 4:2 (1982). Type: SE Tibet, Jiacha (Gyaca), 4900 m, 25.6.1975, *Qinghai-Xizang-exped.* 0752 (Herb. Inst. Biol. Qinghai, holo).

DESCRIPTION. *Tuber* oblong, usually branched. *Stem* branched, subterranean part of stem 2-5 cm, with 1-2 scale leaves, above ground 3-5 cm. *Leaves* fleshy, trifoliate, rather long-stalked with broadly ovate leaflets. *Racemes* 1-5-flowered, very dense, corymbose, borne on distinct peduncles about 2 cm long, becoming recurved in fruit, burying the capsules by the base of the plant. *Bracts* 3-5 x 2-3 mm. *Pedicels* 4-9 mm long, equalling or longer than bracts. *Sepals* 1 mm, dentate. *Corolla* blue, small; inner petals 7 mm. Spur 7 mm long, very narrowly cristate. *Capsule* elliptic, 5-6 x 3 mm. *Seeds* c. 10, 1.5 mm. Fig. 42b.

Only known from the type-collection. Map 34.

Similar to *C. hemidicentra* but much smaller and apparently with geocarpic peduncles. In the following three species, it is instead the pedicels that are geocarpic. Not in cultivation.

SUBSECTION BENECINCTAE

Subsection Benecinctae (Fedde) Lidén in Willdenowia 26:31 (1996); *Benecinctae* Fedde, Repert. Spec. nov. Regni veg. 25: 221 (1928); *Eucorydalis* subsect. *Benecinctae* (Fedde) Fedde in Engler, A. & Prantl, K. (eds), Die natürliche Pflanzenfamilien ed. 2, 17b: 134 (1936); Sect. *Benecinctae* (Fedde) Wu & Shu in Acta Bot. Yunannica 4: 1 (1982). Type species: *C. benecincta* W. W. Smith.

Pedicels elongating and recurved in fruit. *Fruits* not explosively dehiscent.

15. *C. benecincta* W. W. Sm. in Notes Roy. Bot. Gard. Edinb. 9: 90 (1916). Type: China, NW Yunnan, Atuntse (Deqen), 4600-4900 m, July 1911, *Kingdon-Ward* 58 (E).

DESCRIPTION. Superficially similar to *C. hemidicentra* but: *Tubers* more divided. *Leaves* a mottled grey, trifoliate; leaflets often obovate, cuneate at base. *Racemes* much less condensed, usually branched, without a distinct peduncle, 5-15-flowered; flowers strongly fragrant. *Bracts* usually much longer, obovate-oblong, the lower ones often slightly divided. *Pedicels* much longer, thickened, soft, arcuate-recurved in fruit and lengthening to 25-70 mm. *Spur* obtuse, strongly reflexed downward. *Stigma* with lateral and basal geminate papillae. *Fruit* elliptic, 10 x 5 mm with a style 4 mm long (including a short narrow part). *Seeds* 2-2.5 mm with slightly convex epidermis cells and very broad elaiosome.

A very peculiar species which is confined to screes at high altitudes. Two subspecies are recognised:

15a. subsp. *benecincta*

DESCRIPTION. *Tubers* with yellow flesh. *Leaflets* often cuneate at base. *Racemes* usually branched, 5-15-flowered. *Flowers* very broad with low crests, pink to pale purple with dark bluish purple shades towards the apex and with conspicuous pink veins; inner petals 9-10 mm. *Spur* broad, 10-13 mm long. *Fruit* elliptic, 10 x 5 mm with a style 4 mm long (including

Fig. 43. a-c, *Corydalis hemidicentra* (a, cult. KGB 482, NW Yunnan, Beimashan, 4400 m, GB; b, cult. KGB 311, Yunnan/Xizang border, 4400 m, GB; c, Forrest 13141, China, Yunnan, Makong/Yangtse divide, 27° 40' N, E); **d**, *C. benecincta* subsp. *trilobipetala* (Rock 24002, China, S Sichuan, Muli, BM); **e**, *C. benecincta* subsp. *benecincta* (cult. KGB 307, China, Shu La, Yunnan/Xizang border, 4400 m, GB)

a short narrow part). *Seeds* 5-15 (ovaries with up to 20 ovules). 2n=16. Self-incompatible. Fig. 43e; Pl. 83.

DISTRIBUTION. China: NW Yunnan and neighbouring Tibet. Alpine screes (and 'cliff-ledges'?), on 'shale' and limestone; 4000-6000 m (-6400 m!, Kingdon-Ward). Map 35.

From the same screes as *C. hemidicentra* (which see), and with similar succulent, hepatica-like, mimicry leaves. The large flowers are in different shades of pink, red-purple, and white, and mingles with the foliage in a most attractive manner. It is an unbelievable plant. We can only hope that recent introductions will take well to cultivation but have no reason to believe that this will be the case. Plants from these ultimate elevations and extreme environs are usually very difficult to keep.

15b. subsp. *trilobipetala* (Hand.-Mazz.) Lidén in Willdenowia 26:34 (1996); *C. trilobipetala* Hand.-Mazz. in Sitzg. Ak. W.: 114 (1923). Type: China,

Sichuan, Sagani above Muli, 4525 m, 30.7.1915, *Handel-Mazzetti* 7339 (W).

DESCRIPTION. *Plant* smaller than subsp. *benecincta. Tuber* without yellow flesh. *Leaflets* more rounded, often covered with a waxy bloom. *Racemes* more condensed, 2-10-flowered. *Bracts* obtuse and much shorter. *Pedicels* not so much thickened. *Flowers* pale mauve to deep purplish blue; outer petals more broadly crested with distinctly 3-lobed limb; inner petals 8 mm long. *Spur* 9-10 mm long. *Fruit* 6-8 x 4 mm with style 3 mm long. *Seeds* 4-11. Fig. 43d.

DISTRIBUTION. China: NW Yunnan, SW Sichuan. Limestone screes, 4000-5000 m. Map 35.

In SW Sichuan, Muli area (from where subsp. *trilobipetala* is described), the leaflets are more rounded, and covered with a waxy bloom, and the racemes are unbranched. In NW Yunnan the leaflets are less rounded, less waxy, and the racemes are

Fig. 44. a, *Corydalis geocarpa* (type); **b**, *C. dajingensis* (Harry Smith 4352, Sichuan, NE Matang, 5000 m, UPS)

frequently branched, and thus approach the subsp. *benecincta*. The sympatric occurrence, and the presence of intermediate forms between subsp. *benecincta* and subsp. *trilobipetala* in NW Yunnan may be due to secondary contact and introgression.

16. *C. geocarpa* H. Sm. ex Lidén in Willdenowia 26:34 (1996). Type: China, Sichuan, Tatsienlu, Tapao shan, 4500 m, 20.8.1934, in soil-filled rock crevices, *H. Smith* 11282 (UPS-holo; S, iso).

DESCRIPTION. Similar in detail to *C. benecincta*, but with a very different appearance. *Tuber* unknown. *Stems* 7-11 cm, much-branched. *Leaves* several, pinnately divided; lamina ovate-oblong in outline with 2 pairs of pinnae; leaflets ± deeply cut into rounded obtuse segments. *Pedicels* broadly sheathing at base. *Racemes* terminal and often axillary from the uppermost leaf or leaves, lax, 2-9-flowered. *Bracts* stalked, ± deeply divided into obovate to oblanceolate acute lobes, or the upper entire. *Pedicels* as in *benecincta*, 10-35 mm long. *Sepals* 2 mm, dentate. *Corolla* ecristate; outer petals distinctly 3-lobed; inner petals 7-8 mm long. *Spur* short, c. 6 mm long, broad-based, tapering. Fruit as in *C. benecincta. Seeds* 4-8. Fig. 44a.

Only known from the type collection. Not in cultivation. Map 35.

17. *C. dajingensis* C.Y.Wu & Z.Y.Su in Acta Bot. Yunnanica 4: 4 (1982). Type: China, W Sichuan,

Dajing, Barkam, 4100 m, 23.6.1958, *Lee Xing* 77858 (Sich. Univ., holo).

C. cristata var. *pseudoflaccida* Fedde in Repert. Spec. nov. Regni veg. 22: 28 (1925). Type: China, Sichuan, NE Matang, 4800-5100 m, 15.9.1922, *H. Smith* 4352 (UPS).

C. bataliana Maxim., *nomen nudum*; Kam: Hung Chao, *Potanin* (LE).

C. tubero-pisiformis Z.Y. Su in herb.; N Sichuan, Pingwu (KUN)

DESCRIPTION. *Tubers* small, pea-like (only seen on specimens from Pingwu, perhaps juvenile). *Stems* slender, branched; lower part of stems and petioles pale, subterranean. *Leaves* trifoliolate, long-stalked; leaflets obovate, entire or ± deeply 3-fid. *Racemes* without a distinct stalk, 2-6-flowered. *Bracts* about 1 cm, deeply divided into 3-5 oblong-acute lobes. *Pedicels* about 10 mm long in flower, recurved and elongating to 20-30 mm in fruit. *Sepals* 1-1.5 mm, dentate. *Corolla* purple, straight; outer petals with prominent lateral lobes towards the apex (as *CC. geocarpa* and *benecincta* subsp. *trilobipetala*); inner petals 7-8 mm. *Spur* 7-9 mm long, straight, obtuse and recurved at apex. *Fruit* as in *C. benecincta*, 8 x 3 mm with a 2-3 mm long style, 5-9-seeded. Fig. 44b.

DISTRIBUTION. China: N and W Sichuan and neighbouring Tibet, 4000-5000 m. Known from four collections only (see synonyms). Map 35.

Not in cultivation.

SECTION DUPLOTUBER

*D*uplotuber is an easily circumscribed section with several unique characters. It shares an acuminate nectary with subsection Corydalis and there is also a general resemblance in vegetative habit. Tuber development, stigma, and seed, are on the other hand very different and Duplotuber is not related to the other tuberous sections. This has also been confirmed by DNA sequences. Its previous affiliation with Radix-cava (Ryberg 1960) seems difficult to understand but was based on the (supposedly?) monopodial tuber. The section is restricted to east Asia. *C. buschii* is found in Manchuria and North Korea, *C. ternata* is strictly Korean, and *C. decumbens* is distributed in eastern China and southern Japan.

CULTIVATION. The species of this group may qualify for a place in the garden. Although they are by no means spectacular, they possess a quiet charm that makes them useful in the woodland or the peat-garden.

They are easy to grow and multiply quickly. The tubers should be planted around 10 cm deep in a rich woodland compost made up from leaf-mould, peat and a rich loam. *C. ternata* and *C. decumbens* are probably lime-tolerant whereas *C. buschii* prefers an acid soil.

Corydalis section Duplotuber Ryberg in Acta Horti Berg. 19: 223 (1960). Type species: *C. decumbens* (Thunb.) Pers.
Ceratotuber Popov in Komarov, V.A. (ed.) Fl. USSR 7: 680 (1937), invalid name (without Latin description), based on *C. buschii*..

DESCRIPTION. *Cotyledons* one (in *C. decumbens*) or two (in *C. buschii*). *Tubers* solid, small, consisting of a swollen stem-portion beset with leaf-scars; new tubers originating from an old tuber as swollen shoots with crowded leaves and emitting roots from the base. *Flower stems* axillary, one to many, each with 2 to several leaves, with or without scale-leaves in the lower part. *Leaves* alternate, one to several times ternately divided. *Bracts* small to medium, entire. *Flowers* white to pink to pinkish purple, rarely blue or bicolored blue and pink. *Spur* shorter than remainder of corolla, straight, or curved downwards at apex, the nectary short, tapering to an acuminate apex. *Stigma* transversely oblong with a papilla at

each end and with two central papillae. *Fruit* linear with one row of seeds. *Seeds* keeled, sparsely covered with vesicular papillae.

In *C. decumbens* and *C. ternata* new tubers are formed close to the old tuber. In *C. buschii* match-thick stolons grow out from the old tuber, apically swelling into new tubers. In *C. ternata* tubers are also formed in the axils of cataphylls in the lower part of the stem: in all species vegetative dispersal is important. In the greenhouse, *C. decumbens* and *ternata* produce lots of radical leaves very early in winter.

KEY TO SPECIES OF SECTION DUPLOTUBER

1. Leaflets serrate   **1. *C. ternata***
1. Leaflets not serrate   **2**

2. Stems without scale-leaves at base; stems unbranched   **2. *C. decumbens***
2. Stems with several scale-leaves at base; stems branched   **3. *C. buschii***
(

1. *C. ternata* (Nakai) Nakai in Bot. Mag. (Tokyo) 28: (28)-(29) (1914); *C. bulbosa* var. *remota* f. *ternata* Nakai in Bot. Mag. (Tokyo) 26: 94 (1912); *C. remota* var. *ternata* (Nakai) Makino, in Iinuma, Somoku-dzusetsu ed. 3, 13: 4 (1913); *C. nakaii* Ishidoya in J. Chosen Nat. Hist. Soc. 2: 91 (1928). Type: Illustration in Y. Iinuma, Somoku-dzusetsu Vol. 13 fol. 4, fig. 4 (1856).

DESCRIPTION. *Tubers* small, 5-12 mm, rounded to oblong; new tubers are produced one on top of the old tuber or axillary to the radical leaves or from the axils of scale leaves on the subterranean part of the stem or, rarely, axillary to the lower cauline leaves. *Stems* 10-25 cm long with a slender subterranean portion, decumbent to erect with 3-4 leaves and a couple of scale leaves at base, usually branched. *Leaves* with 3 elliptic, serrate leaflets, sometimes with purplish blotches in the centre; lower leaves vaginate at base. *Racemes* rather lax, 7-12-flowered. *Bracts* ovate, entire to dentate. Pedicels equalling or usually longer than the bracts, 5-9 mm long, slender, not curved downwards in fruit. *Sepals* minute. *Corolla* rather closed at apex, pinkish purple; outer petals with

83

84

85

86

87

88

Plate 83. *Corydalis benecincta*, NW Yunnan, Daxueshan
Plate 84. *Corydalis hemidicentra*
Plate 85. *Corydalis conorhiza*
Plate 86. *Corydalis conorhiza*, yellow form
Plate 87. *Corydalis caseana* subsp. *aquae-gelidae*
Plate 88. *Corydalis caseana* subsp. *brandegei*

89
90
91
92
93
94

Plate 89. *Corydalis caseana* subsp. *brandegei*
Plate 90. *Corydalis caseana* subsp. *cusickii*
Plate 91. *Corydalis scouleri*
Plate 92. *Corydalis pachycentra*
Plate 93. *Corydalis oxypetala*
Plate 94. *Corydalis pseudoadoxa*

Fig. 45. a, *Corydalis decumbens* (cult. Fukuhara 89, Japan, Honshu, Kyoto); **b**, *C. ternata* (plant, Oh, S Korea, Kongju, Ch'ungch'ongnam-do, 18.4.1985, GB; flower cult. Fukuhara 90, S Korea); **c**, *C. buschii* (cult. from, *J. Ruksans, sine coll.*, SE Siberia, Oleinij)

limbs slightly spreading, obtuse to slightly emarginate; inner petals 10 mm long. *Spur* short and straight, 5-8 mm long. *Fruit* and *seeds* as in next species. 2n=16. Fig. 45b.

DISTRIBUTION. Korea and NE China; SE Manchuria (Liaoning and Jilin).

Not a very exciting species in the greenhouse. Our plants rarely flower and, when they do, the flowers are very depauperate. It is quite hardy and increases well in the open ground. We grow it in peaty woodland conditions. Not a traffic-stopper.

2. *C. decumbens* (Thunb.) Pers. in Syn. 2: 269 (1806). *Fumaria decumbens* Thunb., Nov. Act. Petrop. 12: 102 (1801). Type: Japan, 1776, *Thunberg* (UPS)

C. gracilipes S. Moore, J. Bot. 226 (1875). Type: E China, Jiangxi, Jiujiang, *Shearer* (K).

C. kelungensis Hayata, J. Coll. Sci. Imp. Univ. Tokyo 30 (art 1): 27 (1911). Type: Taiwan, Kelung, Ariko, 3. 1908, *Kawakami & Shimada* 4298 (not seen).

C. edulioides Fedde in Repert. Spec. nov. Regni veg. 20: 53 (1924). Type: E China, Zhejiang, 'insel Putu im Tschusan-Archipel', *Dubois-Reymond* 73a (B).

C. edulioides var. *haimanensis* Fedde in Repert. Spec. nov. Regni veg. 20: 53 (1924). Type: E China, Tschekiang, Haimen, February 1912, *Limpricht* 305a (B).

C. amabilis Migo in J. Shanghai Sci. inst. sect. 3, 3: 221 (1927). Type: E China, Jiangsu, Shangfang-shan, Soochow, 5.4.1935, *H. Migo* (TI).

DESCRIPTION. *Plant* glabrous. *Tubers* small, rounded, 4-15 mm; new tubers formed on top of the old tuber from the apical meristem or axillary to the radical leaves. *Stems* axillary, usually several from each tuber, 10-25 cm long, weak, slender, not branched, with 2 leaves. *Scale leaves* absent. *Leaves* biternate with obovate leaflets which are entire or deeply divided into acute ovate lanceolate lobes. *Racemes* lax, 3-10-flowered. *Pedicels* 10-20 mm long. *Bracts* small, entire, 5-8 mm long, ovate. *Flowers* whitish to pale pink, often marked with pale blue, usually narrowly crested; lower petal broadly spathulate, usually without basal gibbosity; inner petals with rather broad rounded wings that reach beyond the apex. *Spur* tapering, shorter than limb of the upper petal; nectary short, about one third to a half as long as the spur, tapering at the apex. *Fruit* linear-oblong, somewhat torulose, 13-18 x 2 mm. *Seeds* 6-14. 2n=16. Most strains are self-compatible, and ± autogamous. Fig. 45a.

DISTRIBUTION. S Japan, E China (prov. Anhui, Hubei, Hunan, Jiangsu, Jiangxi, Shaanxi, Zhejiang) and Taiwan. Map 36.

Corydalis decumbens is very variable in the size and form of its flowers. The largest flowered variants are to be found in eastern central China.

Interestingly, this species differs from the next one in having a single cotyledon. However, it deviates profoundly from the other one-cotyledon tuberous groups in that several leaves are produced in the first season. The tubers are small, greyish and potato-like and are formed in profusion; a really good increaser.

It has been readily available in the trade for many years, supposedly from Japanese material. The leaves appears in late autumn. In cold weather they blacken and collapse on the ground but our plants have never failed to recover the following spring. We grow it in woodland conditions in a fertile, woodland soil. Quite a nice little plant of which it could be said that it produces far too much foliage in comparison to flowers but has a pleasant smell like that of *Viola odorata*.

3. *C. buschii* T. Nakai in Bot. Mag. (Tokyo) 28: 328 (1914). Type: (LE).
C. chosenensis Ohwi in Repert. Spec. nov. Regni veg. 36: 49 (1934). Type: Korea: Gekatsuguri in Kannan, *Ohwi* 46 (B).

DESCRIPTION. *Stem* 10-20(-30) cm long, branched, erect, slender, with 2-4 leaves and 1-3 scales at the base. *Leaves* long-stalked, thin, biternate with deeply divided leaflets, papillose-scabrid on margins and veins, the ultimate lobes lanceolate; lower leaves vaginate at base, the vaginas thin and membranous. *Raceme* short and dense, 5-10(-15) flowered. *Bracts* broadly ovate to obovate, apically dentate or the lowermost divided into acute teeth. Pedicels short, straight and thin, 3-5 mm long, equalling the bracts. *Flowers* purple to pinkish red, rather broadly winged; lower petal broadly saccate at base; inner petals with narrow wings. *Spur* equalling or longer than the lower petal. *Fruit* glabrous or rarely slightly papillose-hairy. *Capsule* linear, 14-18 x 2 mm. *Seeds* 5-12. 2n=16. Self-incompatible. Fig. 45c.

DISTRIBUTION. From E Russia (the Vladivostok area) to N Korea. Wet meadows and forest glades. Map 36.

A much leafier and more erect plant than the previous species and with markedly different tubers: these are yellowish, elongated, branched and thin with thicker ends. It is a prolific increaser in cultivation, although definitely not an alpine house plant, but perfect in a rich woodland where it appears rather late in the season. The lush foliage is bright green and, in late May, is just overtopped by dense racemes bearing pinkish-red flowers. A good garden plant which was introduced into cultivation by Janis Ruksans.

NON-TUBEROUS CORYDALIS
A SELECTION

A gardener's guide to *Corydalis* would not be complete without an extensive selection of the non-tuberous species that in reality constitute the major part of the genus, although their representation in cultivation is so far rather modest. Some provide the most exquisite alpine-house, rock-garden and peat wall plants. Others give substantial ornamenal value in both foliage and flowers and are excellent woodland garden plants. Some of the largest are useful and beautiful perennials that thrive by watercourses.

Some of them prolong the corydalis-season well into June or July and start to colour our gardens when the tuberous species have gone dormant. Others, like *C. wilsonii*, start blooming in January in the alpine house and act as 'appetisers' for the coming tuberous species.

In recent years there has been a rapid increase in the number of non-tuberous species in cultivation and this is mainly due to the opening up of western China to western botanists. Accessions from Central Asia also account for some of the novelties. Some have great potential as garden plants, especially species in the sections Archaecapnos, Fasciculatae, Elatae, Capnogorium, and Chrysocapnos. At present many of the newly introduced species are rare in cultivation but they are being tried by a few botanic gardens and private enthusiasts. In due time the most promising will certainly become available on a larger scale. Still, few will become so rapidly popular in cultivation as the now widely grown *C. flexuosa*.

For reasons explained below, we give a fuller treatment of the section *Archaecapnos*, the giants of the genus, while the remainder of the non-tuberous sections are more superficially mentioned with mainly those represented in cultivation included.

SECTION ARCHAEOCAPNOS

A distinct group of five or six species, distributed in western North America, eastern Siberia, Manchuria, Korea and Japan.

Section Archaeocapnos Popov ex Michajlova. *Plants* distinguished by their considerable size, (30-) 50-220 cm. *Stems* fleshy and thick, 1-5 cm diameter, hollow. *Stipules* rounded, membranous. *Flowers* white to purplish pink, appearing late (May-August in cult.). *Stigma* rectangular. *Fruits* rather thick-walled, explosively dehiscent, reflexed on erect pedicels.

In nature the species in this section are all dependant on a constant supply of cool, moving water and are, accordingly, found mainly in close proximity to seeps, springs, tributaries and small streams, in cool humid places. Occasionally, populations may gain a root-hold by larger streams. Some can tolerate a rather dense leafy canopy but a semi-shaded or open situation is preferred by the majority.

Despite being most garden-worthy plants, only one representative, *C. scouleri*, is in general cultivation today. In Gothenburg we are also growing *C. gigantea* and the various subspecies of *C. caseana* and we believe that these have a promising future as ornamental plants.

CULTIVATION. The species require a well aerated, water-retentive, slightly acid soil with a high content of nutrients. The soil should be deep, extremely well-drained but never allowed to become dry. In gardens they prefer decent light but are sensitive to a dry atmosphere and high temperatures that will induce premature dormancy. In areas with hot, dry summers a slightly shaded position, sheltered from drying winds, should be selected. *C. scouleri* actually prefers rather deep shade.

Seed is the best means of propagation. Seed viability is very short and the large seeds should be sown immediately when ripe or stored in a slightly moist medium. The seeds need a warm-cold treatment to germinate. Sow them in a slightly acid, peat-based compost and keep them moist. After one winter they will sprout and form distinct, broadly triangular, rather large cotyledons. In cultivation the first true leaf will appear during the summer if they are regularly watered and fed: with the shorter season of their native haunts it is possible that cotyledons only are produced in the first year. Ownbey suggests that it takes at least four years for them to reach flowering size in the wild. Under ideal conditions in cultivation they will take three to four years to mature. When the first true leaf appears they can be pricked out individually into pots and then grown on for another year before they are placed in a permanent position in the garden.

Division is particularly easy for *C. scouleri* with its shallow stolons. These are best separated in late winter or early spring when they can be transplanted to a new position (or into pots) and they will establish easily. The other species can only be divided when they have produced separate crowns but this takes time. When the original rootstock starts to disintegrate, a clump of short rhizomes will have been formed. Sometimes adventitious roots have been produced on these rhizomes, while in other instances they remain in contact with the remnants of the original taproot. Division of such plants is risky but possible: it should be carried out just as growth commences. Normally the form of the divisions makes potting up impossible and placing them in a permanent position is recommended. The divisions normally grow on without any problems and may even flower in the same season.

KEY TO SPECIES OF SECTION ARCHAEOCAPNOS

1.   Inner petals distinctly tipped with blackish purple; stem leaves 3-5, held in multiple planes; seeds about 2-2.5 mm diameter   **1. *C. caseana***
1.   Inner petals not distinctly tipped with a darker colour; stem leaves about 3, held in a more or less single plane; seeds about 3.5 mm diameter   **2**

2.   With long and slender rhizomes; forming dense stands; N America   **2. *C. scouleri***
2.   Tap-rooted, clump-forming; solitary plants; E Asia   **3**

3.   Spur curved downward or horizontal; sepals 1 - 2 mm long, persistent   **3. *C. paeoniifolia***
3.   Spur curved upward; sepals deciduous in bud or early anthesis   **4**

4.   Inflorescence profusely branched; flowers 16 - 20 mm long; sepals 1-2 mm long, furrowed   **4. *C. multiflora***
4.   Inflorescence not or slightly branched; flowers 20 - 40 mm long; sepals 4-15 mm long, smooth   **5. *C. gigantea***

1. *C. caseana* Gray

DESCRIPTION. *Perennial*, 40-220 cm high, with a thick vertical rootstock. *Cauline leaves* 3-6, along the entire stem, 3-4 (-6)-pinnate, glaucous or yellowish green above, glaucous beneath. *Racemes* usually with 30-200 flowers. *Flowers* 15-25 mm long, white to pinkish purple, with the inner petals tipped with blackish purple, with or without wing margins and with or without crest.

DISTRIBUTION. W USA; moist forests, 370-3400 m.

Corydalis caseana has a wide but scattered distribution in the western USA, being found in California, Oregon, Washington, Idaho, Utah, Colorado and New Mexico. It is always very local and restricted to suitable environs.

Before Ownbey's monograph (1947) there were eight different species described from the distribution area but he put them into perspective. We wholly agree with his treatment and include the later described *C. aquae-gelidae* as an additional subspecies. To quote Ownbey: '*C. caseana* is an excellent example of the type of morphological divergence commonly met with when component parts of a species are isolated geographically'.

In the wild it is found at mid-altitudes, mainly in subalpine forests and is always associated with cool, running water: plants mostly grow just beside or in small streams, where seasonal water level fluctuations are limited. The thick, brittle roots find their way deep into the mineral substrate, which generally consists of coarse gravel and sand but sometimes clay or silt. Old and well established individuals can be found away from visible streams, seemingly growing in organic matter. On examination, however, it will be found that their huge root-system reaches mineral soil and moisture less than 30 cm down. Such plants are probably very old and grow in ancient stream beds. Stunted growth has been observed in plants found on purely organic soils.

Plants prefer open sunny situations but can tolerate some shade. It is our impression that the establishment of new colonies requires a somewhat disturbed soil, lack of competition from other herbs and a fair amount of light. Once the plants are big enough they can endure an increasing overgrowth of trees, but not competition from large coarse perennial herbs. If, on the other hand, the canopy becomes too dense, flowering decreases and the plants eventually die.

KEY TO SUBSPECIES OF CORYDALIS CASEANA

1. Wing margin of outer petals narrow (or lacking), lower petal acute   **2**
1. Wing margin of outer petals moderately to highly developed, lower petal not acute   **3**

2. Leaves 3 (2-4) times pinnate; spur 12-16 mm long; California (N Sierra Nevada) **1a. subsp.** *caseana*
2. Leaves 4 (-6) times pinnate; spur 9-11 mm long; N. Oregon, S Washington
   1b. subsp. *aquae-gelidae*

3. Outer petals rounded, sometimes mucronulate, the wing margin scarcely folded back upon the keel   **4**
3. Outer petals emarginate, the wing margin folded back upon the keel   **5**

4. Plants mostly 100-150 cm tall; flowers pink or white; outer petals mucronulate, crested; Colorado and N New Mexico
   1c. subsp. *brandegei*
4. Plants mostly 40-100 cm tall; flowers white; outer petals rounded, occasionally barely retuse, not mucronulate; crest obsolescent or lacking. Utah   **1d. subsp.** *brachycarpa*

5. Inflorescence not profusely branched; upper petal, including spur, 18-24 mm long; limbs of outer petals broad, not erose (i.e. having an irregularly toothed or apparently gnawed margin); NE Oregon, S Idaho   **1e. subsp.** *cusickii*
5. Inflorescence profusely branched; upper petal, including spur, 16-20 mm long; limbs of outer petals narrow, minutely erose; N Idaho
   1f. subsp. *hastata*

1a. subsp. *caseana*
C. bidwilliae Watson

DESCRIPTION. *Plant* 40-100 cm high. *Leaves* 2-3-pinnate, glaucous. *Flowers* light pink to white, 16 - 22 mm long, with a crested hood.

DISTRIBUTION. USA: California; N. Sierra Nevada, Butte, Lassen, Placer, Plumas, Shasta, Sierra, Tehama, and Tulare counties. 1200-2800 m. Flowers June and July.

The 'Sierra corydalis' is rather uncommon in the wild though it is not considered to be threatened. During our travels we have searched for it in some of its classical sites but only been able to find a few weak plants. Horticulturally, we judge it to be the least important of the subspecies, with pallid, small flowers and a weak constitution.

The Californian plant was the first to be noted and was in cultivation in Britain as early as 1886, twelve years after it had been described. Since then it was lost to cultivation but reintroduced as seed in 1994.

The latest 'The Jepson Manual' (Hickman 1993) states that it is 'Toxic, eaten by naive [sic] livestock'; rather cute wording.

1b. subsp. *aquae-gelidae* (Peck & Wilson) Lidén & Zetterlund

DESCRIPTION. *Plant* 40- 120 cm high. *Leaves* 4-6-pinnate, glaucous. *Flowers* pale to deep pink with a trace of purple, 15-20 mm long , with a conspicuously crested hood. Pl. 87.

DISTRIBUTION. USA: Washington (Clark and Skamania counties); Oregon (Clackamas, Multnomah, and Marion counties). 370-1300 m. Flowers mid-June to mid-August.

The 'Clackamas corydalis' was first found in 1942 and described as a species in 1956. In the original description there is no reference or comparison to *C. caseana*. All modern floras has treated it as an independent species but in 'Vascular Plants of the North West' its close relationship to *C. caseana* is noted. In 1994 one of us had the opportunity to study *C. aquae-gelidae* in Oregon and Washington. After having seen all subspecies of *C. caseana in situ* and in cultivation it is our firm conviction that, if we are to follow Ownbey's concept, *C. aquae-gelidae* must be considered a subspecies of *C. caseana*. The only difference is that the leaves are four (to six) instead of three (to four) times pinnate.

This Spotted Owl of the plant kingdom has been considered to be rare and threatened. Recent surveys have revealed about fifty populations in Oregon, mainly from within the Mt Hood National Forest area, giving a figure of around 75,000 plants.

In 1959 it was found in the Gifford Pinchot National Forest in southern Washington and is now known from about forty sites in that area. It grows in typical *C. caseana* environs in the *Tsuga heterophylla* and *Abies amabilis* zones. The sites are more sheltered from wind than those of the other subspecies; the finely divided leaves are probably particularly sensitive to drying winds.

It is a lovely plant with numerous pink flowers in dense racemes, which contrast perfectly with the lace-like, glaucous foliage. Some populations are dwarfer, up to 50 cm tall, and these are really the prettiest. If it takes well to cultivation every effort should be made to distribute it as widely as possible.

1c. subsp. *brandegei* (Watson) G.B.Ownbey

DESCRIPTION. *Plant* 100-220 cm high. *Leaves* (2) 3 (-4)-pinnate, glaucous. *Flowers* white to rosy pink, 18 - 25 mm long, with a broad wing margin, rounded at the apex and with a crested hood. Pl. 88, 89.

DISTRIBUTION. USA: New Mexico, Rio Arriba County; Colorado, Archuleta, Conejos, Mineral, Hinsdale, Gunnison and Delta counties. 3000-3400 m. Flowering mid-June to mid-August.

A stately perennial which was predicted a great horticultural future by Joseph Dalton Hooker in 1902. Predominately a Colorado plant with an outpost in northern New Mexico, this magnificent subspecies forms extensive colonies in places of easy access. At the western slopes of Kebler Pass near Crested Butte it is really abundant in a white to pale pink form. A little further to the west, on the southern slope of Grand Mesa, the majority of the plants are white and guarded by huge swarms of aggressive mosquitoes.

The most promising form that we have seen is that from the Wolf Creek Pass, NE of Pagosa Springs. Here it is found in a lovely rosy pink form that forms large stands right at the pass itself as well as down on the western side. It is also said to grow near the Monarch Pass.

It has settled well in cultivation but not yet reached the size it can attain in nature. The tallest plants seen (220 cm) were at the lower altitudinal limit below Kebler Pass, growing with nettles and other nitrophilous plants.

1d. subsp. *brachycarpa* (Rydb.) G.B.Ownbey

DESCRIPTION. *Plant* 40-100 cm high. *Leaves* (2-) 3 (-4) -pinnate, glaucous. *Flowers* white, 18 - 22 mm long, with a broad wing margin, rounded at the apex, crest on hood lacking or rudimentary.

DISTRIBUTION. USA: Utah; Wasatch Mts (Weber, Wasatch, Salt Lake and Utah counties). 1700-3050 m. Flowering July.

This is probably the rarest of the subspecies. Ownbey states that 'it is possible that the adult population numbers no more than a few hundred individuals'. Since that time it has been found in Wasatch and Weber counties, sites we know little about. We have only seen the few specimens at Alta, the *locus classicus*, where it is threatened by the development of the growing skiing resort. It is a nice compact plant that should be tried in cultivation but only by means of controlled seed collection.

1 e. subsp. *cusickii* (Watson) G.B.Ownbey
C. hendersonii Fedde non Hernsley
C. idahoensis Fedde

DESCRIPTION. *Plant* 80-200 cm high. *Leaves* (2-) 3 (-4)-pinnate, glaucous or green. *Flowers* white or pink, 18 - 24 mm long, with a reflexed, extremely broad wing margin, deeply notched at the apex; crest on hood lacking or inconspicuous. Pl. 90.

DISTRIBUTION. USA: Idaho, Boise Mountains (Boise, Camas, Elmore and Valley counties); NE Oregon, Wallowa Mountains, Blue Mountains (Union and Baker counties). 1500-2300 m. Flowering mid-June and July.

A plant of great potential, for some reason growing only in close proximity to bonanza ghost-towns like Bourne, Cornucopia and Atlanta, giving nostalgic images of old shacks and ruined saloons. Its large size and substantial, wide-winged flowers make it highly decorative. In Idaho, between Rocky Bar and Atlanta, there is a huge colony with flowers of the loveliest pink shades. The 'Blue Mountain form' collected above Sumpter, is a stronger grower with almost ivory-white flowers. Both are promising plants in cultivation and some gold-dust mixed into the compost may certainly be beneficial!

1f. subsp. *hastata* (Rydb.) G.B.Ownbey

DESCRIPTION. *Plant* 100-200 cm high. *Leaves* (2) 3 (-4)-pinnate, glaucous or green. *Flowers* white or pale pink, 16-20 mm long, with a reflexed, moderately well developed, wing margin, retuse at the apex; crest low.

DISTRIBUTION. USA: N Idaho (Clearwater and Shoshone counties, Clearwater Mountains and North-western part of the Bitterroot Mountains). 900-1300 m. Flowers mid-June and July.

An impressive plant in nature as well as in cultivation but perhaps not as desirable as subsp. *brandegei* or subsp. *cusickii* because of its smaller flowers, but still of great value.

It has a limited distribution in the Idaho panhandle. With increased lumbering, access to the area has been improved, revealing new corydalis sites. Our impression, from a brief visit in 1992, is that it is quite common within its natural limits.

2. *C. scouleri* Hook.
C. macrophylla Nutt.
C. allenii Fedde

DESCRIPTION. *Plant* a stoloniferous perennial, 50-120 cm high. *Cauline leaves* usually 3, near or above the middle of the stem, 3(-4)pinnate, green above, glaucous beneath. *Racemes* unbranched, usually with fewer than 25 flowers. *Flowers* light to deep purplish-pink, 25-30 mm, wing margin absent, crested. Pl. 91.

DISTRIBUTION. USA: Washington (Clallam, Clark, Grays Harbor, Jefferson, King, Mason, Pacific, Pierce, Thurston and Wahkiakum counties); Oregon (Benton, Clackamas, Clatsop, Columbia, Hood River, Marion, Multnomah, Tillamook, Washington and Lane counties). Canada: British Columbia. 0-1100 m. Flowers mid-April to mid-June.

Corydalis scouleri is a widespread species in the Pacific North-west from Vancouver Island southwards at least to Fall Creek in the Siuslaw National Forest, Lane County, Oregon.

Like the preceding species this plant is confined to wet, cool habitats, but is generally found at lower elevations. The fact that *C. scouleri* prefers a much shadier situation and a different substrate (humus-rich), often combined with larger rocks, usually keeps the two species apart in the small area where they overlap. In Tanner Creek they actually grow along the same stream but no hybrids have been reported.

Corydalis scouleri is easily recognised by its colonising way of growth. It is quite variable, particularly with respect to the incision and texture of the leaves. The common form in cultivation has finely

dissected, thin, pale-green leaves, whereas more recent introductions have more coarsely cut, thick and dark-green foliage.

This species has been in cultivation at least from the 1890s, when it was grown at the Royal Botanic Gardens Kew from material donated by Cannon Ellacombe. As early as 1898, evaluations and cultural instructions by S. Arnott were found in *The Garden*: '..charming foliage...and pretty flowers...a position sheltered from strong winds.....which destroy the tender leafage and shrivel it up as by fire....it likes partial shade....may be divided for propagation'. That covers it well, may we only add that it is an excellent plant for the woodland garden; further, it comes early into growth and can be decapitated by hard frosts.

Corydalis scouleri has a very high chromosome number (2n= c.140), three times higher than in any other species of *Corydalis*.

3. *C. paeoniifolia* (Steph.) Pers.
C. redowskii Fedde

DESCRIPTION. *Plant* 25-60 cm high. *Leaves* 2-3, near the middle of the stem, short petioled, 2 (-3)-pinnate, green above, glaucous beneath. *Racemes* simple to slightly branching. *Sepals* 1-2 mm long, scarious. *Corolla* pink-violet, 22 - 25 (30) mm long; wing margin broad, ovate, obtuse; lower petal pouched. *Spur* stout, curved downward or horizontal.

DISTRIBUTION. Russia: E. Siberia (Lena-Kolyma, Dauria); Far East (Zeya-Bureya, Uda River area, Ussuri, Okhotsk). Flowers from May to July.

We have no experience of this compact large-flowered species but imagine that it is very attractive. It is said to grow in 'shady, moist, or swamp forests, and along forest streams', hardly surprising for a plant from this section. Cultivation will certainly be similar to that for *C. gigantea*.

4. *C. multiflora* Michajlova
C. gigantea sensu Popov (1937) *pro majora parte*.

DESCRIPTION. *Plant* 100-120 cm high. *Leaves* 3 (-4)-pinnate. *Racemes* profusely branched, 15-20 cm long, with up to 200 flowers altogether. *Sepals* 1-1.5(-2) mm long, thick and rugose. *Corolla* dirty violet, 16-18(-25) mm long. *Spur* straight (also in bud?).

DISTRIBUTION. E Russia: Sakhalin and closely

neighbouring parts of the mainland (De Kastri).

The east Asian species are more difficult to define than the American ones and we have seen far too few specimens of them to take a standpoint regarding their taxonomy. For the time being we follow Charkevicz (1987) in our treatment of the eastern Asiatic species. Small-flowered and rather small-sepalled forms of *C. gigantea* from the northern part of the distribution area (here belongs, for example, the type of *C. gigantea*) were previously considered synonymous with the Sakhalin taxon, but were shown by Michajlova (1982) to be distinct.

Corydalis multiflora is reported to grow in forests by small rivers and streams. As far as we know, this plant is not in cultivation.

5. *C. gigantea* Trautv. & Mey.

?*C. curvicalcarata* Miyabe & Kudo
C. gigantea var. *amurensis* Regel
C. gigantea var. *macrantha* Regel; *C. macrantha* (Regel) Popov
C. zeaensis Michajlova

DESCRIPTION. *Plant* (30-) 60-120 cm high. *Leaves* (2-) 3 (-4)-pinnate, green to dark green above, glaucous beneath. *Racemes* simple to branched, 5 - 12 cm long with 10-20 flowers. *Sepals* (2.5-) 4-10 (-15) mm, scarious, soon falling, smooth, not or slightly dentate. *Corolla* dirty red to red, (20-) 30-40 mm long, acute; wing margin narrow. *Spur* stout, narrow and strongly curved upwards in bud, but becoming thick and straight at maturity.

DISTRIBUTION. Russia: Far East (Zeya-Bureya, Ussuri and Uda River area); China: Manchuria; N Korea; Japan: Hokkaido and Mt. Furano). Flowering June to August.

In nature *C. gigantea* grows in typical moist environs and often forms large colonies. Quite recently a plant from spaghnum bogs in the Zea River system was recognised as *C. zeaensis*: this is a compact form, about 30 cm high, with flowers 30 to 40 mm long and leaves four times pinnate, but it is not accepted by Charkevicz (1987). This publication also questions Mikhailova's view that *C. gigantea* is a hybrid derivative of *CC. macrantha* and *multiflora* and treats *C. gigantea* and *C. macrantha* as synonyms. We have tentatively also included *C. curvicalcarata*, as we fail to find any distinguishing characters; however, we emphasise that this conclusion is based on descriptions and photos only.

This is the only Asian representative with which we have any experience. In 1978 we received material from Moscow Botanic Garden originating from near the town of Obluchye (quite close to the type locality of *C. zeaensis*) and the species has been with us ever since. It is a lovely plant with large red flowers and does not exceed 60 cm in height.

We are growing our plants in an open, sloping peatwall; an old plant grown in a less well-drained, flat position suffered a premature death. The soil is a deep fertile peaty loam which is kept uniformly moist over the summer. With age, the centre of the taproot dies off and the plants spread slowly by short rhizomes. An old plant can be divided in spring, immediately after the new leaves start to appear.

C. longicalcarata X.Zhuang & Z.Y.Su

This species has rather large two- to three-times pinnately divided leaves. The single slender stem is terminated by a few-flowered raceme of large long-spurred flowers, with large entire caducous sepals. It grows in deep humusy soils in forests on Omei Shan and Wawu Shan in West Sichuan. The related *C. anthriscifolia* Franch. differs in having acute leaf-lobes. They differ from the section Mucronatae in stigma, underground parts and seeds, and are better placed in a separate section. Recently introduced into cultivation.

OTHER NON-TUBEROUS SPECIES

In the treatment below, species not known to be (or to have been) cultivated are indicated by an *.

SUBGENUS CORYDALIS

SECTION FASCICULATAE

This is the largest of all *Corydalis* sections with about 70 species. It is characterised by fasciculate swollen storage roots crowned by bulb-like hibernation buds. Like the tuberous species, at least some (*C. cashmeriana*) of them germinate with one cotyledon only (but produce true leaves during the first growing-season), and the stems are similarly attenuated towards their subterranean attachment. Except for a couple of Burmese endemics, all are native to China and Tibet (Xizang). Some of them are also found in Nepal, Sikkim, Bhutan and/or India.

Plate 95. *Corydalis kokiana*, NW Yunnan, near Betahai
Plate 96. *Corydalis kokiana*
Plate 97. *Corydalis calcicola*, NW Yunnan, Beimashan
Plate 98. *Corydalis melanochlora*, NW Yunnan, Beimashan
Plate 99. *Corydalis appendiculata*

100

101

102

103

104

Plate 100. *Corydalis juncea*
Plate 101. *Corydalis atuntsuensis*
Plate 102. *Corydalis lathyrophylla*
Plate 103. *Corydalis flexuosa*, W China, Sichuan, Wolong
Plate 104. *Corydalis elata*

CORYDALIS CASHMERIANA GROUP (3 SPECIES)

Corydalis cashmeriana, a representative of the many blue-flowered Fasciculatae, is one of the most famous and popular species in the genus. In the wild it is common in the Himalaya from Kashmir to Bhutan. West of Annapurna in WC Nepal the inflorescence is generally 3-6-flowered, whereas east of Annapurna it is usually only 2-flowered. The similar *C. ecristata* from E Nepal to Bhutan, can be recognized by its more finely divided leaves and bracts, smaller flowers and fruits, as well as by its very broad truncate lower lip. The Tibetan dwarf *C. jigmei* is similar to *C. ecristata* in its short ovate fruit, but has flowers like *C. cashmeriana*, although much smaller. The species in this group grow mainly in alpine turf.

Corydalis cashmeriana Royle.

This well known species made its first appearance at the Alpine Garden Society's spring show in 1934 and '....created quite a furore by reason of its unearthly beauty'. The material is stated to have been introduced by Ludlow and Sherriff from Bhutan — ' pounds and pounds of whose tubers Ludlow and Sherriff later distributed to gardens in Britain ...' (Fletcher, 'A Quest of Flowers'). Apparently, there was also an import of viable seed during this same era. In 1938 G.W. Robinson states '*C. cashmeriana* ... has attracted a great deal of attention in recent years. My own experience with it has been disappointing, for raising from imported seed one gets a high proportion of poor-coloured forms bordering to magenta and not worth growing..' (RHS Journal).

For many years the Bhutanese form was the only one grown. Lately other forms have been introduced from Kashmir and Nepal.

Ever since its introduction it has held a position amongst the most popular and written up alpine plants. It was awarded a Certificate of Merit in 1934, an A.M. in 1938 and a F.C.C. in 1955.

Corydalis ecristata (Prain) D.G. Long

This species was apparently not introduced until 1976 when George F. Smith collected it in the Barun Valley in east Nepal. This was subsequently thoroughly written up in the Alpine Garden Society *Bulletin* in 1979 and has later been introduced by others. In cultivation it is a weaker and much smaller plant, trickier to keep and only in the hands of a few specialist growers.

Corydalis jigmei C.E.C. Fischer & Kaul.

A few plants are around in cultivation but neither this nor *C. ecristata* will rival *C. cashmeriana* in gardens.

CULTIVATION. Being a devotee of alpine altitudes, *C. cashmeriana*'s keyword is 'cool'. With the right climate, cultivation is easy. Scotland is famous for its colonies and in Scandinavia it is an excellent plant. It is best grown in the peat-garden, where it responds well to a well-drained, aerated but moisture-retentive, slightly acid, soil with a good nutrient content. A mix of equal parts of coarse peat, loam and sand, enriched with leafmould or well-rotted manure, will suit it.

The site should be on the well-lit side; the cooler the climate, the more light it can take. More light improves the intensity of the flower colour and keeps plants compact. In hotter areas it is best grown away from direct sun but without a leafy canopy.

It comes into flower in May or early June, revealing its flowers of celestial blue with a touch of turquoise that makes the blue even more vivid and a perfect contrast to the light green foliage. Around midsummer the heat induces a premature semi-dormancy with only a few pathetic leaves left to feed the red spider-mite and the greenfly that can prove bothersome at this time of the year. The cooler days of late August revive its spirits and a second flush of growth is produced, often together with some stray flowers that lack the lustre of the spring flush. Later it is defoliated by the hard frosts and hides away until its resurgence the following spring.

PROPAGATION. Division is the most common means of propagation and, also, a necessity to keep plants growing vigorously. When a plant has become well established, it quite rapidly builds up into rather dense clumps. With density the risk of damping off increases and regular division is the obvious answer to this problem; we prefer to lift and divide our plants every third year.

Division can be carried out in spring, before, or just as, new growth is visible. The best period, however, is just as the autumn growth is about to begin. Lift the clumps in late August and carefully separate the root-bundles into individual crowns. Plant them with the top of the white-scaly growing points 2-3 cm below the soil-surface. The plantlets will grow on and should become well established during the autumn, showing no setback when they flower the next season. Grown well you will get nice large mats of this corydalis!

Seed is not often set in cultivation: we obtained some capsules after careful cross-pollination of different clones. The fruits are explosive and must be checked at regular intervals! The seeds were sown immediately in late June and they germinated in late September. The solitary cotyledon was soon followed by tiny regular leaves and they managed to build up decent roots before dormancy. The introduction of new clones into cultivation will probably improve future seed-production, so this method will eventually become more important.

C. pachycentra Franch. Pl. 92.

This species is in the *C. curviflora* group and is easily distinguished from *C. cashmeriana* by the broad upward-curved spur and undivided or rarely three-lobed bracts. The flower colour varies from white to a deep azure. In the wild it grows in alpine meadows and open woodland or scrub in NW Yunnan north to central Sichuan, and is replaced further north by the closely related *C. curviflora* Maxim.* and the yellow-flowered *C. cytisiflora* (Fedde) Lidén & Z.Y.Su* *ined.*

Many forms of this delightful plant have been introduced over the last few years. They show a surprisingly wide range in variation regarding plant and flower size. Some forms spread efficiently by thin underground stems, whereas others are sedentary. In nature it inhabits the meadow areas where snow melts comparatively early; it flowers in late May to June. The natural soil is a thin turf in rather rocky areas.

In cultivation some of the collections can take more exposed, dryish situations than others. Despite this, we still recommend a similar treatment to that for *C. cashmeriana*.

C. oxypetala Franch. (Pl. 93)

A rare species with rather thick dark green, slightly divided, leaves and a handsome spike of blue flowers with short straight spurs. It is known from Cangshan (Tsangshan) above the old city of Dali (Tali) in Yunnan, and neighbouring mountains and is replaced towards the north by its close relatives *C. balfouriana* Franch.* and *C. multisecta* C.Y.Wu & X.Zhuang*. *C. trifoliata* Franch.*, which has a wider distribution from Yunnan to east Nepal, can be distinguished by its trifoliate leaves. *C. cheirifolia* Franch.* is another related species with beautifully curved and tapering spurs; it is so far only known from the type collection.

We found *C. oxypetala* in the Cangshan on a west-facing slope just below the summit, rooted between slabs of stone in a burn. It is very elegant when it reveals its sky-blue flowers on a slender 25 cm tall stems. It is to early to predict its future in cultivation, but it has similar demands to *C. cashmeriana*.

C. pseudoadoxa (C.Y.Wu & X.Zhuang) C.Y.Wu & X. Zhuang. Pl. 94.

Similar to *C. oxypetala* in its leaves but with shorter stems and dense racemes, flowers with a longer and more recurved spur, and quite a different underground structure. The dormant bulbs are composed of large white fleshy scales and are similar to those of *C. melanochlora*. It is common in NW Yunnan and SE Tibet in alpine meadows, especially where snow has lingered.

We (KGB Expedition) collected it in several locations in NW Yunnan, always in depressions, where it apparently displays its main flush of flowers in late September!

Being a decided snowmelt plant we first suspected it to be difficult to cultivate. Surprisingly, this is not the case and it seems to be one of the easier in the section to grow; we are growing it like *C. cashmeriana*. In May it puts on its show and grows on through the summer. The flowers are not as celestial blue as those of *C. cashmeriana* but they are still very attractive. They are produced on 10 cm scapes above particularly attractive shiny dark green foliage. Some hybridisation with *C. cashmeriana* would be interesting to try.

C. kokiana Hand.-Mazz. Pl. 95, 96.

This species is easily recognised by its branched stems and the comparatively large much-divided leaves with acute lobes. The flowers are blue to purple with rather short obtuse recurved spurs. Quite common in NW Yunnan, where it (unlike other species in the section) grows in rather dry situations on limestone. We encountered it once on a dry rock in a fountain just by our hotel in Zhongdian.

The two forms we (KGB) collected are most attractive with red-tinted stems up to 30 cm tall, carrying several flowers of a lovely pale sky-blue. To date we have given it the *C. cashmeriana* treatment, notwithstanding the different niche it occupies in nature. However, one must remember, that dry in Yunnan at 3300 m altitude does not mean dry by European standards. Still we recommend some coarse gravel to be mixed in with the compost and suspect that *C. kokiana* can succeed in more exposed sites.

C. appendiculata **Hand.-Mazz.** Pl. 99.

This species is characterised by a minute cornute spurlet at the base of the lower petal of its bright blue flowers. It grows in wet places in SW Sichuan and NW Yunnan.

We collected it in wet moss by Wangshui in north-western Yunnan at 3100 m, a rather low altitude. In cultivation it is a smallish but nice plant when grown in the peat-garden.

C. scaberula **Maxim.*** and *C. glycyphyllus* **Fedde***

The large dense racemes of flowers borne in the middle of the large glaucous, pinnate to bipinnate, leaves that spread close to the soil-surface, makes these plants truly striking . The flowers are broad with short curved obtuse spurs. The yellow-flowered *C. scaberula* grows in Qinghai and neighbouring areas, whereas the closely related white- to rose-flowered *C. glycyphyllus* is found in north-central Sichuan. Both inhabit screes in the wild.

C. calcicola **W.W.Smith.** Pl. 97.

Similar to *C. glycyphyllus* in ecology and general habit but with more divided leaves, while the purple flowers have long arcuate spurs which taper to a narrow tip. It is native to NW Yunnan and W Sichuan. The related cream-flowered *C. trachycarpa* Maxim.* (which is probably not in cultivation) is a native further north in Qinghai, N Tibet, Gansu and NW Sichuan. *C. calcicola* has a pronounced geographical differentiation in Yunnan. Our plants from Da Xue Shan (Big Snow Mountain) are rather compact with finely cut, very glaucous, leaves, whereas plants from the Beimashan are laxer with broader and greener leaflets and broadly crested flowers.

Corydalis calcicola has been introduced on several occasions. In nature it is a smashing plant but in cultivation the reddish-purple of the flowers is obscured by a smoky hue. Despite its preference for exposed limestone or schist screes in nature, it has not been successfully established in the open rock-garden but seems to do much better with *C. cashmeriana* treatment in a cooler peat-bed. A good amount of chippings was used to dilute the rich compost and a particularly raised position was chosen which, as for *C. cashmeriana*, shows plants off to the best advantage.

C. melanochlora **Maxim.** Pl. 98.
(including *C. adrienii* Prain)

A very beautiful species with blue, purplish-blue, white or bicolored flowers with long curved cylindrical spurs, much-divided glaucous leaves and a large underground 'bulb' made up of white fleshy scales. It is quite common in alpine screes from NW Yunnan northwards to Gansu. There is a marked difference between populations from the Da Xue Shan and the Beima Shan in NW Yunnan, a difference which in fact is more pronounced than the north-south differentiation.

Several colour-forms have been introduced and it has settled down in cultivation but is not as easy as *C. cashmeriana*. In nature it shares its screes with *C. calcicola* and should be grown under similar conditions.

C. inconspicua **Bunge ex. Ledeb.**
C. tenella Kar. & Kir., non Ledeb.

Similar to *C. melanochlora* in the underground organs but an inconspicuous small-flowered plant from Tarbagatai and Tienshan.

C. juncea **Wall.** Pl. 100.

A slender herb with a single entire lanceolate cauline leaf, and a spike of yellow dark-tipped flowers. It is common in alpine meadows of Nepal and Bhutan, where it is often seen growing up through dwarf shrubs that gives support to the stems and the slender thin petioles of the radical leaves.

It is a disappointment in gardens. It simply lacks stamina and is too floppy. In addition, the flowers are rather small and not at all showy. We have lost it but do not miss it.

C. lathyrophylla **C.Y.Wu.** Pl. 102.

A lanky plant with glaucous pinnate leaves and long narrow racemes of peculiar short but broad, dentate flowers variegated in pale bluish-lilac and pale pink. It is restricted to the Beimashan in NW Yunnan, where it is locally common in wet situations.

It seems to be one of the easier species to grow, increasing well in cultivation. It is not one of the most exciting when it comes to colour but we find it quite attractive.

C. linarioides **Maxim.*** and allies

A large group of species distributed from N Yunnan to N Gansu. They are characterised by their pinnate leaves with narrow stiff leaflets with revolute margins, often stiffly papillose-hairy on the veins beneath. The flowers are yellow with distinct veins. *C. atuntsuensis* W.W.Smith and *C. eugeniae* Fedde are presently in cultivation from the KGB expedition. They have quite different roots but are otherwise rather similar. Both grow in alpine pastures around 4000 m.

Corydalis atuntsuensis (Pl. 101) is the more interesting species from the horticultural point of view. The dark-green, shiny foliage is in proportion with, and a perfect contrast to, the golden flowers, borne on 20 cm long stems. Cultivation: as for *C. cashmeriana*.

Corydalis eugeniae is a slenderer and slightly more floppy plant but worth growing.

C. densispica C.Y.Wu

A very common plant in NW Yunnan and neighbouring areas to the north (but, surprisingly, rarely collected by the classic plant hunters!) Like *C. juncea,* it is often found hiding in dense shrubs. It is related to the *C. linarioides* group, but has more slender, branched, stems with a few stalked ternately divided leaves. The margins of the lower petal is peculiarly rugged, almost corrugated.

Not one of our favourites, behaving like *C. juncea* and with small yellow flowers. However, it is easy to grow in an open peatbed.

SECTION ELATAE

This section is virtually restricted to the Chinese province of Sichuan and contains about 20 species. Their thin rhizomes or stolons are clothed with thick fleshy scales, very densely so on the main clumps, but at least some of the species sometimes produce 'runners' bearing a few distant scales only. The flowering stems are usually erect and sparsely branched and grow to a height of 25-50 cm. The flowers are often large and pleasantly scented. They are all self-incompatible, and thus have to be cross-pollinated to produce seeds, but they are easy to multiply vegetatively; some of them even produce 'bulbils' in the leaf-axils.

C. flexuosa Franch. sensu lato. Pl. 103.

C. balsamiflora Prain

This species has received much attention during the last decade. It has erect leafy stems and dark-green foliage. The racemes are dense at first but become long and lax in the fruiting stage. The blue flowers with long narrow straight or curved spurs are borne on thin ascending stalks. The fruit capsules are narrowly linear, pendent from straight erecto-patent pedicels. It has a very restricted distribution in central-western Sichuan. The complicated taxonomy of the *C. flexuosa* group is not fully solved at present. Several subspecific taxa have been suggested by Dr Zhuang Xuan in Kunming.

In nature it is a plant of mixed deciduous and evergreen forest or shrubberies at altitudes from 1800-3000m. It grows in loose, moist, humus-rich soil on steep slopes, sometimes along river banks, together with robust herbs like *Cardiocrinum giganteum* var. *yunnanense*, *Androsace henryi*, *Anemone demissa* and *Paris polyphylla*. There is a picture of it in the wild in 'Perennials' by M. Rix & R. Phillips, showing a lovely combination of the bright-green fronds of *Matteuccia* and the blue of *C. flexuosa*; quite exquisite!

It was first introduced in 1986 by Reuben Hatch who collected it in the vicinity of the Wolong Panda Reserve, west of Chengdu. In 1989 a team consisting of James Compton, John D'Arcy and Martyn Rix saw it in the Baoxing (Moupin) valley as well as in the Wolong valley and introduced material from which three cultivars were selected.

Corydalis flexuosa is perfect for horticulture, since it combines exceptional beauty with exceptional ease of propagation. Accordingly, it has had a career in gardens that is hard to rival. The 1989 introduction was rewarded a P.C. in 1990 and an A.M. in 1991. It is now widely offered by nurseries and widely available to gardeners and seeds itself around vigorously in some gardens, provided that there are more than one clone grown.

CULTIVATION. It grows happily in any decent humus-rich soil. Those who know claim that it will tolerate a high pH. Considering its native habitats, one might suggest that a deep, humus-rich soil mainly consisting of leaf-mould, a sloping surface, and light shade will be best for it. Yet it even succeeds well, in ordinary border soil in the dry regions of eastern England!

It has a rather awkward growth-cycle. The leaves appear with the cool days of autumn and remain green over the winter. In frost they attain 'the cooked look' but rise again unaffected upon the return of mild weather. The growth continues through the spring and from March to June the flowers are present. With the summer-heat the plants go dormant for about two months. A sloping soil-surface will help the plants over the winter in areas were the climate is more severe; this will provide surface drainage for rain on frozen soil and so help keep fungal rots away.

Hardiness has not yet been wholly explored. The altitude where it grows in Sichuan is on the low side and it is possible that it will be killed by severe frosts, although it is known to survive -23 degrees C.

PROPAGATION. The basal parts consist of short horizontal stems which are densely clothed with thick pale fleshy scales and these divide readily. Some cultivars also produce scaly stolons and runners that makes propagation even easier. Leaf-cuttings, with the fleshy bases intact, will also form new plants. Some cultivars have been subject to micro-propagation, which may prove economically beneficial if one wants to earn some money on a new cultivar, but it will not be profitable after the first release.

Division can be made in early spring but is best carried out when the autumn-flush is about to begin (by mid-August). Simply lift the plant, tear it apart and plant the tiny divisions; you cannot fail! Late planted specimens often continue growing throughout the summer and may still be in flower in October.

If seed is set, sow it directly after harvest onto a slightly acid to neutral, sterilised compost, cover it and keep moist. Germination can probably be expected in September and the plants should be able to grow large enough to survive the first winter.

Five cultivars are available, all with considerable merits:

'Blue Panda' (R. Hatch). The most common one grown in the Pacific North-west (USA) and becoming increasingly common in Europe. It has pale blue-green, unmarked, leaves and sky-blue flowers with curved spurs. It is clump-forming without any tendency to produce runners. This introduction comes closest to the type of *C. flexuosa*.

'Purple Leaf' (C.D.&R. 528a). The leaves and stems are reddish purple with dark blood-red markings at the base of the leaflets; flowers up to 28 mm long. The neatest clone.

'Père David' (C.D.&R. 528b). The leaves are glaucous with blood-red markings on and near the midrib; flowers up to 35 mm long; very freely stoloniferous.

'China Blue' (C.D.&R. 585). The leaves brownish-green in winter, with small red blotches at the base of the lobes; flowers greenish- to sky-blue, up to 31 mm long.

'Balang Mist' (C. Grey-Wilson, 1993) is a newcomer from the Balangshan above Wolong. It is quite similar to the C.D.&R. collections but flowers are pale and whitish with a very pleasing flush of blue. Clump-forming and non-stoloniferous, like 'Blue Panda'.

C. elata Franch. Pl. 104.

This species has been recently brought into cultivation. It is similar to *C. flexuosa* and grows in the same area but it can be distinguished by its broader leaflets, broader claw to the lower petal and by the narrowly obovoid fruit. Like *C. flexuosa*, it is an extremely polymorphic species, whose pattern of variation still needs to be clarified.

The clone that we are growing is about 40 cm tall in flower. The clear dark blue flowers are borne in a compact few-flowered raceme and are about the size of those of *C. flexousa*. It is generally a taller plant which comes into flower several weeks later.

It spreads slowly but continuously by means of the root-stock. Contrary to *C. flexuosa* it is not green through the winter but with an ordinary perennial growth-cycle, which can make it a better plant in some gardens.

Cultivation and propagation as for *C. flexuosa*. It will self-sow in favoured gardens.

C. leucanthema C.Y.Wu

A frequent species on Mount Omei (Emei Shan) and neighbouring mountains in Sichuan. It is similar to *C. elata* but with a lax pyramidal raceme of elegantly nodding purple (rarely white) flowers. Recently introduced into cultivation.

C. temulifolia Franch.

This deviates from the other species in this section by its compound leaves with large crenate-dentate leaflets. The flowers are few and large. Recently introduced into cultivation and it is hoped that it will soon settle down.

SECTION MUCRONATAE

A small group of 3 species from Central Sichuan.

C. mucronata Franch.

A very elegant plant with crenate leaflets and a long spike of purple, acuminate flowers, 25 mm long with long narrow, sometimes strongly upcurved spur, and peculiar long triangular stigma. It is grown in a few British gardens and is pictured in 'Perennials' by Rix & Phillips (1991) as *C. sheareri** S.Moore (this is a more eastern species). The similar *C. vivipara** Fedde produces conspicuous bulblets in the leaf axils. *C. pseudomucronata** C.Y.Wu is distinguished from *C. mucronata* mainly by a short and broad stigma and smaller sepals.

SECTION HAMATAE

This section comprises low-growing perennials with several thick soft roots subtending a basal distichous rosette of oblong pinnate leaves. We grow one representative from each of the two distinctive subsections:

C. polyphylla Hand.-Mazz. Pl. 105.

This interesting species has a stalked umbel of purplish-blue flowers above a rosette of finely divided oblong leaves. It is known from NW Yunnan and SE Tibet. The flowers are inconspicuous and of short duration in the self-compatible plants from the wetter southern parts of the Beimashan that we grow. Larger-flowered forms are found in the wild: Frank Kingdon-Ward recorded it as being 'beautiful' on one herbarium label. Judging from herbarium specimens, its large-flowered cousin, *C. pseudofluminicola* Fedde*, from S Sichuan is, despite its ugly name, a real beauty with large blue or purplish flowers.

C. hamata Franch. Pl. 107.

This species can be found in NW Yunnan and neighbouring areas to the north but is replaced in central Sichuan by the more robust *C. pseudohamata* Fedde* and in Tibet by *C. conspersa* Maxim*. They are all quite similar, with leafy ascending stems and very dense cylindrical racemes of blue-tipped yellow flowers, arising from a basal rosette of attractively dissected blue- or grey-green foliage.

In nature *C. hamata* is confined to moist mineral-soils and frequently stands with its yellow cord-like roots in running water. In gardens, conditions like that can be difficult to reproduce. We have planted a few in ordinary peat-garden soil in an open north-slope on the rock-garden. To date it has thrived, producing nice clumps of decorative, roundly lobed, glaucous leaves and it has flowered well. Seed has also been set in the garden, so it may remain in cultivation.

Corydalis pseudohamata (Pl. 106) appears to be an even more attractive plant due to its more upright habit, although it is probably not in cultivation. The Editor (CG-W) has seen it in several localities in northern Sichuan, particularly in the vicinity of Juizhaigou where it inhabited marshy gorund in association with *Caltha palustris*, *Primula secundiflora* and other moisture-loving species.

SECTION CAPNOGORIUM

This section comprises a number of robust tap-rooted or rhizomatous perennials. Unlike the species of the next section, the fruit is not explosively dehiscent. They are found mainly in Gansu and Qinghai provinces. They agree with the core tuberous groups in fruit and seed-structure and may well be closely related to these. Most of the species grow in Qinghai, W Gansu and N Sichuan, including some very large-flowered ones. Keep your eyes open for *CC. cristagalli* Maxim., *potanini* Maxim., *grandiflora* C.Y.Wu & Z.Y.Su, and *livida* Maxim. next time you are in that neighbourhood..

C. nobilis (L.) Pers. Pl. 108.

A widespread park-ornamental in Sweden and Finland, with large globular heads of yellow and white, dark-tipped flowers. However, it is much rarer in gardens in Britain and the rest of Europe. Together with the species of section Archaecapnos, probably the most conspicuous and eye-catching species in the genus. It comes from the Altai Mountains southwards to the Tienshan.

This species was described by Linnaeus in 1767 as *Fumaria nobilis*. He had received seed from his disciple, Eric Laxman, who had collected it on the high snow-clad mountain Sinisopka by Kolyvan in the Siberian prefecture Tomsk. Linnaeus predicted a great horticultural future for the species but its distribution in gardens is still limited.

Swedish floras list it as a garden escape and it can be really invasive in park-environments. It grows up to 50 cm tall, forming lush stands of glaucous, dissected foliage superseeded by dense flowerheads. In Sweden it blooms from April to early June but by midsummer, when seed has been set, it dies back to a coarse, fleshy taproot.

It is much requested by gardeners and can be ordered from seed-lists. The seed will survive fairly well; we have raised a new stock from wild-collected seed that had been stored for six months.

Corydalis nobilis produces only two cotyledons during the first season and, in that respect, shows some affinity with the tuberous species. The second year, growth rate is higher and the first plants may flower in the third season. Once established it is soundly perennial and can start to conquer your garden.

C. flaccida Hook. f. & Th. Pl. 109.

This rhizomatous forest floor herb has a wide distribution from Nepal to Sichuan in western China. The stiff leafy stems sometimes reach a metre in height. The lower leaves are large and much-divided with small rounded leaflets. The flowers are small with a short spur and broad obtuse lips, and are often peculiarly variegated in purple, pink and blue.

We have seen it wild in Yunnan, growing in a fertile humus-soil by small brooks in the shade of *Abies*, together with *Primula septemloba, Aquilegia rockii,* and *Cardamine macrophylla.* In Gothenburg we have chosen a shady, cool spot in the peat-garden where it seems to enjoy life. A collection from Sikkim was once grown but subsequently lost.

With this species the grey-green *Thalictrum*-like foliage is the main attraction (of course, the flowers are also extremely beautiful, that is when observed through a magnifying glass).

SECTION OOCAPNOS

Oocapnos, which contains three species, was once segregated as an independent genus (*Cysticorydalis* Fedde ex Ikonnikov) but, apart from the vesicular (bladderlike) fruits, it fits reasonably within *Corydalis.* Like the tuberous groups, species of this section germinate with one cotyledon only.

The two cultivated species originate from dry areas and are difficult to grow in the open garden. We find them best kept in the alpine house. To hold on to the unstable mountain-screes, the underground part of the stem is long and tough, and a deep pot is recommended. The compost should be well-aerated and dominated by mineral material. A good amount of water and liquid feeding should be supplied during the growing season, somewhat withheld in summer, and resumed in August. During dormancy they should be kept on the dry side.

C. crassifolia Royle Pl. 110.
(including *C. crassissima* Camb.)

Easily distinguished by the leaves with their few broad leaflets, sometimes almost entire. The leaves are very fleshy and mottled grey; it is interesting to note that leaves similar in form, texture and coloration

have also evolved in a few species of section Dactylotuber. The flowers are pale blue or white with purplish margins, obtuse at apex, and without dorsal crests on the outer petals. It inhabits rough screes at high altitudes in West Himalaya. Per Wendelbo (1974) restricted the name *C. crassifolia* to the East Kashmir plants, using *C. crassissima* Camb. for the majority, but we have adopted a broader concept.

We first saw this plant by the Batura Glacier in Northern Pakistan and were struck by the leathery, sunburnt leaves. It is one of the most aberrant species of the genus. Seed is occasionally available and tolerates dry storage. It is slow to germinate and may require two to three winters before the cotyledon appears. This is followed by one or a few tiny true leaves in the first season.

In cultivation leaves are formed all through the growing season. At first they are a nice sight; succulent, metallic blue-green with a red petiole. In summer mildew ruins them and aphids devour the juicy, new growth. It is not an easy plant to maintain but we have flowered (and lost) it in the alpine house.

C. fedtschenkoana Regel. Pl. 112.

The leaves of this species are strongly glaucous, ovate, and pinnately divided into many small acute lobes. It has a wide distribution in the Pamirs.

For a long time this was an unattainable dream-plant of ours. Lately seed has been introduced under a variety of names by Joseph Halda — bless him. These introductions have been listed as *Cysticorydalis* and the descriptions tells us that the foliage is 'gorgeous chalky-blue', 'whitish pubescent' or 'dark green', more or less finely divided. The flowers vary from purplish, to pale violet, pink and white.

For the names *Cysticorydalis alaica* and *C. turczaninovii* of Josef Halda's seed lists we have not been able to find any references. The plants depicted are very similar to *Corydalis fedtschenkoana.*

Seed has germinated well after two to three winters but it is a very difficult plant to grow on and we have not yet flowered it.

SECTION CHRYSOCAPNOS

This section comprises Himalayan perennials with long, densely scaly rhizomes, leaves crowded at base and yellow flowers. The explosively dehiscent fruit capsules are born on recurved pedicels. The section was considered part of section Capnogorium sensu lato in Lidén & Zetterlund (*Bulletin Alpine Garden*

Society Vol. 56), but it seems much closer to section Ramoso-sibiricae.

CULTIVATION. Several species have been tried in cultivation. They are short-lived perennials, growing well for two or three years but later, when the leaf-rosettes become crowded, they tend to rot off. Seed is the best means of increase. They can be dried off and still remain viable; however, they require one or two winters in order to germinate but the young seedlings are quite easy to grow on. They generally flower from their second year.

Those species that do not produce seed by selfing can be propagated by division. This is best carried out in the early spring just as the leaves are starting to grow. Lift the plants and clean them, detaching individual rosettes with as long a portion of rhizome as possible. Plantlets with an ample set of roots can be potted and grown on but rosettes with few or no roots should be treated as cuttings. In nature they inhabit different situations and climatic regions and, accordingly, require different garden environments. Most species are best grown in an exposed, acid scree, but some do better on an open peat-wall. Initially they are safest in an alpine house where they grow into good-looking specimens.

C. tibetica Hook. f. & Th.
C. pseudocrithmifolia Jafri

A usually papillose-hairy alpine from the inner parts of Kashmir, distinguished from similar species by its greyish habit, linear fruits and tuberculate seeds.

This is a common plant in the Karakoram, where it grows on cliff-walls at 3000-4500 meters altitude. Previously in cultivation in Gothenburg (photo in *Bulletin Alpine Garden Society* Vol. 56) but lost by accident and we miss it. It was a nice dwarf plant with fine-cut grey foliage and large yellow flowers.

C. govaniana Wall.

A rosette-forming early-flowering plant, widespread in the Himalaya eastwards to east Nepal. The flowering stems bear two small opposite leaves and the bracts are pectinate-dentate.

A rather lush plant in cultivation with flowers unfortunately engulfed by the foliage.

C. crithmifolia Royle

Similar to the preceding species but with far fewer, smaller, less divided, more narrow-lobed, olive-green leaves and entire narrow bracts. The flowers are well-presented so it is a better garden-plant than the previous. We are growing a collection from Nanga Parbat in northern Pakistan which we found in gravel in the conifer-zone. It is native to the W Himalaya.

C. gortschakovii Schrenk.

A more conspicuous plant with erect, leafy, branched stems. It grows from the Altai southwards to NW Pakistan with three vicariant subspecies. It is similar to the two following species but more robust and larger-flowered. It has been introduced to cultivation by Gert Böhme and Josef Halda.

Corydalis moorcroftiana Hook. f. & Th., a related species from Ladak and SW Tibet, is not known to be in cultivation.

C. pakistanica Jafri. Pl. 113.

A short-lived glaucous perennial with branched leafy stems, producing bright yellow flowers in profusion. It is self-compatible but the capsules and seeds are surprisingly small and are easily overlooked; they should be harvested before they explode! Quite common in moist depressions at alpine altitudes in the Pakistan Himalaya.

Two SEP collections of this species (nos. 141 and 181, initially distributed as *C. thyrsiflora*) are established in Gothenburg. Indivudual plants will live for two or three years. The blue-green rosettes are most decorative and the golden flowers makes it a superb plant for a cool part of the rock-garden where it sows itself prolifically.

C. thyrsiflora Prain.

A more easterly plant, similar to *C. pakistanica*, but longer lived and with larger and more divided leaves. The racemes are very dense and characteristically pointed in bud. It differs from *C. pakistanica* also in being self-incompatible.

C. pachypoda Franch.*

An interesting yellow-flowered species from NW Yunnan is pictured in the Alpine Garden Society Bulletin (Grey-Wilson, 56:138) but regrettably it is not in cultivation as far as we know. The species grows in damp rocky places and screes, sometimes in low scrub close to the tree line. The yellow flowers are attractively marked with green.

C. chaerophylla DC.

A coarse herb, reaching more than one meter in height. The dark-green leaves look like those of the sweet cicely, *Myrrhis odorata*, and are produced in abundance from a strong 'taproot'. In late summer the dense-branched racemes of small, pale yellow flowers appear. A common woodland herb in the central and eastern Himalaya. *CC. stipulata* Lidén*, *terracina* Lidén*, *geraniifolia* Hook. f. & Th., and *borii* C.Fischer* are closely related larger-flowered species with more restricted distributions.

Corydalis chaerophylla is a good plant for a rich, moist soil in a woodland garden where it can be allowed to develop. The foliage is most decorative, and capable of swamping weeds, though the flowers are not exciting. It sets seed in abundance and youngsters will pop up if you have found the right spot for it.

SECTION LATIFLORAE

The species of this section are similar to the previous section in their vegetative parts but are lower growing and branched and have very broad, short-spurred, spongy flowers. The pedicels are erect and apically hooked in fruit. They grow at high altitudes in the central Himalaya.

C. latiflora Hook. f. & Th. Pl. 115.
(incl. *C. alburyi* Ludlow and *C. gerdae* Fedde)
A frequent inhabitant of rough screes of the Nepal Himalaya, this lovely species has been found up to 6000 m altitude. It has few-flowered racemes of greyish-blue, very fragrant, flowers with green and purplish markings, which barely overtop the loose cushion of greyish leaves. It is an extraordinary beautiful plant, distributed from West Nepal to Bhutan. The geographical variation is rather clearcut, and three or four subspecies could probably be recognised. The most distinctive one is found in West Nepal by Toridwari Banyang and has very large flowers and surprisingly small leaves (Lidén 1989).

We grew this fragile little gem for a few years. It did well and flowered a few seasons in the alpine house, grown in a gritty, acid mix, and kept as cool as possible. It is possible to increase it by means of early spring division and by seed, formed after cross-pollination by hand. In order to stay alive it requires a great deal of attention; unfortunately in the long run we failed to provide this!

C. meifolia Wall. Pl. 111.
This Himalayan species has beautiful and finely cut leaves with very narrowly linear leaflets. The yellow

to orange flowers, often with purplish-brown spurs, are born in conspicuous racemes. Widespread but scattered from Kumaon to Bhutan, it is particularly abundant in the upper reaches of the Barun Khola in eastern Nepal.

A striking plant (the contrast between the grey, filigree foliage and the large, tubby flowers is startling) which we cultivate in the alpine-house, presuming it to be too frail to survive in the open garden. Our plant is grown in an gritty, acid mix, and kept moist through the summer. No seed has set and division is not yet possible, so it is difficult to propagate. It has been repeatedly introduced by various collectors but has never gained a firm foothold in cultivation.

C. stracheyi Prain
Probably related to the above but with slender, branched stems and small inconspicuous flowers. It is found almost throughout the Himalaya on wet stabilised slopes but has been lost to cultivation.

C. megacalyx Ludlow. Pl. 117.
This pretty high alpine Nepalese cushion plant survived less than a season in Gothenburg. The similar *C. clavibracteata* Ludlow* is pictured in Lidén & Zetterlund (*Alpine Garden Society Bulletin* 57:365). In the wild *C. megacalyx* forms a neat hummock of finely dissected leaves smothered in summer by small cream or yellow flowers. It is a denizen of high shales and screes well above the tree line.

C. hendersonii Hemsl.*
This species, which probably has the altitude record among *Corydalis* (6300 m; i.e. very close to that for flowering plants as a whole), has never been tried in cultivation. Its comparatively large flowers are held vertically with only the apices rising above the dense little cushion formed by the small leaves and bracts.

SECTION RAMOSO-SIBIRICAE

A section which comprises annuals as well as perennials with branched leafy stems, yellow flowers and explosively dehiscent capsules on recurved pedicels. Some species are more or less weedy, and are often found in botanic gardens, introduced intentionally or unintentionally. This section is difficult to demarcate from section *Chrysocapnos*. It includes perhaps 10 species in China, the Himalaya, Japan, Korea and SE Russia.

C. vaginans Royle

A leafy branched erect biennial or annual, the flowers with deeply dentate crests. Too uninteresting and weedy to be let into your garden; the same could be said about the following species.

C. ochotensis Turcz.

A more juicy and straggling herb with the flowers partly concealed by entire bracts.

C. acropteryx Fedde

A species from N Sichuan which survived one season at the Royal Botanic Gardens Kew. It differs from *C. ochotensis* in its more upright thinner and tougher habit, smaller divided bracts and narrow curved spurs.

C. cornuta Royle

C. mildbraedii Fedde

Similar to *C. vaginans* but with entire crests and ornamented seeds. It has a remarkable distribution, being found in the Himalaya and the mountains of East Africa (Lidén 1993b).

C. capnoides (L.)Pers.

A diffuse little biennial with small pale yellow flowers subtended by large divided bracts. Recently introduced from the Tienshan. It has a wide and scattered distribution which includes eastern central Europe, the Urals, Mongolia and the Chinese Tien Shan.

SECTION FUMARIOIDES

This section owes its name to the vegetative likeness of many of its species to the European broad-leaved fumitories, *Fumaria*. It is mainly an eastern Himalayan group, but reaches to Kashmir in the west and Siberia in the north. About 10 species are or have been in cultivation, but are of no ornamental interest (they include *CC. cavei* D.G.Long, *zhongdianensis* Z.Y.Su & Lidén, *pseudotongolensis* Lidén, *yui* Lidén, *calycina* Lidén, *casimiriana* Prain, *longipes* DC., *gracillima* C.Y.Wu, *aconitiflora* Lidén, *sibirica* (L.) Pers., *impatiens* DC.).

SECTION DAVIDIANAE

This section comprises large, erect, leafy yellow-flowered perennials with a dense cluster of long wiry roots. The leaves are large with triangular repeatedly ternate laminas. The section is heterogeneous and *C. davidii* (unfortunately the type of the section) may in fact be more closely related to Section Elatae.

C. tenerrima C.Y.Wu, Z.Y.Su & Lidén. Pl. 114.

Previously only known from a single specimen collected by T. T. Yü near Atuntse (Dechen, Deqen) in NW Yunnan, this species was refound by the KGB expedition in 1993. It formed dense stands in the semi-shade of mixed woodland from 3200 to 4000 m. It is distinguished from the other species in the section by its more divided leaves with less discrete lobes, as well as by its many-flowered racemes of short, broad-lipped flowers, produced in late summer.

A useful woodland plant in gardens. It does not provide much in the way of colour, but a frail, delicate effect that is quite pleasing. Propagation is easily done in spring by separating the growing points that crown bundles of long, cord-like roots.

C. yunnanensis Franch. Pl. 116.

(incl. *CC. pterygopetala* and *delphinoides*)

This species is widespread in W Yunnan. Compared with *C. tenerrima*, it is more branched from the base, has less divided leaves and the flowers are narrower but larger. A very variable early summer flowering species, that possibly should be split up.

The plants that we are growing are about 70 cm tall in flower. The *Thalictrum*-like, bright-green foliage is of a thin texture and sensitive to direct sun and drying winds. The elegantly curved, yellow flowers are borne on slender pedicels and gives a pleasingly refined effect. They also have a strong fragrance, by some considered very pleasant, but others compare it to horse-manure. It is certainly worthy of a prime position in the woodland garden.

Propagation: as for *C. tenerrima*.

C. saltatoria W.W.Smith*

One of the strangest species of *Corydalis*. The peduncles, pedicels and bracts are extremely thin. We quote Reginald Farrer: 'very thin textured and squashy, flowers falling in long graceful loose flights of golden sparks'. It comes from the Burma/Yunnan border region but is not in cultivation.

C. davidii Franch.

A common roadside plant in mountains of SW China. Recently introduced into cultivation.

SECTION ASTEROSTIGMATA

This section comprises much-branched herbs with leafy stems, usually with narrow capsules and purple flowers. They are found mainly in Yunnan and southern Sichuan, but *C. leptocarpa* Hook. f. & Th.* goes west to Nepal.

C. taliensis Franch.

This species grows on walls and in waste places in the old city of Dali and further north as far as Lijiang. If given favourable conditions it branches profusely and can attain astonishing proportions.

If hardy, it will be a nice plant for walls and crevices, producing attractive cascades of foliage in an attractive olive-green with lighter markings. The flowers are sweetly scented, of a decent size, lilac to purple, and produced in compact racemes. Our plants have proved easy to propagate; the nodes of the shoots tend to root if they come into contact with a moist medium. So far we have only tried it in the alpine house; however, one must remember that it is a plant of a warm-temperate region.

C. smithiana Fedde. Pl. 118, 119.

A plant similar to *C. taliensis* but with acute leaflets, laxer racemes and lanceolate instead of linear fruits. It grows in stony places (roadsides etc.), from Lijiang in NW Yunnan northwards to S Sichuan.

Corydalis smithiana is a biennial that was first introduced by the CLD expedition, but much of the material at present in cultivation came in from the ACE and KGB expeditions. The seeds survive dry storage and require one or two cold periods to germinate. In the first year it forms a rather inconspicuous rosette. The following summer the red-purple to lilac or almost white flowers are borne on 20 to 30 cm tall branched stems. They are rather large and heavily perfumed with a mysterious, musky scent.

It has proved easy in the garden where it can be grown either amongst rocks or in peat and where it will self-sow readily; lots of seed is set and this germinates freely and quickly; a nice and welcome little 'weed'.

SECTION PUBICAULES

C. petrophila Franch.

An annual or short-lived perennial collected by the KGB expedition around Deqen (Atuntse) in NW Yunnan. In nature it grows on walls, as well as in shady positions in secondary shrub, and is extremely plastic. It is superficially similar to *C. smithiana* but the fruits are short and broad, reflexed on erect pedicels. The flowers are creamy white in shade, but become reddish in brighter, more exposed sites.

SECTION INCISAE

A section of annuals and biennials with branched erect stems and erecto-patent straight pedicels with pendent explosive fruits. The two species mentioned below are both found in a tap-rooted annual form and (more commonly) in a 'tuberous' biennial form.
The seeds will survive dry storage.

C. incisa (Thunb.) Pers. Pl. 120.

A common species in Japan, Korea and eastern China. It has dentate leaflets and shortly crested violet-blue flowers, which in combination with the swollen root (like a pale radish) makes it easily distinguishable.

A startling biennial. The seeds of this species germinate in the spring and build up small, bright green rosettes. In the summer it withdraws to the root to continue growth in the autumn. The rosette remains green through the winter and, in the following spring, it produces compact racemes of dramatically coloured flowers.

C. linstowiana Fedde. Pl. 121.

A charming plant confined to the Sichuanese mountains. It is a nice plant with (purplish-)blue uncrested obtuse flowers and a root similar to a small carrot. It differs from *C. incisa* also by its large fimbriate sepals, the entire leaf-lobes and by the peculiar fimbriate stipules.

Rather a good garden-plant; biennial and a prolific seeder.

SECTION ORIENTALES

C. bungeana Turcz.

A small lowland annual from E China with small white and dark purple flowers.

SUBGENUS CHREMNOCAPNOS

SECTION BIPAPILLATA

This section comprises two species of erect perennials with tall leafy stems and dense racemes of yellow flowers. They differ from all other *Corydalis* in the small stigma with two erect lobes and the lack of elaiosomes on the seeds.

C. semenovii Regel & Herder
Native to the Tienshan, this species was in cultivation in the late 1800s. It is an erect perennial growing 30-60 cm tall, with foliage reminiscent of *Thalictrum minus*. The flowers are about 15 mm long, white or yellow, and are borne in a compact raceme. A plant of spruce-forests and probably an easy garden plant.

SECTION STRICTAE

In arid parts of Central Asia and China there are about 20 species of the section *Strictae* to be found. They are often chasmophytic (cliff dwellers), with very glaucous and fleshy stems and leaves and yellow short-spurred flowers.

Some species are attractive, forming dense tufts of short stems crowned by small rosettes of decorative foliage and interestingly formed and, sometimes, intriguingly coloured flowers, while others are more erect and lax. Their seeds can be dried off, so they can be safely ordered from seed-lists.

Being either decided cliff-dwellers, or plants of arid regions, they require a very well-drained compost and a restrained rootgrowth in cultivation. In the open garden they stand the best chances in a trough or a raised bed.

C. rupestris Boiss. Pl. 123.
This, the most widespread species of the subsection in cultivation, is a cushion-like chasmophyte, with pinnately divided, markedly glaucous leaves and dense racemes of golden flowers. Very handsome, and producing plenty of seeds through selfing. The fruit is tough-walled, ovate and tapering. It is native to arid regions of Iran, Baluchistan and Afghanistan.

It is safest grown in the alpine-house where it seeds around in the plunge material.

C. fimbrillifera Korsh.
This species has rosettes of olive-green, narrowly segmented leaves, erect leafy stems up to 25 cm high,

and dense heads of deeply fringed flowers in a very strange yellow-orange. A native of Chitral.

A most peculiar, yet attractive species.

C. adunca Maxim.
Large plants with basal rosettes of much-divided, very glaucous leaves and erect stems to 70 cm tall, branched and rather lax. Thin sprays of small yellow and copper flowers appear during the summer. It is native to western China from Gansu southwards to Yunnan with a couple of vicariant races. A roadside weed of the dry valleys. Several accessions are in cultivation.

This species is really too large for the alpine house. In the rock-garden it is short-lived or, in some cases, annual. If the summer is warm and long enough, it will set plenty of seed in the open to ensure its existence. In areas that experience a less certain climate it is best started off in a greenhouse.

C. flabellata Edgew.
The attractive feature of this species is its rosettes of oblong, once-pinnate, round-lobed, *Adiantum*-like, succulent, grey-green leaves. The yellow flowers are rather inconspicuous. Native to dry regions of the W Himalaya, being especially abundant in some valleys in western Nepal, where it inhabits dry cliff crevices.

C. bucharica Popov. Pl. 122.
A rather small, branched plant with orange flowers in which the spur is at least half as long as the limb (in the above-mentioned species about a third or less). Native to the Pamir Mountains. Not terribly exciting.

SUBGENUS SOPHOROCAPNOS

SECTION CHEILANTHIFOLIAE

Branched annuals, biennials or perennials with small to medium-sized flowers with a short blunt spur and narrow capsules with numerous small seeds. It comprises only five species, three of which are of interest here:

C. ophiocarpa Hook. f. & Th.
A biennial with leafy branched erect stems and small creamy (usually purple-tipped) flowers borne in long narrow spikes. The capsules are narrow and contorted. It is a widespread and somewhat weedy species from Bhutan to Gansu and Taiwan. Plants from Taiwan differ in their shorter racemes of wholly pale flowers.

A biennial garden-weed with large rosettes of juicy foliage, in a peculiar shade of bronzy-blue and a strange translucent look with the flowers disturbing the picture. Actually, best avoided. Sometimes grown under the name *C. tashiroi*, which is in fact a plant in section *Sophorocapnos*.

C. cheilanthifolia Hemsl. Pl. 124.

More or less scapose perennial with a large rosette (to 45 cm diameter) of pinnately divided oblong, fern-like leaves with acute leaflets. These attain attractive shades of light- and dark-green during the growing season and remain through the winter, attractively flushed with rust. The golden flowers are formed in profusion in long racemes in early spring. Native of China (Hubei, Guizhou and E Sichuan) where it is found amid stones on the banks of streams in the higher mountains.

It is an excellent garden-plant that will take to a wide range of environments, being at home in the rock-garden, the peat-garden as well as in the wood-land border. It was introduced by E. H. Wilson in the early 1900s and has remained in cultivation ever since. In 1969 it was rewarded an A.M. by the Royal Horticultural Society. Plants can be divided with ease in the late summer or early autum and even unrooted pieces will root readily when planted directly into the garden. The seed can take dry-storage so it is well distributed in Western gardens. When established it spreads efficiently by seed.

C. moupinensis Franch.*

This species, which comes from Baoxing (formerly Moupin), is very similar to the above but has larger flowers and broader obtuse leaflets. It is not in cultivation.

C. racemosa (Thunb.) Pers.

An annual eastern Chinese and Japanese weed, similar to a small-flowered Fumitory and of little garden merit.

SECTION THALICTRIFOLIAE

A section containing chasmophytic (cliff-dwelling) perennials, including some very good ornamental ones.

C. saxicola G.S.Bunting
C. thalictrifolia Franch., non Regel.

A low-growing branched perennial, with broad-lobed, *Thalictrum*-like foliage, light green when fresh,

coppery red with age. Flowers rather large, pale yellow in a lax few-flowered raceme. In nature a limestone lover, growing in rocky soil on ledges and cliffs in warm situations at low altitudes, sometimes together with *Primula sinensis*. It is quite widespread in Central China from Guangxi to Shaanxi.

This tender plant was introduced by E. H. Wilson from West Hubei and distributed by Messrs. Veitch & Sons, flowering in cultivation for the first time in 1901. In 1902 it was written up in *Curtis's Botanical Magazine* (tab. 7830). On the 10th of June 1902 it was awarded an F.C.C. by the Royal Horticultural Society It is still with us, being a useful plant for the conservatory but unfortunately it is not hardy outdoors, even in milder parts of Britain. The flowering period is long and lots of seeds are produced; these will take dry storage readily.

C. saxicola x wilsonii

These two species cross quite easily, producing fertile offspring. The F1 generation is in every respect intermediate but the F2 generation varies tremendously. All are attractive plants well worth cultivating and free-flowering.

C. wilsonii N.E.Br. Pl. 125.

A most valuable species with its low habit and long dense racemes of rather large, intensely yellow, fragrant, pointed flowers. The leaves are twice pinnately divided and very glaucous, appearing pale blue. It was found by E.H. Wilson on dry rocks at c. 3050 m, at Fang in Hubei.

A lovely tender plant which is safest in the alpine house where it starts flowering in early spring and continues through the summer. Originally introduced by E. H. Wilson it flowered for the first time in cultivation in 1903. The ancestors are still cultivated. It was awarded an A.M. in 1905. Seed is formed in profusion and new plants appear in strange nooks and crannies in the alpine house. It was pictured in *Curtis's Botanical Magazine* in 1904 (tab. 7939).

C. tomentella Franch.
C. tomentosa N.E.Br.

Closely related to the preceding species but finely puberulent and with smaller flowers, like a tinier, slightly furry version of *C. wilsonii*. Native to Hubei, Sichuan and Shaanxi provinces of China.

This species was first introduced to Europe in 1894 by M. de Vilmorin and later by E.H. Wilson. It received an A.M. in 1937 when shown at the Royal Horticultural Society. It remains in cultivation, and has the same demands and qualities as *C. wilsoni*, though it is even more susceptible to excess water, especially during the winter.

C. fangshanensis W.T.Wang*

Similar to *C. wilsonii* but with white flowers tipped with purple. It grows only a couple of hours away from Beijing, and so is within easy reach. It is found in Hubei, Shanxi, Henan and Gansu provinces. Not in cultivation but certainly worth an expedition.

C. latiloba (Franch.) Hand.Mazz.

A variable species related to *C. wilsonii* but with shorter racemes, longer pedicels and shorter and broader fruits. It was seen by the KGB expedition in NW Yunnan (Wangshui), on very dry otherwise bare rocks and later captured in the dragon fountain outside a hotel in Zhongdian, NW Yunnan, where it was clinging to the roof of a small depression in a tufa block. Similar to *C. rupestris* but even more condensed and with quite different stigmas and seeds.

In cultivation it produces tight tufts of rather small leaves.

SECTION SOPHOROCAPNOS

This section, which contains about twenty species, is distributed on both sides of the Pacific and includes mostly yellow-flowered annuals and biennials. Though some of them can be quite striking early in the season, they later attain a rather diffuse and untidy look. Some of the species are occasionally cultivated. The Japanese *CC. speciosa* Maxim., *hondoensis* Ohwi [= *C. pallida* (Thunb.) Pers. var. *tenuis* Yatabe], and *heterocarpa* Sieb. & Zucc. are recommendable biennials producing stems about 40 cm tall bearing rather large, golden flowers from decorative glabrous, glaucescent rosettes. They require woodland conditions. *C. foetida* C.Y.Wu & Z.Y.Su, is a small yellow plant from C China for the rock-garden. *CC. aurea* Willd., *flavula* and *micrantha* are three American species that form neat rosettes of glaucous, almost blue foliage, over which short-stalked, yellow flowers appear. Nice 'weeds' for dry parts of the rock-garden.

SECTION AULACOSTIGMA

C. edulis Maxim.

The only species in the section is an erect annual from C and SE China with broadly obtuse, rather pretty pink flowers.

Snipp, snap, snut-så var sagean slut!

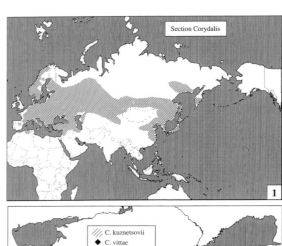

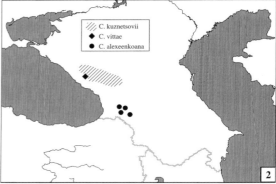

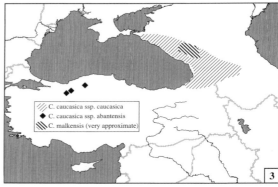

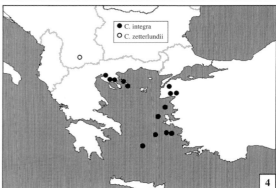

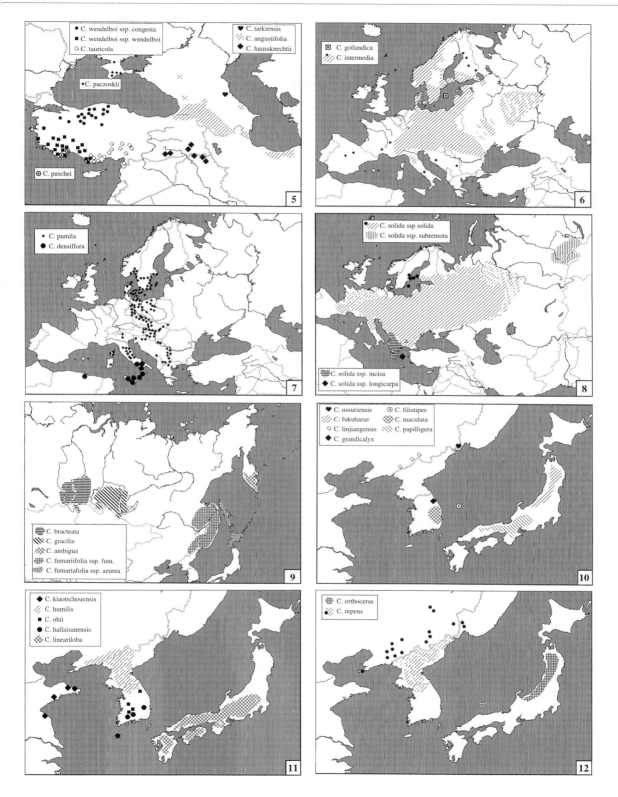

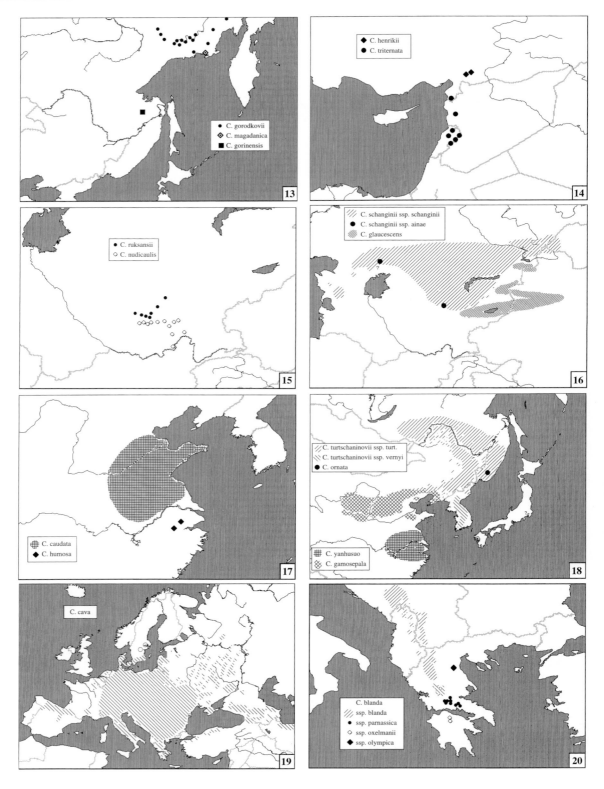

Plate 105. *Corydalis polyphylla*
Plate 106. *Corydalis pseudohamata*, W China, NW Sichuan, Juizhaigou
Plate 107. *Corydalis hamata*, SW China, NW Yunnan, Beimashan
Plate 108. *Corydalis nobilis*
Plate 109. *Corydalis flaccida*

Plate 110. *Corydalis crassifolia*
Plate 111. *Corydalis meifolia*
Plate 112. *Corydalis fedtschenkoana*, in fruit
Plate 113. *Corydalis pakistanica*
Plate 114. *Corydalis tenerrima*

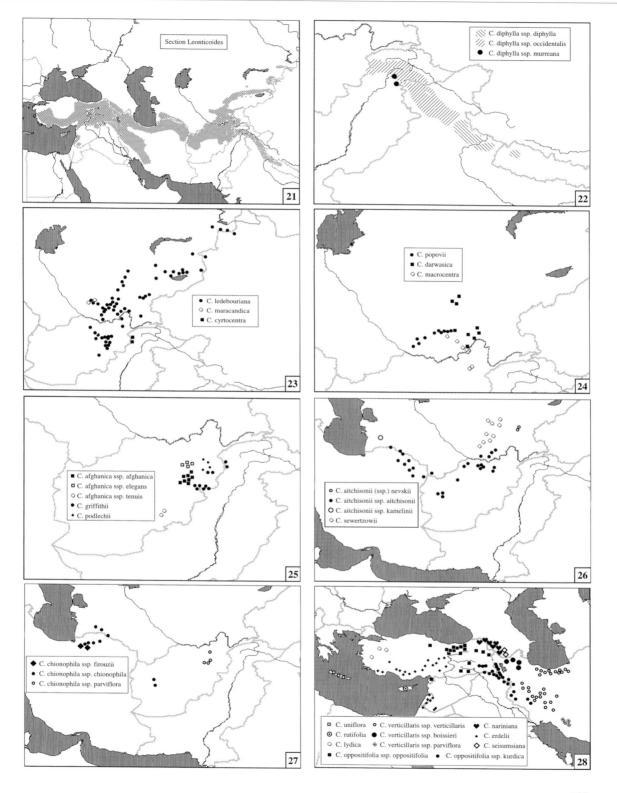

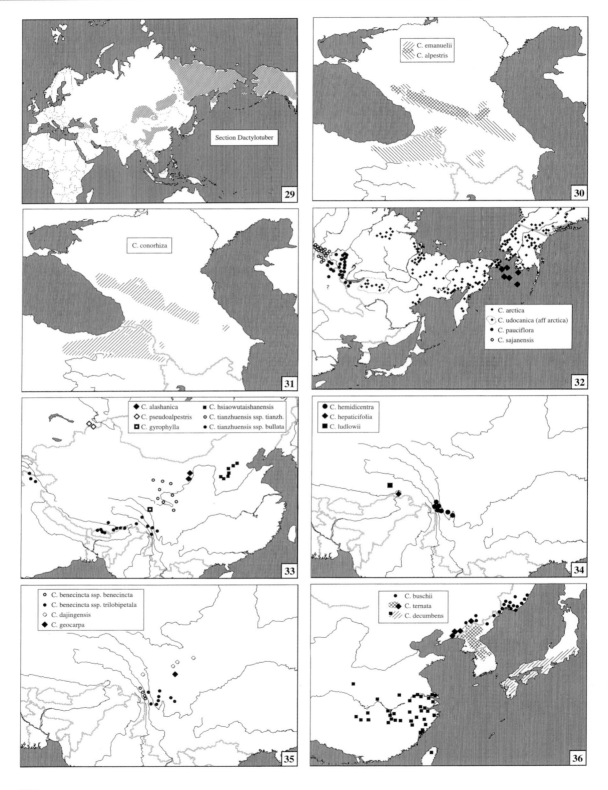

REFERENCES

Bao D. 1988. Control studies of the downy mildew of yanhusuo. Bulletin of Chinese Materia Medica 13 (5): 14-16, 61.

Baskin, J.M. & Baskin, C.C. 1994. Nondeep simple morphophysiological dormancy in seeds of the mesic woodland annual *Corydalis flavula* (Fumariaceae). Bull. Torrey Bot. Club 121: 40-46.

Beattie, A. J. 1985. The evolutionary ecology of ant - plant interactions. Cambridge University Press.

Brückner, C. 1985. Zur Samenmorphologie in *Corydalis*. Gleditschia 13: 53_61.

Brückner, C. 1993. Comparative carpology in the tuber-bearing sections and sect. *Capnogorium* of *Corydalis* (Fumariaceae). Bot. Jahrb. 115: 367-420.

Candolle, A. P. de. 1821. Regni veg. syst. nat. 2. - Paris

Charkevitz, S. S. 1987. Plantae Vasculares Orientis Extremi Sovietici 2. - Leningrad.

Cullen, J. & Davis, P. H. 1965. in: Davis, P. H. (edit.) Flora of Turkey and the East Aegean Islands. 1.

Decraene, L.P.R. & Smets, E.F. 1992. An updated interpretation of the androecium of the Fumariaceae. Canad. J. Bot. 70(9): 1765-1776.

Dymock, W. 1890. Pharmacographia indica. - Calcutta.

Fedde, F.F. 1936: Papaveraceae. In: A. Engler & H. Harms (eds.), Die natürlichen Pflanzenfamilien ed. 2, 17b: 5-145. - Leipzig.

Fu X., He Z., Liang W. & Tu G. 1989. Chemotaxonomic characterization of yanhusuo. Acta Bot. Yunnanica 11: 193-197.

Fukuhara, T. & Lidén, M. 1995a. Pericarp anatomy in Fumariaceae. Bot. Jahrb. Syst. 117: 499-530.

Fukuhara, T. & Lidén, M. 1995b. Seed coat anatomy and phylogeny in Fumariaceae. J. Linn. Soc. Bot. 119: 323-365.

Goldenberg, D. 1990. Draft Species Management Guide For *Corydalis aquae-gelidae*. Report submitted to the Oregon Department of Agriculture for the Mt. Hood National Forest.

Grey-Wilson, C. 1988. Journey to the Jade Dragon Snow Mountain, Yunnan 2. Quarterly Bull. Alp. Garden Soc. 56(2): 115-130.

Grossheim, A.A. 1950. Flora Kavkaza ed. 2, 4. - Moskva.

Hager, H. 1883. Handbuch der pharmaceuthischen Praxis 1, 1. - Berlin.

Hegi, G. 1958. Illustrierte Flora von Mitteleuropa, ed. 2 (F. Markgraf), IV (1): 55.

Hickman, J.C. 1993 (ed.). The Jepson Manual. Higher plants of California. University of California Press. - London.

Higashi, S., Ohara, M. & Arai, H. 1988. Robber-like pollinators: overwintering queen bumblebees foraging on *C. ambigua*. Ecological entomology 13: 411-418.

Hitchcock, C.L., Cronquist, A. 1964. Vascular Plants of the Pacific Northwest, 2: 422 - 427.

Jafri, S.M.H. 1974. Fumariaceae. Flora of West Pakistan 73.

Kosenko, V.N. & Mikhailova, M. 1991. The morphology of pollen in the genus *Corydalis*. Bot. Zhurn. (Moscow & Leningrad) 76 (4): 556-564.

Johnson, M.A.T. 1989. An unusually high chromosome number in *Voaniaola gerardi*. Kew Bull. 44: 207-210.

Lamarck, J. B. de & Candolle, A. P. de. 1805. Flore francaise ed 3, 4. - Paris.

Lidén, M. 1981. On the typification of *Corydalis* nomen conservandum. Taxon 30: 322-325

Lidén, M. 1986. Synopsis of Fumarioideae with a monograph of the tribe Fumarieae. Opera Bot. 88. 136 pp.

Lidén, M. 1989a. Tuberous *Corydalis* in the Med-Checklist area. Notes Roy. Bot. Gard. Edinb.45: 349-363.

Lidén, M. 1989b. The genus *Corydalis* in Nepal. Bull. Brit. Mus. (Nat. Hist.) Bot. 18: 479-539.

Lidén, M. 1991a. Notes on *Corydalis* sect. *Corydalis* in the Baltic area. Nord. J. Bot. 11: 129-133.

Lidén, M. 1991b. New tuberous species of *Corydalis* (Papaveraceae). Willdenowia 21: 175-179.

Lidén, M. 1993a. Fumariaceae. *In:* K. Kubitzki (ed.), Families and genera of vascular plants, 2. - Springer-Verlag.

Lidén, M. 1993b. *Corydalis cornuta*, a Himalayan/ Afro-montane disjunct species. Opera Bot. 121: 45-46.

Lidén, M. 1995. A revision of *Corydalis* sect. *Fumarioides*, part II. Rheedea 5: 1-36.

Lidén, M. 1996. New taxa of tuberous *Corydalis* species. Willdenowia 26: 23-35

Lidén, M., Fukuhara, T. & Axberg, T. 1995. Phylogeny of *Corydalis*, ITS and morphology. Pl. Syst. Evol. Suppl. 9: 183-188.

Lidén, M., Fukuhara, T., Rylander, J. & Oxelman, B. 1997. The phylogeny and classification of Fumariaceae with emphasis on *Dicentra sensu lato* based on the chloroplast gene *rps*16 intron. Pl. Syst. Evol. (in print).

Lidén, M. & Staaf, R. 1995. Embryo growth in tuberous *Corydalis* species. *Bull. Torrey Bot. Club* 122: 312-313.

Lidén, M. & Zetterlund, H. 1988. Notes on the genus *Corydalis*. Quarterly Bull. Alp. Garden Soc. 56(2): 115-130.

Lobstein, M.B. & Rockwood, L.L. 1993. Influence of elaiosome removal on germination in five ant-dispersed plant species. Virginia J. Science 44(1): 59-72

Medikus, F.C. 1789. Philosophische Botanik 1. - Mannheim.

Mikhailova, M. 1981. De generis *Corydalis* Vent. (Fumariaceae) speciebus nonnullis ex Asia Media. Novosti Sist. Vyssh. Rast. 19: 81-98.

Mikhailova, M. 1981. Revisio specierum generis *Corydalis* Vent. (Fumariaceae) sect. *Archaecapnos* M. Pop. Novosti Sist. Vyssh. Rast. 19: 98-105.

Mikhailova, M. 1981. Subsect. *Strictae* (Fedde) Fedde generis *Corydalis* Vent. (Fumariaceae) revisio critica. Novosti Sist. Vyssh. Rast. 18: 191-196.

Nakanashi, H. 1994. Myrmecochory in *Corydalis* in S Japan. Ecological research 9(1): 1-8.

Oh B.-U., Chung G.-Y. & Kim Y.-S. 1993. A systematic study of Korean *Corydalis* species on the embryological characters. I. Seed-coat development and structure. Kor. J. Pl. Tax. 23: 131-*147*.

Ohara, M. & Higashi, S. 1994. *Corydalis fumariifolia* pollinated by overwintering queens of *Bombus hypocrita*. Oecologia (Berlin) 98(1): 25-30.

Olesen, J.M. 1994. A fatal growth pattern and ways suspected of postponing death. Corm dynamics in *Corydalis cava*. Bot. J. Linn. Soc. 115: 95-113.

Olesen, J.M. & Knudsen, J.T. 1994. Scent profiles of flower colour morphs of *Corydalis cava* (Fumariaceae) in relation to foraging behaviour of bumblebee queens (*Bombus terrestris*). Biochem. Syst. Ecol. 22(3): 231-237.

Ono, Y. 1995. Life cycle of 'Cerotelium' asari (Uredinales). Sydowia 47: 54-64.

Ownbey, G.B. 1947. Monograph of the North American Species of *Corydalis*. Ann. Missouri Bot. Gard. 34 (3): 187-260.

Persson, K. 1992. *Colchicum feinbruniae* sp. nov., and allied species in the middle East. Israel. J. Bot. 41: 75-86.

Popov, M. 1937. Papaveraceae. In: Komarov, V. A. (ed.) Flora USSR 7. - Moskva.

Prain, D. 1896. Novitiae Indicae X. Some additional Fumariaceae. J. As. Soc. Bengal. nov. ser. 65, 2(1): 10-41.

Reimeier, C., Schneider, I., Schneider, W., Schaefer, H.C. & Elstner, E.F. 1995. Effects of ethanolic extracts from *Eschscholzia californica* and *Corydalis cava*. Arzneimittel-Forschung 45(2): (124-)132-136.

Ryberg, M. 1955. A taxonomical survey of the genus *Corydalis* with reference to cultivated species. Acta Horti Berg. 17 (5): 115-175.

Ryberg, M. 1960. A morphological study of the Fumariaceae, and the taxonomic significance of the characters examined. Acta Horti Berg. 19 (4): 121-248.

Sokolovskaya, A.P. 1966. Geograficheskoe rasprostranenie polyploidnykh vidov rasteniy. Vestnik Leningr. Univ. 1966 ser. Biol. 3:92-106 (not seen).

Stojanov, N., Stefanov, B. & Kitanov, B. 1966. Flora Bulgarica ed. 4, 1.

Su Z.-Y. & Lidén, M. 1996. *Corydalis* in China I: some new species. Edinburgh J. Bot. (in print).

Su Z.-Y. & Lidén, M. *Corydalis* in China III: checklist. (in prep.).

Velenovsky, J. 1881. Flora Bulgarica. - Prag.

Ventenat, E. 1803. Choix de plantes 19. - Paris.

Wendelbo, P. 1974. Fumariaceae. In: K.H. Rechinger (ed.) Flora Iranica 110. - Graz.

Zhang, Y.-H.1996. A wild hexaploid population of *Corydalis yankusuo* from Zhejiang. J. Pl. Resourc. Environ 5 (2): 63-64.

Zhu X.-Z. 1991. Development of natural products as drugs acting on central nervous system. Memorias do Istituto Oswaldo Cruz Rio de Janeiro 86 (suppl. 2): 173-176.

INDEX

Names are indexed only once, either as **accepted name** (bold), or - if not accepted - as basionym, and always by the last part of the name. Example: *Corydalis afghanica* Gilli subsp. *elegans* Lidén is indexed as: "**elegans** Lidén, afghanica ssp.". Names not described in *Corydalis* are in italics. Main entries are bold.

abantensis Lidén & Zetterlund, caucasica ssp. 29
acaulis = **Pseudofumaria alba** ssp. **acaulis** (Wulfen) Lidén
aconitiflora Lidén 130
acropteryx Fedde 130
Adianta , Series 64
adrienii Prain 123
adunca Maxim. 132
afghanica Gilli 14 15 19 **90**
ainae Ruksans ex Lidén, schanginii ssp. 16 **69**
aitchisonii Popov 15 16 89 **92**
alaica Halda, *Cysticorydalis* 127
alashanica (Maxim.) Peschkova 105
albiflora Kit. ex Schult. 77
albiflora Rupr., caucasica var. 30
alexeenkoana N.Busch 16 19 22 **27** 35
alpestris C.A.Mey. 12 16 99 100 **101** 107
alpina J.Gay 37
alpina Koch, non J.Gay 97
allenii auct. hort. 15 **49**
altaica Ledeb., *Fumaria* 104
amabilis Migo 113
ambigua Cham. & Schltdl. 14 23 **49** 56
amurensis Maxim., ambigua var. 51
angustifolia (M.Bieb.) DC. 12 16 22 **33**
angustifoliolata Nakai, orthoceras var. 59
anthriscifolia Franch. 120
appendiculata Hand-Mazz. 123
aquae-gelidae (Peck & Wilson) Lidén & Zetterlund, caseana ssp. 5 **117**
aquilegifolia DC., pauciflora var. 104

araratica Rupr., *Capnites macrosepala* var. 103
Archaecapnos, Sect. 13 **115**
arctica Popov 99 **105**
Asterostigmata, Sect. 131
atuntsuensis W.W.Smith 16 **123**
Aulacostigma, Sect. 134
aurea Willd. 13 134
australis Hausm., solida var. 42
azurea Lidén & Zetterlund, fumariifolia ssp. 51
balansae Prain 9
balcanica Velen. 46
balfouriana Franch. 16 **122**
balsamiflora Prain 124
bataliana Maxim. 111
bayerniana Rupr., *Capnites pallidiflora* var. 101
benecincta W.W.Sm. 12 16 99 108 **109**
Benecinctae, Subsect. 109
bicalcarata Velen. 42
Bipapillata Lidén, Sect. 132
blanda Schott 19 76 **79** 80
boissieri (Prain) Wendelbo, verticillaris ssp. 98 **99**
brachyloba Boiss., solida var. 64
bracteata (Willd.) Pers. 15 19 **47** 64
bracteosa Batt. & Trabut, solida var. 40
brandegei (Wats.) Ownbey, caseana ssp. 118
Brevinectaria, Subsect. 66
brevipedicellata Lidén 36
brotherusiorum (Fedde) Fedde, conorhiza var. 103
bucharica Popov 132
bulbosa L., *Fumaria* 10 40 77
bullata Lidén, tianzhuensis ssp. 107
bungeana Turcz. 9

buschii Nakai 14 16 19 112 **114**
cabulica Gilli 87
calcarea Albov 101
calcicola W.W.Smith 16 **123**
calycina Lidén 130
capillaris Makino, bulbosa var. 55
capillipes Franch. 59
Capnogorium, Sect. 126
capnoides (L.) Pers. 10 **130**
caseana Gray 116
cashmeriana Royle 14 15 18
casimiriana Prain 130
caucasica DC. 12 13 15 22 27 **29** 30
caudata (Lam.) Pers. 71
cava (L.) Schweigg. & Körte 9 10 14 17 19 67 76 **77**
cavei D.G.Long 130
Ceratotuber, Sect. 112
chaerophylla DC. 8 **128**
chamissonis Fedde, pauciflora var. 105
cheilanthifolia Hemsl. 133
Cheilanthifoliae Lidén, Sect. 132
cheirifolia Franch. 122
chionophila Czerniak. 15 19 82 **93**
chosenensis Ohwi 114
Chremnocapnos, Subgenus 12 13 132
Chrysocapnos, Sect. 13 127 129
clavibracteata Ludlow 129
claviculata = **Ceratocapnos claviculata** (L.) Lidén 7
congesta Lidén & Zetterlund, wendelboi ssp. 36
conorhiza Ledeb. 12 16 99 102 **103**
conspersa Maxim. 126
cornuta Royle 130

Coronatae, Series 86
Corydalis, Sect. 13 18 19 **21**
Corydalis, Series 39
Corydalis, Subsect. 27
crassifolia Royle 108 **127**
crassissima Camb. 127
crispa Prain 9
crithmifolia Royle 128
curviflora Maxim. 122
cusickii (Wats.) Ownbey,
    caseana ssp. 118
cyrtocentra Prain 86
cytisiflora 122
Dactylotuber, Sect. 13 18 19 **99**
Dactylotuber, Subsect. 101
dajingensis C.Y.Wu & Z.Y..Su
    99 **111**
darwasica Regel ex. Prain
    15 16 83 **89**
Davidianae, Sect. 13 **130**
davidii Franch. 130
decipiens Nyman, Schott &
    Kotschy 46
decumbens (Thunb.) Pers.
    9 12 13 18 112 **113**
densiflora C. & J.Presl
    21 36 **40** 46
densispica C.Y.Wu 16 **123**
dentata Y.H.Chou, ambigua f. 51
depauperata Schur 39
diffusa Michajlova, maracandica
    var. 87
digitata Schrank, *Fumaria* 41
diphylla Wall. 15 19 82 83 **85**
Duplotuber, Sect. 13 18 **112**
ecristata (Prain) Long 16 **121**
edulioides Fedde 113
edulis Maxim. 9
elata Franch. 16 **125**
Elatae, Sect. 124
elegans Lidén, afghanica ssp.
    92
Elegantes, Series 90
Elongatae, Subsect. 100
emanueli C.A.Mey.
    12 16 99 100 **102**
erdelii Zucc. 15 16 **97**
eugeniae Fedde 16

fabacea Retz., *Fumaria* 37
fangshanensis W.T.Wang 134
Fasciculatae, Sect. 13 18 **120**
feddeana Poelln. 42
fedtschenkoana Regel 127
filistipes Nakai 12 **75**
fimbrillifera Korsh. 132
firouzii (Wendelbo) Lidén,
    chionophila ssp. 15 16 **94**
flabellata Edgew. 132
flaccida Hook. f. & Th. 127
flavula 18 134
flexuosa Franch. 14 16 **124**
foetida C.Y.Wu & Z.Y.Su 134
fukuharae Lidén 16 49 **52**
fumariifolia Maxim.
    9 15 16 21 23 **50**
Fumarioides, Sect. 13 **130**
fungosa = **Adlumia fungosa**
    (Ait.) Britton, Stern &
    Poggenburg
gamosepala Maxim. 72 **74**
geocarpa Harry.Sm. ex Lidén
    99 **111**
gigantea Trautv. & Mey. 120
glabra Takeda, ambigua var. 51
glareosa Sommier & Levier 101
glaucescens Regel 16 23 **70**
Globosae, Subsect. 24
glycyphyllus Fedde 123
gorinensis Van 16 21 23 **64**
gorodkovii Karav. 62
gortschakovii Schrenk. 16 128
gotlandica Lidén 12 14 19 22 **38**
govaniana Wall. 10 **128**
gracilipes S.Moore 113
gracilis Ledeb. 13 16 **49**
gracillima C.Y.Wu 130
grandicalyx B.U.Oh &
    Y..S.Kim 57
grandiflora Bornm. & Gauba,
    verticillaris var. 98
griffithii Boiss. 14 15 **90** 91
gyrophylla Lidén 107
haimanensis Fedde, edulioides
    var. 113
haitaoensis Y.H.Chou &
    C.Q.Xu, turtschaninovii f. 74

hallaisanensis H.Lév. 57
halleri Willd., *Fumaria* 41
hamata Franch. 9 16 **126**
Hamata, Sect. 126
hastata (Rydb.) Ownbey,
    caseana ssp. 118
haussknechtii Lidén 16 23 **32**
Helicosyne, Series 27
hemidicentra Hand.-Mazz.
    12 16 99 **108**
hendersonii Hemsl. 13 **129**
hennigii Fedde, kolpakowskiana
    var. 70
henrikii Lidén 16 23 **65**
hepaticifolia Wu & Y.Su 109
heterocarpa Sieb. & Zucc. 134
heteroclita K.T.Fu, remota var.
    74
heteropetala Otschiauri 102
holanschanica Fedde, pauciflora
    var. 105
hondoensis Ohwi 134
hsiaowutaishanensis T.P.Wang
    106
humilis B.U.Oh & Y.S.Kim 54
humosa Migo 71
humosoides Y.H.Zhang, repens
    var. 71
(X)hybrida Michajlova 47 49
hyrcana Wendelbo 98 99
impatiens DC. 130
incisa (Thunb.) Pers. 13 18
incisa Lidén, solida ssp.
    9 15 16 41 **46**
Incisae, Sect. 131
inconspicua Bunge ex. Ledeb.
    123
integra Barbey & Fors.-Major
    16 23 **31**
intermedia (L.) Merát
    12 13 17 19 21 22 **37** 39
ivaschkeviczii Aparina 58
jezoensis Miq. 51
jigmei Fischer & Kaul 16 **121**
juncea Wall. 123
kamelinii (Kurbanov) Lidén,
    aitchisonii ssp. 93
kashgarica Rupr. 71
kelungensis Hayata 113

kiaotschouensis Poelln.   55 74
kokiana Hand.-Mazz.   16 **122**
kolpakovskiana Regel   70
kurdica (Cullen & P.H.Davis)
    Lidén, oppositifolia ssp.   96
kusnetzovii Khokhr.   16 **28** 30
lanceata Ohwi, lineariloba var.
                              55
lathyrophylla C.Y.Wu   16
latiflora Hook. f. & Th.
                    13 16 **129**
Latiflorae, Sect.   129
latifoliolata Nakai, orthoceras
    var.   59
latiloba (Franch.) Hand.-Mazz.
                    16 **134**
latiloba Maxim., pauciflora var.
                             107
laxa Fr.   40 43
laxa Franch. & Sav., non Fr. 55
ledebouriana Kar. & Kir.
    14 15 18 19 82 86 **87** 89 94
Leonticoides, Sect. 13 18 19 **81**
Leonticoides, Series   92
leptocarpa Hook. f. & Th.   131
leucanthema C.Y.Wu   125
linarioides Maxim.   123
lineariloba Maxim, remota var.
                              72
lineariloba Siebold & Zucc.
    14 16 17 21 23 **55** 56
linjiangensis Z.Y.Su   **53**
linstowiana Fedde   9 18 **131**
lobelii Tausch   39
longicalcarata X.Zhuang &
    Z.Y.Su   120
longicarpa Lidén & Zetterlund,
    solida ssp.   46
longiflora Willd., *Fumaria* 68 71
longipes DC.   12 13 130
ludlowii Stearn   8 **109**
lutea = **Pseudofumaria lutea**
    (L.) Borckh.   8
lydica Lidén   16 **96**
macrocentra Regel   16 83 **92**
Macrocentrae, Series   92
macrosepala Rupr., *Capnites*103
maculata B.U.Oh & Y.S.Kim **61**

magadanica Khokhr.
                    14 16 23 **62**
major Roth, *Fumaria*   71
majori Poelln.   31
malkensis Galuschko
        12 14 15 16 22 **30**
maracandica Michajlova
        14 16 82 **87**
marschalliana Pall. ex. Willd.,
    Fumaria   77
megacalyx Ludlow   16 **129**
meifolia Wall.   16 **129**
melanochlora Maxim.   16 **123**
micrantha Ohwi, lineariloba var.
                              58
micrantha   134
minor Roth, *Fumaria*   41
modestum Schott, *Cryptoceras*
                              97
Monstruosa Lidén, Subsect. 75
moorcroftiana Hook. f. & Th.
                             128
moupinensis Franch.   133
mucronata Franch.   16 **125**
Mucronatae, Sect.   125
multifida Y.H.Chou, ambigua f.
                              51
multiflora Michajlova   119
murreana (Jafri) Lidén**,**
    diphylla ssp.   86
nakaii Ishidoya   112
nariniana Fed.   16 83 **97** 98
nevski Popov   16 93
nivalis Boiss. & Huet   101
nobilis (L.) Pers.   10 13 14 **126**
nonapiculata Ohwi,
    turtschaninovii var.   57
nudicaulis Regel 16 19 23 **66** 76
Numullaria, Subsect.   71
ochotensis Turcz.   131
ochroleuca Rupr., *Capnites* 103
ochroleuca = **Pseudofumaria
    alba** (Miller) Lidén
Officinales, Subsect.   72
ohii Lidén   13 **56**
oliganthus Trinajstic, *Bulbo-
    capnos solidus* ssp.   47
olympica Lidén, blanda ssp. 80

Oocapnos, Sect.   18 **127**
ophiocarpa Hook. f. & Th.   132
oppositifolia DC.   15 16 82 **96**
ornata Lidén & Zetterlund
        16 23 72 **74**
orthoceras Siebold & Zucc.
            12 14 **59**
ovalioblonga Ohwi, lineariloba
    var.   55
oxelmannii Lidén, blanda ssp.
                              81
oxypetala Franch.   122
pachycentra Franch.   16 **122**
pachypoda Franch.   128
paczoskii N.Busch   12 22 **34**
paeonifolia (Steph.) Pers.   119
pakistanica Jafri   16 **128**
pallida (Thunb.) Pers.   134
pallidiflora (Rupr.) Lipsky,
    emanueli var.   99 100 102
pamiroalaica Soskov,
    glaucescens ssp.   67
papillata Ohwi, turtschaninovii
    var.   58
papilligera Ohwi14 16 19 23 **60**
papillosa Kitag., turtschaninovii
    var.   72
papillosa Takeda, ambigua var.
                              51
parnassica (Orph. ex Heldr.)
    Lidén, blanda ssp.   80
parviflora Lidén, chionophila
    ssp.   94
parviflora Lidén, verticillaris
    ssp.   99
parviflora Regel, pauciflora var.
                             105
paschei Lidén   16 23 **36**
pauciflora (Willd.) Pers.
            85 100 **104**
pauciflora Pacz., solida var.   34
pectinata Kom., remota var.   51
persica Cham. & Schltdl.
            16 97 98 99
Pes-gallinaceus, Sect.   24 100
Petiolatae, Series   85
petrophila Franch.   131
pirotensis Adamowic   42

podlechii Lidén 90
polyphylla H.-Mazz. 14 **126**
popovii Nevski ex Popov
14 15 19 87 **88**
pseudoadoxa (C.Y.Wu &
X.Zhuang) Wu & Zhuang 16
pseudoalpestris Popov 106
pseudocava Pant. 77 80
pseudocrithmifolia Jafri 128
pseudoflaccida Fedde, cristata
var. 111
pseudofluminicola Fedde 126
pseudohamata Fedde 126
pseudomucronata C.Y.Wu 125
pseudotongolensis Lidén 130
Pubicaules, Sect. 131
pulchellum Schott, *Cryptoceras*
97
pumila (Host) Rchb.
12 13 19 21 22 38 **39** 40
purpurans Schott, *Cryptoceras*
97
racemosa (Thunb.) Pers. 9 **133**
Radix-cava, Sect. 13 **76** 81
ramosa Pacz., solida var. 34
Ramoso-sibiricae, Sect. 13
Raphanituber, Series 62
repens Mandl & Mühld.
14 21 49 **58** 71 73
Repentes, Series 49
roseopurpurea Rupr., *Capnites*
marschalliana var. 77
rotundiloba Maxim, remota var.
72
ruksansii Lidén 16 19 23 **67**
rupestris Boiss. 132
ruprechtii N.Busch, conorhiza
var. 103
rutacea Th.Fr. 43
rutifolia (Sm.) DC. 15 **94**
sajanensis Peschkova 105
salangensis Wendelbo, griffithii
ssp. 92
saltatoria W.W.Smith 130
saxicola G.S.Bunting 133
scaberula Maxim. 123
schanginii (Pall.) B.Fedtsch.
19 21 23 **68**

scouleri Hook. 115
seisumsiana Lidén 16 83 **97** 98
semenovii Regel & Herder
13 **132**
sempervirens = **Capnoides**
sempervirens (L.) Borckh.
senanensis Franch. & Sav. 59
sewerzowii Regel 89
shearteri S.Moore 14 125
sibirica (L.) Pers. 130
sibirica Regel, pauciflora var.
105
simplicifolia Fedde, sewerzowii
var. 93
slivenensis Velen. 42 43
smithiana Fedde 16
solida (L.) Clairv. 10 13 14 15
16 17 18 19 21
22 36 38 39 **40**
sommieri Fedde, conorhiza var.
103
Sophorocapnos, Sect. 134
Sophorocapnos, Subgenus
13 132
speciosa Maxim. 134
stracheyi Prain 129
Strictae, Sect. 132
stummeri Pant. 77
subremota Popov ex Lidén &
Zetterlund, solida ssp. 42
subuniflora Boiss. & Heldr.,
rutifolia var. 95
swanetica Krasnov 101
taliensis Franch. 16
tangutica Peschkova 107
tarkiensis Prokh. 27 34 **35**
tashiroi 133
tauricola (Cullen & P.H.Davis)
Lidén 19 23 **37**
taygetana Fedde, solida var.
densiflora subvar. 46
teberdensis Khokhr. 28
temulifolia Franch. 125
tenella Ledeb. 29
tenerrima Wu, Su & Lidén 16
tenuis Lidén, afghanica ssp. 91
tenuis Schott, Nyman, &
Kotschy 46

tenuisecta Boiss., solida var. 36
ternata (Nakai) Nakai 19 **112**
ternata Ohwi, turtschaninovii
var. 73
thalictrifolia Franch. 15 133
Thalictrifoliae, Sect. 133
thasia Stoj. & Kitan., solida var.
46
thyrsiflora Prain 16 **128**
tianzhuensis M.S.Yan &
C.J.Wang 12 99 **106**
tibetica Hook. f. & Th. 128
tomentella Franch. 15 **133**
trachycarpa Maxim. 123
transilvanica Schur, solida var.
speciosa.. 42 43ff
trifoliata Franch. 122
trilobipetala (Hand.-Mazz.)
Lidén, benecincta ssp. 110
triternata Zucc. 16 23 **64**
tuberosa DC. 77
turczaninovi Halda,
Cysticorydalis nom. nud. 127
turtschaninovii Besser
14 16 23 64 **72**
udokanica Peschkova 105
uniflora (Siebold) Nyman
12 15 83 **95**
ussuriensis Aparina 16 23 **52**
vaginans Royle 130
vernyi (Franch. & Sav.) Lidén,
turtschaninovii ssp. 73
verticillaris DC. 15 83 **98**
vittae Kolak 16 **29**
vivipara Fedde 14 125
watanabei Kitag. 58
wendelboi Lidén 16 19 23 **35** 37
wettsteinii Adamovic 31
wilsonii N.E.Br. 133
yanhusuo (Chou & Xu) Wang
ex Su & Wu 9 14 17 22 **74**
yezoensis = jezoensis
yunnanensis Franch. 16 **130**
zeaènsis Michajlova 120
zetterlundii Lidén 16 23 **31**
zhongdianensis Z.Y.Su & Lidén
130

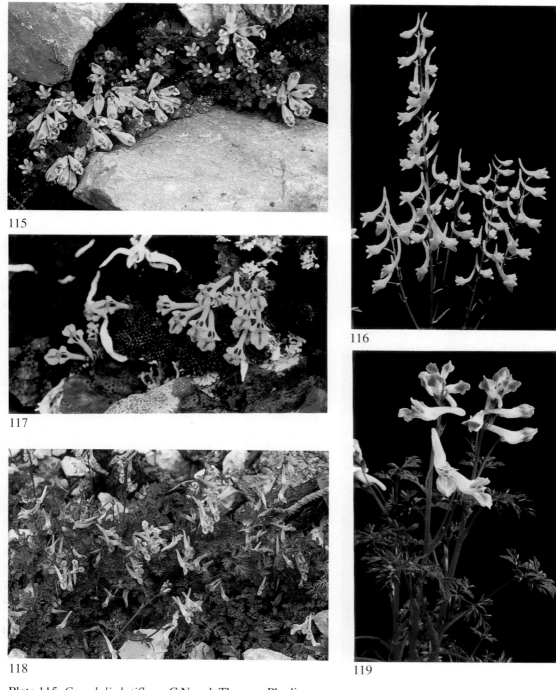

Plate 115. *Corydalis latiflora*, C Nepal, Thorong Phedi
Plate 116. *Corydalis yunnanensis*
Plate 117. *Corydalis megacalyx*, C Nepal, Thorong La
Plate 118. *Corydalis smithiana*, SW China, NW Yunnan, Napahai
Plate 119. *Corydalis smithiana*, in cultivation

120

121

122

123

124

125

Plate 120. *Corydalis incisa*
Plate 121. *Corydalis linstowiana*
Plate 122. *Corydalis bucharica*, close up of flowers
Plate 123. *Corydalis rupestris*
Plate 124. *Corydalis cheilanthifolia*
Plate 125. *Corydalis wilsonii*